910
P77g

49892

DATE DUE			
Jan 17'73			
Jan 24'73			
GAYLORD M-2			PRINTED IN U.S.A.

THE GEOGRAPHIC PATTERN
OF MANKIND

BY

JOHN E. POMFRET
PRINCETON UNIVERSITY

D. APPLETON–CENTURY COMPANY
INCORPORATED

NEW YORK   LONDON

1935

910
P77g
49892
May, 1965

IN MEMORIAM
DANA CARLETON MUNRO

EDITOR'S PREFACE

It is becoming increasingly apparent that an accurate and thorough understanding of the nature and development of human society is prerequisite to the solution of the problems faced by individuals in the complex civilization of to-day. The social sciences are rightly receiving increasing attention among research workers and in educational institutions. From many points of view the light is being focused upon the behavior of human beings as individuals and in groups, large and small, organized loosely or compactly. It is, however, imperative that the right attitude of mind should be possessed by those who are engaged in such studies.

Man is not living in a vacuum. He is an inhabitant of the earth; his activities display an unmistakable geographic pattern. In the classical story of the encounter between Hercules and Anteus, "the son of Gea," the offspring of Mother Earth, Anteus personifies the human race. As long as he maintains contact with the earth which mothers him, he has strength sufficient even for the competition with so mighty an antagonist as Hercules. When that contact is broken, he suffers defeat. Even among the artificialities of modern life, that principle holds true. If we approach our problems with the constant thought that we must keep our feet upon the ground, must always be aware of our relations to the sum total of the environmental conditions provided by the earth, there is at least a possibility that we may be victorious. Without that attitude of mind, we are certain to fail.

This book provides an admirable stimulus for developing such a mental attitude. It surveys with rare judgment the various elements of modern civilization and shows with keen appreciation of values the many ways in which man is adjusting himself to diverse physical environments in various parts of the earth. It is a splendid introduction to the social sciences and goes far toward stimulating that sense of relationship between man and earth, which is fundamental to progress in perfecting the art of living.

At the same time, this volume is appropriately considered as a contribution in the field of "earth science." For the special student of modern geography who has profited by systematic training in the principles of that science, it provides an imposing array of "cases" by which those principles may be tested, or to which they may be applied, as he pursues his studies beyond the introductory stages. Thus it effectively bridges the chasm which long existed between the sciences dealing with the earth and those concerned with human society.

KIRTLEY F. MATHER.

PREFACE

The student who makes any serious excursion into the field of social science should be equipped with a certain degree of knowledge and understanding of the physical stage upon which man works. In many institutions of learning there has been a conscious attempt, either in the survey course or in the general geography course, to provide such a background. The student of politics, economics, and kindred subjects is interested in the world of reality; hence in a consideration of the relation between man and his environment the treatment must necessarily focus upon the socio-physical unit rather than upon a set of geographical principles illustrated at random. Only the first chapters of this book are concerned with the elements of the science of geography; the larger portion deals with the definite relationships that exist between what Dr. Bowman terms the "natural landscape" and the "cultural landscape" in various regions.

To Mr. Joseph C. Green of the Department of State, a former colleague, the writer owes much. He has borrowed lavishly from Mr. Green's store of knowledge and ideas. He wishes also to acknowledge the suggestions of Mr. Walter Hall, Mr. Walter Wright, and Mr. Wheaton Lane, his colleagues, Mr. Robert Cunningham of Phillips Exeter Academy, Mr. Howard Smyth of Union College, and the assistance of the members of the staff of the Princeton University Library. The diagrams and maps were drawn by Miss Sarah Nusbaum of Philadelphia. The materials of such a broad survey, however, represent the labor of many workers in the field of regional geography, and much of this book is a tribute to their scholarly researches. Not the least helpful has been the coöperation of hundreds of Princeton undergraduates who, as members of the survey course in social science (History 101), have patiently submitted to the experimenting of their mentors.

J. E. POMFRET

CONTENTS

ix

LIST OF FIGURES

LIST OF FIGURES

LIST OF PLATES

KEY TO CLIMATE MAPS OF THE CONTINENTS

There are four climatological maps for each of the continents: two representing the isotherms, isobars, and prevailing winds for January and July, and two representing rainfall for January and July. They are based upon more highly graduated representations of similar phenomena by Professor J. Paul Goode (see his *School Atlas,* Rand McNally & Company, 1925).

As the accompanying table shows, ALTITUDE is represented in shading as follows:

dark, sea level to 1,000 feet.

medium, 1,000 to 5,000 feet.

light, above 5,000 feet.

black, water bodies.

The shading of a continent other than the one which is the subject of the map is not intended to show altitude.

PARALLELS OF LATITUDE, at intervals of ten degrees, are indicated by these fine lines.

ISOTHERMS—imaginary lines connecting places of equal temperature—are heavy black lines. They are the boundaries of the *temperature zones.* Thus in Africa in January three temperature belts are shown (see Plate II): above 70°F. (70°+); from 50°–70°F; and below 50°F. (50°–).

ISOBARS—imaginary lines connecting places of equal pressure—are broad white lines. They are the boundaries of the *pressure zones,* and are indicated in inches. Thus in Africa in January there are pressure areas of 29.9", 30.0" and 30.1" (see Plate II).

PREVAILING WINDS are indicated by white or black arrows. The arrow indicates the direction toward which the wind is blowing, but the wind takes its name from the direction from which it comes. Thus, in Africa in January (see Plate II), may be distinguished the Northeast Trades over the Sahara, and inshore winds of monsoonlike character about the Gulf of Guinea.

ISOYETS—imaginary lines connecting places of equal rainfall—are heavy black lines. They are the boundaries of the *rainfall zones.* On these maps the following rainfall belts are indicated: 0"–10", 10"–20", 20"–40", and over forty inches (40+). Thus, in Africa, in January (see Plate IV) all three rainfall régimes are represented. By June (Plate V), however, their locations have shifted considerably.

The reader's appreciation of this book will be considerably heightened by reference to this series of maps. Man's geographical environment changes greatly with the shifting seasons, and the variations in the physical phenomena underlying climate are most clearly expressed by maps.

THE GEOGRAPHIC PATTERN
OF MANKIND

THE GEOGRAPHIC PATTERN
OF MANKIND

CHAPTER I

HUMAN GEOGRAPHY AND CULTURE

1. The Study of Human Geography

Human geography is the study of the relationship between the physical environment and the social environment. It is a social study because, like politics, anthropology, economics, and history, it is chiefly concerned with human society. Politics is interested in those institutions that society has fashioned for the governing of various groups of men, while economics investigates the manner in which men make their living. History has to do with the past experiences of human society, while anthropology examines human culture in the hope of determining more precisely the causes of its rise and development. All these studies and many others, then, are engaged in the examination of man and his culture. All hope to arrive at generalizations regarding the behavior of the social group that will be helpful in our understanding of the human species. The more optimistic investigators hope to establish laws that will guide man in his conduct. As yet, however, little has been achieved in this direction.

It cannot be emphasized too strongly that the social studies have as their function the examination of the various activities of man, past and present. In other words, all of them are concerned with the same subject, and all make use of the same materials. The historian, the economist, the sociologist, the geographer, the political scientist, and all the other students of man share a common interest and seek to attain a common end. Man's behavior is very complex, and the activities in which he participates are manifold; in consequence countless studies have arisen which have to do with the forces that influence human behavior, the various activities of man, and the various phases of his diverse culture. But a particular social science is useful only in so far as it contributes to an understanding of human society. Many enthusiastic teachers and scholars fail to keep in mind that their respective specialties are only media through which an understanding of the whole is to be gained. The political scientist who, for example, attempts to explain everything in the light of political causation is not only forgetful of the essential unity of all knowledge but is forever dealing in half-truths. In reality there is only one social science, but there are numerous angles from which human culture and human activities may be viewed.

Human geography, if rightly understood, is a valuable instrument of study. It is believed that the physical environment as well as the genetic factor and the social factor have exerted a real influence upon human culture and human activities. Men live in groups, and every social group is attached to some place or region. Every such region affords a certain type of topography, a certain type of soil, certain mineral and metal resources, and a certain type of climate. These things constitute the physical environment of the group. To this environment the social group must adjust itself. With this adjustment or relation human geography is principally concerned. Attempts have been made by short-sighted geographers—the so-called "environmental determinists"—to explain the form and content of culture largely in terms of geographical influences. Their gross exaggerations have occasioned much ridicule. It is true that topography, soil, climate, and other geographical features are more or less constant, but it is equally true that man's reactions are not fixed. Man is constantly surmounting disadvantages of physical environment. Poor soil is overcome by the use of fertilizers; lack of rainfall by the introduction of irrigation works; handicaps of relief by the building of roads, tunnels, and canals; and so on. The chief interest, therefore, in the study of human geography lies in the manner of man's adjustment to the physical environment, not in the elements of that environment.

Human geography is a particularly valuable medium for the study of contemporary society. Many social scientists, to the bewilderment of their readers, draw their materials from the whole gamut of human history, apparently regarding history as a convenient grab-bag.

Yet, as any historian will testify, the materials of substantiation are only too available in turning the pages of the past. The historian who neglects the geographical factors in his synthesis is a shoddy worker, but the geographer who seeks at random facts in history with which to illustrate his principles lays himself open to serious criticism. There is a second objection to the historical approach to human geography. No reader is familiar enough with the various forces influencing past cultures or with the form and content of those cultures to weigh the validity of the geographical inferences. Historical geography, unless the social environment is thoroughly analyzed, is likely to be of little value. But we can escape many of the pitfalls of half-truths if we examine the influence of *place* upon the activities of present-day man. The materials for studying the physical environment and describing the social environment of any people stand in sharp relief. Far from being obscured by the passage of time, they can be actually observed. Thus the findings of human geography arising from the study of contemporary social groups and their physical environments are likely to portray clearly and authoritatively the interaction between man and his physical environment.

A survey of the human geography of the modern world will serve as a broad introduction to social science. In any place an observation of the geographical factors cannot fail to reveal the nature of the social environment. In studying a great port, for example, the geographical equation cannot be properly interpreted without reference to the activities of the social group. A consideration of the physical properties of the harbor compels a discussion of man's efforts to accommodate the harbor to shipping. A consideration of the topography of the surrounding region involves a discussion of the means employed for distribution of goods. A consideration of the geographical resources of the hinterland poses the question of their utilization, while the climatic factor tells us much of the healthfulness of the community, of its agricultural potentialities, and so on.

A single port or city, however, is but a part of a larger environment. Owing to the nature of the climatic controls, the whole surface of the earth may be divided into natural regions. Within any such region the human responses are apt to be similar over wide areas. The social environment and the cultural adjustments tend to coincide with the geographical unit. All peoples living within the bounds of a natural region tend to arrive at adaptations that are in harmony with the landscape. Even in going from country to country, one will frequently find that crop specialization and agricultural methods are identical. This is so because the opportunities afforded by the physical environment for the raising of certain crops are identical. Along the Mediterranean coasts, for example, there exists a common agricultural pattern because of the climatic uniformity of the whole area. If environmental influences are dominant, the cultural province may coincide with the geographical unit rather than with the political entity. We speak to-day of a *Euramerican culture,* which embraces the countries of Western Europe and most of North America. Throughout this whole area a common way of life tends to prevail. The approximate uniformity of the physical environment has had a part in the shaping of this culture.

Human geography is important, then, because of its close relation to the activities and the culture of the social group. In examining the influences of geographical elements upon the social environment, one is drawn inevitably into a consideration of the entire culture of the group. In surveying numerous environments one touches upon many cultures and reaches an appreciation of the breadth and scope of man's social experiences. Hence there is gained not only a broad background for more particularized social studies but an understanding of the social heritage of the human race. Human geography is not an end in itself, any more than any other social study, but it does provide a valuable medium for the study of human society.

2. The Social Environment and Human Culture

Human geography, like many of the other social studies, deals not with individuals but with the social group. After all, an individual has little importance except as a member of society. Men live together, indeed they cannot live apart; in consequence, the coöperative behavior of men is objectively more important than the acts and thoughts of an individual. In fact, it must be admitted that what most individuals do and think is more important to themselves than to any one else. Our vaunted individualism is only a small part of our behavior, and for it society makes liberal allowances. The larger part of our behavior is identical with that of those among whom we live. Although we are rarely aware of it, most of our waking hours are spent in doing and thinking as others do and think. In other words, our social environment almost, though not completely, engulfs us. Were it not for a single saving grace, the capacity of human beings to react in various ways to an identical stimulus, our behavior would be as fixed and as rigid as that of the termites.

The social environment constitutes the entire cultural surroundings of the individual. Each individual is confronted with the problem of adapting himself to the mannerisms and customs of those among whom he lives. Our whole education, whether technical or liberal, is concentrated upon this end. Although our school system prides itself upon manufacturing good Americans, its more sober purpose is to equip the individual with the tools for making his entrance into society as frictionless as possible. A higher education is merely a heightening and refining of the process. It is fundamentally an inquiry into the "way of life" that prevails in the group with which one is associated. From a knowledge and understanding of his social environment the individual gains not only an appreciation of the variety and richness of life about him; but if he is a thinking person, he will also arrive at a set of values that will enable him more easily to take his place as a member of society.

There are many different types of social environment in the world. Judged by our standards, some men are backward and to us their social environment is poor and inadequate. We regard ourselves and a few other groups as civilized; the remainder we regard as primitive and uncivilized. Yet every group, however uncivilized, possesses a social environment that is similar in *form* or pattern to our own. The Hottentots, for example, have their own political, social, economic, religious, and esthetic adjustments. It is in *content* that social environments vary. Each social group, then, has a culture which in *content* varies from that of every other group. Culture is merely the sum total of the adjustments or adaptations worked out by any social group. For the individual it is the culture of the group which constitutes his social environment.

Viewed in one aspect the world of man is divisible into a number of cultures. Some of the units are small, embracing only a few tribes; others include many millions of people, speaking a variety of languages and living under many flags. Sinitic culture and Hindu culture are participated in by millions of men, while the so-called Euramerican culture extends over several continents. Yet the cultures of such groups as the Samoans, the Lolos, and the Kolarians are not without significance, for they represent distinct group experiences.

Social scientists are interested in the entire culture of the social group rather than a particular activity or a single institution. The archæologist, excavating in Crete or Yucatan, is intent upon reconstructing completely Cretan or Mayan society. Books upon the history of the Middle Ages or the Renaissance no longer concern themselves with purely political relationships but treat of every activity manifested during the period. To-day attempts are being made to interpret to us the culture of Europe and America. Such studies are valuable because every cultural synthesis represents a complete groupexperience. A comparison, however remote in time or in space, should assist us in interpreting the significance of our own type of culture.

On the other hand, many other methods have been attempted in surveying the universe of man. An examination that employs the political unit as its medium soon leads to confusion. One British subject, for example, may have nothing in common with another except allegiance to the same flag. They may be separated by thousands of miles, speak different languages, and live in entirely different manners. Yet the inhabitants of Western Europe and the United States, in spite of their different citizenship, live in much the same way because they are participants in what is essentially a common cultural heritage. Similar difficulties arise in grouping men according to language, religion, occupation, or social class. Race studies are popular because it is quite possible to classify men in groups based upon dominant physical traits. But racial character, contrary to a popular belief, does not account for cultural status. Members of the same race may participate in different cultures, and conversely different races frequently share in a common way of life. Race, like physical environment, may and quite possibly does influence human culture, but it determines neither the form nor the content of culture.

Culture represents an accretion of group experience which under normal circumstances increases in richness and fineness from generation to generation. This is, or ought to be, the social scientist's conception of human progress. Decay is not so much the loss of cultural content, for very little of intrinsic value to the group is ever lost. Rather the so-called "lost arts" are usually lost because they have been replaced by something deemed better, not because of any physical or mental debility of the group. Cultural decay, however, results from a "state of mind" that is hostile to change; which rejects innovations by members of the group and those coming from another group. A static society is impervious to change; a dynamic society seeks and accepts changes in content wherever the new represents a better adaptation than the old.

Culture, in one sense, is a vast accretion of traits, the sum total of the experience of the group. It has been built up through the course of thousands of years. A portion of it is endemic, that is, owing to inventions and discoveries contributed by members within the group and accepted by the group. An invention is not significant culturally until it is adopted by the group. Much of any culture, however, is not indigenous but has been borrowed from other groups as a result of direct or indirect contact. Barter and war in ancient times paved the way for the exchange not only of commodities but of uses, processes, and ideas. To-day, with the obliteration of physical obstacles due to modern facilities of communication and transportation, a new trait circles the globe in no time at all. Receptive people, like the Japanese, have been quick to adopt ideas and inventions transmitted to them, thus greatly augmenting their culture and better fitting it for the exigencies of modern civilization.

The culture of a social group, then, is a vast accretion of traits, the bulk of which have been handed down from the past. Each generation is the recipient of a social heritage to which it adds something through invention or borrowing. The social heritage constitutes the chief part of any culture. A moment's reflection will reveal the truth of this statement. The institutions of law and religion, for example, have been transmitted almost in their entirety by our forbears. Culture, however, is dynamic; alterations, for the most part finer adjustments, are ever being made, and, whether the consequence of invention or of diffusion, life changes preceptibly from generation to generation.

3. The Physical Environment and Human Culture

Physical environment is simply the surroundings provided by nature: principally climate, land and water bodies, soil, and vegetation. This term must not be confused with *social environment*. One is socialized by virtue of conforming to the social environment into which he has been thrust, usually at birth. Each individual must adjust himself to the culture of the group to which he belongs. But there is another type of adaptation that man must make and that is the adjustment to the physical environment. The relationships that arise from the contact of man with nature constitute in large measure the field of human geography.

The influence of the physical environment upon the culture of the social group is regarded, by anthropologists especially, as rather obvious and hence unworthy of much consideration. "It is of course plain," writes one of them, "that a primitive tribe under the equator would never invent the ice box, and that the Eskimo will not keep their food and water in buckets of bamboo. . . . The materials and opportunities provided by nature may be made use of by each people, while other materials not being provided, other arts or customs can therefore not be developed. . . . Obviously natural environment does impose *limiting conditions* on human life; but equally obviously, it does not cause inventions or institutions." [1] It would be absurd, as any but the determinist would agree, to assert that the physical environment any more than any other single factor had given rise to the culture of a social group. Indeed most geographers would admit that cultural development has been more influenced by historical causes than any other factor. Yet, as an examination of subsequent chapters of this book ought to show, the culture of every group is colored, even "shot through," at every turn by the influences of the physical environment. The Eskimo, for example, makes garments of fur; he carves and etches on bone; he has a house of snow during the winter season; his kayak is made of thongs, skins, and bones; and all the other traits of his material culture represent, in masterly fashion, adjustments to an environment that, with its cold, snow, storm, darkness, and paucity of materials, is one of the most hostile that any social group has been called upon to face. His higher needs, religion and mythology, have also been influenced by his physical surroundings. The saga of Sedna, the Goddess of Winds and Sea Mammals, whose function it is to furnish a plentiful supply of game and to protect her humble adherents from storm and famine, is symbolic of the utter weakness of man before the omnipotent forces of nature. A few hundred miles south live the Northwest Indians, in a far different type of environment. They dwell among the great

[1] A. E. Kroeber, *Anthropology*, pp. 181, 182.

coniferous forests of the west Pacific coast. They, too, hunt and fish, but the content of their culture is dominated by the wood motif. Their great houses and their large canoes are the result of a plentiful supply of wood. Their totem poles, masks, ceremonial batons, dishes, spoons, and utensils are also of wood. Their realistic art, both painting and sculpture, must be attributed to the presence of this workable medium. So influential is the use of wood that women weaving blankets adhere to patterns and designs that are far more suitable for the working of wood than of wool. Their mythology and social systems are wholly in keeping with the environment. Their potlatches, or great feasts, by which the social status of the individual is fixed, are possible only in a place where vast stores of food are readily obtained. "Rivals fight with property alone and the best way to humiliate a rival is to flatten him out with a sumptuous feast." The more lavish the destruction and consumption of fish, game, and oil, the more highly esteemed is the giver of the feast.

It cannot be asserted, however, that geographical environment, either in the case of the Eskimo or in that of the Northwest Indian, has *determined* the content of the culture; or that the mores and institutions arose out of the properties of the environment. Yet obviously it would be futile to embark upon a study of either group without an examination of the possibilities and the limitations of the environment. Man must eat to live, and some sort of adjustment must be made with nature if man is to survive. The food-obtaining complex is inseparably bound up with the environment, and all other traits and concepts are likely to represent responses that are colored by it. A culture is quite likely, therefore, to coincide in extent with a certain type of environment and to undergo transformation where its limits are reached.

Another sweeping conclusion has it that environment is a passive influence in the affairs of men, especially in modern times where the degree of emancipation from nature is admittedly large. If it is true that modern man has triumphed over nature, it is equally true that nature never surrenders. To-day, with all our cultural trappings, we are constantly reminded that nature has not graciously assumed the passive rôle assigned her by man. Floods and inundations in the Mississippi and the Yangtze valleys, earthquakes in Japan and California, drought in Russia and the central United States are reminders, none too gentle, of this truth. Each community has problems of this nature. One Floridian sleeps with a barometer by his bedside, fearful of the West Indian hurricane; another consults the thermometer hourly, fearful of the frost that may visit his citrus crop. Indeed, every farmer in the world is aware of the penalty of a few days' neglect. That we have won a high degree of emancipation from our physical surroundings it would be foolish to deny. Indeed millions in this country live and die without a thought of the conditioning of the physical environment. Considerations of this nature are left to the farmer and others in close contact with the vagaries of nature. Possibly our vaunted emancipation explains the prevailing state of ignorance regarding matters of geography.

The influence of environment upon the history of man and upon the shaping of human culture has been tremendous. Indeed the task incumbent upon each society at the start was to arrive at an adaptation that would enable it to survive. Each social group discovered certain helps to be gained from nature, and these had a hand in shaping the peculiar complexion of its culture. Likewise each had its obstacles to overcome, and the ways of meeting them were reflected in the culture pattern. Early cultures, because the groups lived in isolation to a large extent, reveal a highly indigenous or endemic quality. Since the struggle for existence was great, the relation between man and nature appears in every phase of the tribal culture. Through thousands of years of isolation and inbreeding, members of various groups took on the especial physical characteristics that have resulted in the division of men into various races. Geography has had, then, an influence in the formation of races, as well as of cultures. The point to keep in mind, however, is that the early cultures represent just so many local solutions of the problem of existence. Since man is found to-day in almost every nook and cranny of the earth, it would seem that he has the capacity for adjusting himself to any type of environment. The task has never been an easy one. There has been much loss of life, and, as history bears witness, defeat and annihilation have often resulted. At present, thanks to the social heritage, the consequence of untold generations of struggle, every existing social group has arrived at an adjustment to the environment in which it lives.

It is among primitive peoples to-day, the isolated and the backward families of the human race, that this fundamental relationship between man and the physical environment is most clearly seen. The

Pygmies of the Congo basin, remote from the paths of spatial diffusion, are influenced largely in their manner of living by their geographical surroundings. They utilize their native milieu to the fullest extent. Their food, their shelter, their utensils and weapons are all products of the rain forest in which they live. But even here it cannot be maintained that the cultural relationships between man and man are entirely dictated by the environment. We do not know, for example, the origin of their exogamic institutions, but even if they do not represent a borrowing, we may be sure that environment did not oblige them to adopt this type of social structure, for the identical adjustment has been found among peoples living in wholly dissimilar and dissociated environments. Once the adjustments necessary to maintain the essential supplies in food, shelter, and other material needs have been effected, the limits of the culture are fixed only by the bounds of the physical and mental equipment of the human species, which have not yet been reached.

4. Human Geography and Culture

Human geography, we said, is the interrelation between the physical environment and the social environment of any group. The study of the subject is important because in endeavoring to establish the relationships that exist between social groups and their environments much is learned of man's manner of living and of the different cultures he has erected. A terrestrial view of the world is gained, a view afforded by no other social science. Even history, the most catholic member of the group, confines its narration of man's experiences largely to that of the development and diffusion of Western civilization.

Nature has provided certain fixed vantage points from which mankind and his manner of living upon earth can be viewed. We shall find that nature has plotted identical environmental conditions in various portions of the globe. There are trade wind deserts, for example, in the Old World and in the New World; in the northern hemisphere and in the southern hemisphere. One of our problems is to ascertain to what extent the cultures of peoples living in identical environments are similar, thus measuring—crudely, to be sure—the extent of the environmental influences. Do men living in trade wind desert environments ever progress beyond the so-called "leather cultures"? Must men living in the damp equatorial forests of the Congo and the Amazon rest content with the crude "rain forest cultures" that repeat themselves in this type of environment? These and problems of similar interest fall within the scope of human geography.

Certain peoples, we shall find, have been more successful in coping with their physical environment than others. One hesitates to speak of inferior and superior peoples or of inferior and superior cultures, for one does not wish to minimize the achievements of such primitive peoples as the Masai, for example, who have succeeded in maintaining themselves in the East African Highlands in an environment of intense heat, poor soil, famine, and pestilence. On the other hand, there are many people who have consciously forsaken a poor environment to seek a better one; others who either with the aid of, or in defiance of, their environment have attained a more adequate adaptation and a richer culture. Finally, there are those who have so mastered their environment that they mold it, almost at will, to their advantage. We shall find that physical environment has much to do with the cultural status which certain peoples have been privileged to attain.

One last inquiry remains. There is on earth to-day, for better or worse, one outstanding civilization, the Euramerican, with its nuclei in Western Europe and the United States. Its forces are so tremendous that its marginal areas reach round the globe. Few peoples in the world have escaped its influences in some form or other. Peoples, conscious of its force, are everywhere endeavoring to adjust themselves to meet its impact. Some, like the Japanese, have wilfully substituted much of its content in the place of the indigenous culture. Others like the Chinese and the Hindus have made a determined stand, if not against Euramerican culture as a whole, certainly against those manifestations which they believe to be at variance with their own way of life. As a result there is much conflict and readjustment in the world. The primitive peoples, for the most part unaware of the immensity of the forces that are seeping in upon them from every quarter, are everywhere threatened with destruction. Only by ethical and legal suasion are they protected and preserved against the uglier manifestations of our civilization. Yet the responsible carriers of this culture, from motives of gain and altruism, sincerely hope that the contact between the cultures will benefit both. The Euramerican needs the products of the native environment, while the native, it is hoped, will succeed in adapting himself to the social heritage of the dominant culture and so discover a happier way of life.

Euramerican culture bears a conqueror's relation to environment. It strides the whole earth seeking grist for its industrial mill. All environments are forced to pay it toll. From the rain forest, from the jungle, from the steppe, and from the desert raw materials are gathered. Euramerican enterprises are changing the physical surface of the earth. In conformity with the geographical principle that similar environments are capable of producing identical products, Brazilian rubber has been planted in Java and Liberia, American cotton in India and Egypt, and Old World coffee in Brazil and Mexico. Wheat, barley, potatoes, tobacco, and other semi-tropical products have been shifted hundreds of miles poleward. All over the globe materials such as coal, copper, tin, iron, and a host of others are disemboweled and carried to the factories of Euramerica. The soils of the earth are arbitrarily treated, and mixed in accordance with scientific formulas. The streams are harnessed and their waters distributed according to dictate. The entire transformation we cannot discuss, for it is partly historical and does not fall within the limits of this volume. But the subject of the relation of Euramerican culture to other environments is vital, and with that much of the book will deal.

The influences of the physical environment are never stilled. Yet in its destructive aspects it has been made to recede to the background, emerging only in time of catastrophe to remind men of the eternal struggle for which it stands. All peoples have won in some measure a victory, and the extent to which the social group has advanced beyond the level of mere subsistence is the measure of its progress. Those groups that have forced from a reluctant environment a surplus are free to pursue their higher needs.

CHAPTER II

PRIMARY LAWS

5. Rotation and Revolution

It has been said that human geography is a terrestrial science, for it deals with the whole of the earth and its inhabitants. Every human being, regardless of where he lives, is subject to certain primary laws of the physical universe. Land, water, air, light, and heat are the things that make life possible. The distribution of the latter two is dependent upon the motions of the globe. The earth rotates and the limits of day and night are set. The earth revolves about the sun, determining the duration of the year. The inclination of the earth's axis from the perpendicular gives rise to seasons. Light and heat from the sun are distributed to man in accordance with the dictates of a rotating, revolving, and inclined sphere.

From earliest times man has been observant of the motions of the earth and of its relations to other celestial bodies. His concepts of time are derived from the periodicity of the motions of the earth; and his measurements of space owe their accuracy to a knowledge of the relationship between the earth's inclination and the earth's rotation. Surveying and navigation, two practical arts, are based largely upon the earth's relations to various celestial bodies. The tides, regulated by moon and sun, play a prominent part in man's activities. A knowledge of the laws of the earth, then, is fundamental to the study of geography.

Accurately speaking, the earth is not a sphere, but a spheroid. Because of rotation about an axis, the earth like any other rotating mass tends to flatten slightly at the poles. Thus it is that the distance from pole to pole is about twenty-seven miles shorter than the diameter of its equatorial plane. The shortest diameter is 7,899.7 miles, the longest 7,926.5 miles.

The earth rotates about its axis once in twenty-four hours in a direction which is counter-clockwise as viewed from the north pole.

The most obvious effect of rotation is the alternation of day and night. The sun rises and the sun sets, we say. This is a misconception but does no harm. Rather it is the earth that rises and sets. Hold an electric bulb near any small globe. One half will be light, the other dark. In rotating this sphere, any fixed point upon it will encounter light, then darkness, as it passes within and without the illuminated

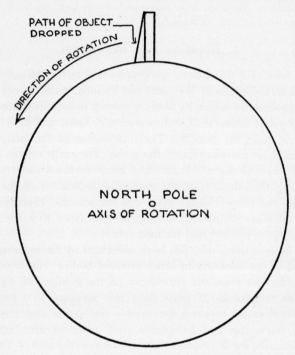

FIG. I—PROOF OF ROTATION EXPERIMENT
(*See pages 17-18*)

surface. Similarly light from the sun illumines half the surface of the earth at all times. Any place within the Great Circle of Illumination experiences daylight. If the earth were not inclined upon its axis all places would have twelve hours day and twelve hours night.

That the earth rotates can be demonstrated by a simple experiment. A body dropped from a great height, such as a tall building, will fall not to the point immediately below, but a little to the east, in fact, the deviation is about one inch for each 500 feet of fall. The explanation is that the velocity of a point in a rotating body increases with its distance from the axis of rotation. Accordingly the top of the building in this example will be moving at a greater rate than the surface below it, just as the rim of a wheel moves faster than the hub. Thus a body loosed into space will have a greater forward velocity above the surface than at the surface. Since the falling body always falls slightly to the east, it is taken as proved that the earth rotates in a counter-clockwise direction.

The earth revolves in an elliptical orbit about the sun once during the year, in 365¼ days approximately. Revolution can also be proved but only with the aid of complex astronomical observations. The direction is counter-clockwise when viewed from the north pole. The path of revolution is not a circle, but an ellipse with the sun as one of the foci. For this reason the distance of the earth from the sun varies. At *perihelion,* which happens to fall in January, the earth is 91.5 million miles from the sun, while at *aphelion,* which falls in July, the distance is 94.5 million miles. This phenomenon gives rise to slight differences in temperature between the northern and southern hemispheres. Since perihelion occurs in January, winter in the northern hemisphere is slightly less severe than in the southern hemisphere; likewise, as aphelion occurs in July, summer in the northern hemisphere will be slightly moderated. Conversely the seasons in the southern hemisphere will be in a corresponding degree intensified.

6. Inclination and the Seasons

The earth's axis inclines 23° 30′ [1] from the perpendicular to the plane of its orbit, and it is for this reason that there are seasons. Suppose, for purpose of illustration, that the axis of the earth did not incline. The edge of the Great Circle of Illumination would at all times pass through the north and south poles. Exactly half of every parallel of latitude would be illuminated by the sun. In other words, day and night would be equal in length in every place on the surface of the earth, and under these conditions there would be no seasons except the minor differences set up by perihelion and aphelion.

The north pole, however, during the whole time of revolution is inclined and points, allowing for a slight variation, toward a fixed spot in the heavens, the North Star. It is this inclination of 23° 30′

[1] Actually 23° 27′ 8″.

which gives rise to the varying length of day and night. In common parlance we say that during the course of the year the sun travels north from the equator 23° 30′ to the Tropic of Cancer, which it reaches on June 21; then returns to the equator on September 23,

A. SIMPLIFIED GLOBE WITH VERTICAL AXIS

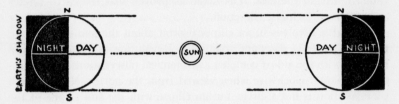

B. WITH INCLINED AXIS

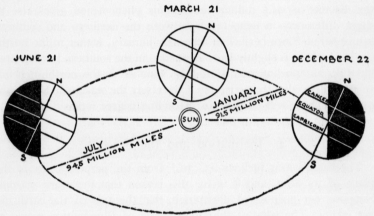

Fig. 2—Inclination and the Seasons
(*See pages 18–21*)

completing half its journey. During the second part of the year it travels southward to the Tropic of Capricorn, which it reaches on December 21, finally completing its journey on March 21, at the equator. When the sun is on the Tropic of Cancer in June, we know that day is longer than night; and conversely when the sun is at Capricorn in December, night in the northern hemisphere is longer than day. This whole journey, however, is an illusion.

The true state of affairs can be visualized readily by the use of an electric bulb and a globe. If the axis of the globe be inclined 23° 30' toward a fixed point on the ceiling as the globe is slowly revolved about the bulb there will be no danger of missing the significance of the experiment.

First observe closely the relations between sun (bulb) and earth (globe) when the north pole is most inclined toward the source of light. This is roughly the state of affairs on June 21. The farthest point south touched by the Great Circle of Illumination will be 66° 30' from the equator. No light will fall upon the southern extremity of the earth. A point in rotation at 66° 30' S. describes the Antarctic Circle. Ninety degrees north of that latitude, at 23° 30' N., the sun's noonday days will fall perpendicularly upon the surface of the globe. Thus originates the *Tropic of Cancer,* the farthest latitude north where the sun's noonday rays fall perpendicularly upon the earth. Since this takes place only once during the year, on June 21,[1] we speak of it as the *summer solstice,* the time at which, apparently, the sun stands still before turning southward. At that time the area encompassed by the Great Circle of Illumination is, as always, half of the surface of the globe, but more of the northern hemisphere is illuminated than of the southern. In fact, on June 21 all areas within 23° 30' of the north pole have twenty-four hours of daylight, but lands within 23° 30' of the south pole have no daylight. Indeed there will be no night at the north pole and no day at the south pole until the autumnal equinox, September 23. Because of inclination, then, during half the year, from March 21 until September 23, the length of day exceeds that of night in the northern hemisphere, and conversely night is longer than day in the southern hemisphere.

Now if the globe under consideration be revolved counter-clockwise 90° through an imaginary orbit, the new position will correspond with that of sun and earth on September 23. The light rays now fall vertically upon the equator, while the Great Circle of Illumination just touches the north and south poles. Upon that day, the *autumnal equinox,* day and night are equal at all places on the earth. At both poles the sun can be seen on the horizon. A single day later, however, the sun's rays are perpendicular at a point just south of the equator and in consequence the Great Circle of Illumination favors the southern hemisphere. The day, then, everywhere in that hemisphere is

[1] Actually the dates vary slightly from year to year.

slightly longer than the night, and the north pole is plunged into darkness until the succeeding equinox, March 21.

If the globe be revolved an additional 90°, the north pole will be pointed as far as is possible away from the plane of the Great Circle of Illumination. The condition prevailing on June 21 is reversed. On December 21 the day is longest in duration in the southern hemisphere and shortest in the northern hemisphere. The upper margin of the Great Circle of Illumination on December 21 touches the earth at a point 66° 30′ north of the equator, namely, the Arctic Circle; and the sun's rays are vertical at a point 23° 30′ south of the equator, namely, the *Tropic of Capricorn*. This day, when the noonday rays of the sun fall vertically at the furthest point south, is called the *winter solstice*.

Another shift of 90° in the orbit will find the noonday rays again falling vertically upon the equator. This position of earth and sun is the *vernal equinox,* March 21, and with it the experiment comes to a close. It should be noticed that as the Great Circle of Illumination always bisects the equator, day and night there remain equal. Hence the name *equator*.

Thus it is obvious, because of the revolution of an inclined sphere, that day and night are not everywhere equal in length. Since the sun transmits not only light but heat, each part of the earth will receive more heat at certain times during the year than at others. During spring and summer more heat is received than at the other seasons; these are the growing seasons and then nature is bountiful to man. In autumn and winter, the light and heat necessary to plant life are proportionately reduced, and man must draw upon his harvest stores. Polar regions have only two "seasons," day and night; while in low latitudes between the tropics where night and day vary little in length, the seasons vary more in accordance with rainfall than with temperature. There the seasons are either wet or dry.

Seasons in the main, however, are warmer or colder depending upon the length of the day. The amount of daylight enjoyed by any particular place is inexorably fixed by the proportion of the parallel of latitude of that place falling within the Great Circle of Illumination. This amount will vary from day to day as the earth proceeds in its revolution about the sun. Philadelphia, latitude 40° N., has fifteen hours daylight at summer solstice, but only nine at winter solstice.

The amount of daylight, though most important, is not the only factor in the determination of seasons. Naturally the more daylight a place receives, the more heat also; but heat is not distributed uniformly within the Circle of Illumination. Two other factors of importance enter: the varying slant of the sun's noonday rays, and the varying distance traveled by the noonday rays through the atmosphere.

The noonday rays of the sun are vertical at the Tropic of Cancer on June 21. At noon at any place along the parallel 23° 30' N. the sun is at the zenith, that is, directly overhead. All places north and south of this latitude will receive less heat because the rays of the sun will be slanting, not vertical. The further away from the parallel 23° 30', the less will be the amount of insolation. The sun altitude at Philadelphia, for example, will not be 90° but 74° 30'. The varying slant of the sun's noonday rays, therefore, must be taken into consideration as a cause of the seasons.

The earth is covered by a blanket or envelope of atmosphere that absorbs much of the heat from the rays of the sun. The more slanting the rays of the sun, therefore, the more heat will be intercepted by the atmosphere. Philadelphia will receive less heat from the noonday rays of the sun than a point 10° further south, not only because the rays are more slanting, but also because the rays must pass through a greater thickness of atmosphere. But all three factors in the determination of the seasons—the varying length of day and night, the varying slant of the sun's noonday rays, and the varying distance traveled by the noonday rays through the atmosphere— depend ultimately upon the prime factors of rotation, revolution, and inclination.

7. Latitude

Latitude is the angular distance measured in degrees, minutes, and seconds north and south of the equator. *Longitude* is the angular distance, likewise measured, east and west of the *prime meridian* of Greenwich. If the latitude and longitude of a place are known, its position upon the surface of the earth can be ascertained without difficulty.

The whole science of cartography has its basis in two fixed points on the globe. They are the ends of the axis of rotation, the poles.

These are readily discernible, since the upper end of the axis, taken
celestially, points approximately toward the North Star at all times.
The equator is an imaginary great circle, every point on which is
equidistant from the poles. The plane of the equator bisects the earth's
axis and is perpendicular to it. The angular distance from equator to
pole measured along the arc of the earth's surface is 90°. Regions near

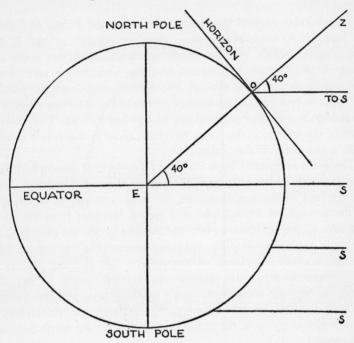

Fig. 3—Method of Computing Latitude (Vernal Equinox)
(*See page 24*)

the equator are said to have low latitude since the latitude of the
equator is 0°, while polar regions are in high latitudes. A parallel of
latitude is simply an imaginary circle parallel to the equator, and thus
every point on it is equidistant from the north or the south pole.
Latitude is measured along meridians, imaginary semicircles passing
from pole to pole. Longitude is measured along parallels. A degree of
latitude varies, because of flattening at the poles, from 68.7 miles at
the equator to 69.4 miles at the poles. For ordinary purposes of calculation, however, a degree of latitude is sixty-nine miles.

Latitude can be readily measured at sea where the surface is uniform. Let us endeavor to determine the latitude of a place due east of the harbor of Philadelphia. The date is March 21. The observations are most easily made at noon when the sun is nearest the zenith, the point directly overhead. With the use of a small instrument, the sextant, the angular distance from the southern horizon

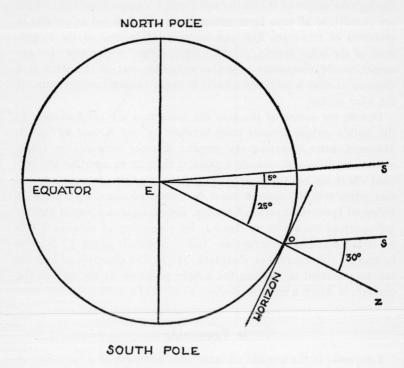

FIG. 4—METHOD OF COMPUTING LATITUDE AT SEA
(*See page 25*)

to the sun is sighted. As the angular distance between the zenith and the horizon is always 90°, and as the sextant in this instance measures 50°, by subtraction the angular distance between the zenith and the noonday sun will be 40°. Now it can be demonstrated by means of plane geometry that the angular distance from the zenith to the noonday sun is equal to the angular distance from the point of observation to the point where the sun's rays are falling vertically.

On the diagram the angle ZOS equals angle OES, for interior exterior angles are equal. Measured on the surface of the earth the angular distance from the equator to the observer is 40°, his latitude; for latitude is measured always from the equator. The latitude is 40° N. because the sun was sighted from the southern horizon. It should be noticed upon the diagram that an extension of the line ZO will pass through the center of the earth; and further that the lines SO and SE are parallel, as all rays from sun to earth are regarded as parallel in problems of this type. This can be assumed because of the magnitude of the solar system. A globe eight inches in diameter, for example, would necessitate a sun seventy-two feet in diameter at a distance of over a mile and a half, in order to duplicate the scale of the solar system.

During the course of the year the sun's rays are perpendicular to the earth's surface at some point between 23° 30′ N. and 23° 30′ S. Mariners, after observing the angular distance between the zenith and the noonday sun, consult a nautical almanac to ascertain the latitude where the sun's rays are falling vertically. The distance between that point and the equator must be computed since all latitude is reckoned from the equator. Suppose, for example, the sun is sighted 30° north of the zenith on April 1. By consulting an almanac it will be found that the sun's rays are falling vertically about 5° N. The latitude of the observer is, therefore, 25° S. The principle of latitude can be mastered by solving the simple problems at the end of the chapter, in which a nautical almanac need not be used.

8. Longitude

Longitude is the angular distance east and west of a meridian. A *meridian* is an imaginary line passing over the surface of the earth from pole to pole. Centuries ago the meridian passing through Greenwich, near London, was arbitrarily chosen as the prime meridian from which all longitude is measured. *East longitude* is the angular distance eastward, measured in degrees, minutes, and seconds, from the prime meridian to the meridian of the observer. *West longitude* is measured similarly. The meridian 180° necessarily marks the extreme point of east or west longitude. As all meridians converge at the poles, the poles have no longitude; the only directions there are north or south. A degree of longitude varies in length from 0 at the poles to

69.6 miles at the equator. Published tables conveniently indicate the length of a degree of longitude along any parallel.

Longitude may be reckoned as easily as latitude; in fact the navi-

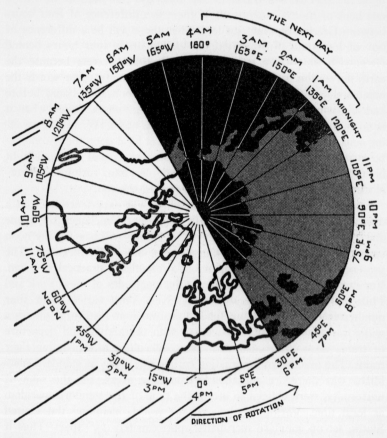

FIG. 5—LONGITUDE AND TIME
(*See pages 26–27*)

gator makes this observation several times daily. Aboard every ship is a clock or chronometer which keeps Greenwich time, the time of the prime meridian. If, for example, at local noon, the time at which the sun is highest in the heavens for that day, the Greenwich time registers 4 P. M., the longitude will be 60° W. If Greenwich time had registered 6 A. M. the longitude would be 90° E. The explanation follows.

The earth rotates upon its axis once in twenty-four hours. A point upon the surface will travel in that time 360°, at the rate of 15° in one hour of time. Consequently if there is a difference of four hours between Greenwich time and local time, there will be a difference of 60° of longitude. Furthermore, if local noon is four hours behind Greenwich time (4 P. M.) the longitude will be west because the earth is rotating in a counter-clockwise direction. In other words the inhabitants of Greenwich have experienced noon four hours before and are, when it is noon at 60° W., awaiting sunset. Again when it is noon at longitude 120° W., the inhabitants at 60° W. will be awaiting sunset. Suppose, as a final illustration, at local noon the chronometer registers 4 A. M. The longitude will be 120° E. and not until eight hours have elapsed will the Greenwich meridian, turning counter-clockwise, be exposed to the noonday rays of the sun.

Every place on the surface of the earth will experience noon at a different time, except those on the same meridian, since the plane formed by the axis and the observer's meridian will pass by the noon sun at a different time than the plane of any other meridian. The presence of innumerable local noons presented a practical problem. For example, the difference between the longitudes of New York and Philadelphia is 1′ 2″. Local noon at New York varies about four minutes from that of Philadelphia. Local noon at Pittsburgh shows a wider variation. Railways concerned with the arrival and departure of trains were confronted with great difficulties in scheduling their trains. The practice of designating certain meridians as standard meridians was therefore adopted. Surrounding areas, for the sake of uniformity, were obliged to accept the time of the standard meridian as local time. Various regions of the world, including the United States, set up standard meridians, approximately 15° apart. Thus it is that Eastern United States keeps the time of the 75th meridian (New York), and Central United States that of the 90th meridian (St. Louis). Mountain time is that of the 105th meridian (Denver), and Pacific time that of the 120th (Reno). A traveler passing from Pittsburgh to Chicago, let us say, will have to set back his watch one hour.

Just as a traveler passing through 15° of longitude should push forward or set back his watch one hour, depending upon the direction of travel, so should the round-the-world traveler change his day. A man setting out westward from New York will find, after he has gone 15°, that his watch has gained an hour and that he will have to set it back, a procedure that will give him twenty-five hours in that day. In 360° of travel he will have changed his watch twenty-four times

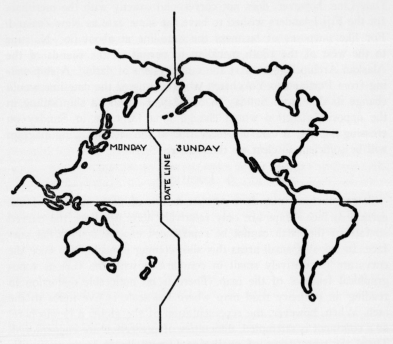

FIG. 6—INTERNATIONAL DATE LINE
(See page 29)

and thus have gained twenty-four hours or a whole day. If, for example, he has kept a diary showing that he left New York on September 1 and has been absent on his trip exactly one year (365 days), he will find on his return that although his diary indicates the day to be September 1, actually it will be September 2.[1] The explanation, of course, is that he has been around the world with

---

[1] This phenomenon was first noted by the members of Magellan's crew, who made the first voyage around the world. The ship's records indicated the day of their return to be September 6, and they were puzzled when told that it was the 7th.

the sun. If his journey had been eastward, he will find the actual date
of his return to be August 31.

To alleviate the plight of travelers and, more important, to adjust
business arrangements in general, the nations have adopted the 180th
meridian as the place where the date is changed. The International
Date-Line, however, does not correspond exactly with the meridian,
for the Fiji Islanders wished to have the same date as New Zealand.
For like purposes of business the date-line at about 60° N. runs
to the west of the 180th meridian to permit all the islands of the
Alaskan Archipelago to have the same system of dating. A ship sailing from Portland to Yokohama when it crossed the date-line would
change its day from Sunday to Monday. Likewise a ship sailing in
the opposite direction would change from Monday to Sunday on
crossing the line. A careful observation of the accompanying diagram
will be sufficient to clear up the matter.

9. Location

A geographical map is a representation of some portion of the
earth's surface. Maps are only relatively accurate, since the curved
surface of the earth cannot be reproduced exactly upon a flat surface. In maps of small areas this shortcoming is negligible, since the
curvature is relatively small in comparison with the various topographical features of the map. There is no noticeable distortion in
reading an ordinary road map where the scale is five miles to the
inch. When, however, the representation of the globe, a hemisphere,
or a continent is attempted, difficulties of projection are encountered.
There are many types of projections (methods of construction de-
vised to draw on a plane surface one that is curved), but in each some
element of truth has to be sacrificed. In geographical maps, truth of
area is of prime importance, and only secondly truth of form. To
achieve these ends great freedom is taken in distorting the relationship between parallels and meridians. In the most satisfactory type of
world projection, *Goode's interrupted homolographic,* the chief ends
of the cartographer are achieved, but at the sacrifice not only of the
network of coördinates but of oceanic unity.[1]

The projections most commonly used are the *Mercator, conic, polyconic, azimuthal* (Lambert) *sinusoidal* (Sanson), and *homolographic*

[1] See *Goode's School Atlas,* Plate I, for examples of this and other projections.

(Mollweide). They all fail in one or more of the following respects: the shapes of the regions are distorted, the areas are wrong, or the distances are wrong. The Mercator map was invented in 1569. A cylinder is wrapped around the globe at the equator and the projection made. In a conic projection a cone is slipped over the globe with the apex resting over the pole of the hemisphere it is desired to reproduce. The other projections are, likewise, drawn in accordance with various geometric principles.

On a Mercator world projection all meridians and parallels are straight lines, but the extent of a degree of longitude is everywhere the same. In consequence, distances, though relatively accurate near the equator, are greatly distorted in high latitudes, so affecting the size and the shapes of areas. On this projection North America is larger than Africa, while Greenland, which is a ninth the size of South America, appears larger. Mercator maps, however, are used by all mariners because by merely calculating the angle between the meridian of their location and the rhumb-line (a straight line connecting two points in their course) they can set their compasses and sail directly to their destinations. On a conic projection the meridians appear as straight lines and the parallels are curves. Areas near the central parallel are relatively true, and therefore this type, and the polyconic for like reasons, are used in the representation of small areas. The azimuthal is important because it most effectively reproduces the shapes of whole continents. The sinusoidal is especially good for projecting small areas. The homolographic is the favorite world map for it not only respects the shapes of the continents, but in it the areas are relatively correct for all the land masses. Each continent has a mid-meridian of its own.

Good maps are essential to the study of geography. Our whole appreciation of distances and their relationships arises from the use of maps. The study of the geographical phenomena of any place begins with correct location, and therefore location is one of the elements of human geography. Without maps we should be confronted with the tedious task of deriving and memorizing the latitude and longitude of every place under consideration, but with the aid of maps we can locate little-known places with reference to the more important places or the geographical features near-by. In studying the geography of three towns, for example, it is more important to see that one lies on the seacoast, another along a river, and a third in a desert than to know merely the latitude and longitude of each.

Maps are important, too, in every comparative study. By their use
we can visualize not only the topographical features but such essentials as the distribution of temperature and rainfall and of population.
We can discover environments where similar climatic controls prevail.
It is possible at a glance to compare regions producing similar crops
and, in many cases, by observation and deduction to account for the
distribution of an agricultural crop.

10. Tides

Celestial bodies, moon and sun, are responsible for the tides. Every
place influenced by the tides experiences high water and low water
twice daily. The tides are of great service to man. Their periodical
ebb and flow keep open many river mouths which would otherwise
silt up. Were there a cessation of the tides, many of the important
ports of the world would have to be replaced by others nearer the
coasts since dredging would be so expensive as to be impracticable.
Moreover the prosperity of certain seaports is directly dependent
upon the height of the flood-tide. As the tonnage of steamships increases, the number of ports that can accommodate them decreases.
Philadelphia, for example, can no longer be reached by the largest
vessels. Southampton has succeeded Liverpool and London as the
passenger port of Great Britain, yet the largest ships cannot proceed
safely up its channel at low water. Tides are also important because
they assist in the disposal of sewage. Recently, because of the com-
plaints of New Jersey, New York City has abandoned the dumping
of garbage in the open sea.

The high tide, known as the *flow tide* or *flood-tide,* occurs twice
daily, as does the *ebb-tide* or low tide. The time at which high tide
occurs is about fifty minutes later each day. Thus at New York high
tides once occurred at 6.41 A. M. and 7 P. M. on October 10 and at
7.29 A. M. and 7.50 P. M. on the following day. This variation results
from the fact that the tides are caused largely by the moon, and the
lunar day is 24.51 hours in length.

The moon and the sun both exert a pull upon the surface of the
earth. The surface of the water, under the gravitational attraction of
the moon, tends to swell up. The center of gravity of the earth-moon
system, owing to the greater mass of the earth, is a point about 3,000

miles from the earth's center, or about 1,000 miles below the surface. The moon has the greatest attraction for the part of the earth nearest it; here its attraction tends to overbalance the centripetal force of the earth upon its surface mass, making the earth bulge up. On the opposite side, the attraction is weakest and tends to be overbalanced by the centrifugal force; there the earth bulges as a result of the differential attraction of the moon. It is known that the solid part of the earth responds to the lunar attraction, but only the waters are sufficiently mobile to be noticeably distorted. These bulges are the high tides, and between them the tides are low.

The earth rotates, and in consequence the high tides shift as the center of gravity shifts. Were the earth entirely composed of water, two great waves would travel about the earth's surface, one always below the moon and the other directly opposite the first. The tidal poles do not correspond with the poles of the earth but shift with the verticality of the moon to the earth's axis. They are shifting poles. The simplicity of the tides is interfered with by the land masses.

Another factor enters, also. The sun, too, exerts a pull on the waters of the earth, which, however, is lessened by its great distance. The pull of the less remote moon exceeds the sun's pull in the ratio of 11:5. Twice during the month, the sun's influence is distinctly noticeable. When the earth, moon, and sun are in a straight line, at conjunction (S-M-E) or at opposition (S-E-M) the tides are more extreme than usual and are known as *spring tides*. The waters of the earth are then subjected to the combined pull of the moon and sun. Twice during the month, at first and third lunar quarters, the pull of the sun is at right angles to the pull of the moon and the pull of the latter is correspondingly counteracted. At such times the *neap tides* occur, and then the tides are least extreme. In other words, at spring tide the highest and lowest tides of the month are occasioned, while at neap tide the high and low tides approach nearest the means for the month.

Tidal waves reach the shores in all directions twice daily, the normal effect of bulging water. If the earth consisted of water surface only, the tidal wave would be between two and three feet high. The tides reach a normal velocity only upon the open seas; elsewhere they are retarded by the configuration of the lands, and particularly by shallowness. Tides are not observable upon the open sea, but along the coasts elaborate tide tables are constructed for the benefit of navi-

gators, fishermen, and bathers. The greatest range in the daily tide
occurs along bays and river mouths and upon lands scarcely elevated
above sea-levels. In the Bay of Fundy in Nova Scotia the range between high and low tide is fifty-nine feet, and at Mont Saint-Michel
in France it is forty-six feet. At river mouths the effect of high tides
is to back up the fresh waters. The tide is felt for 280 miles up the
St. Lawrence, up the Hudson as far as Troy, and up the Delaware

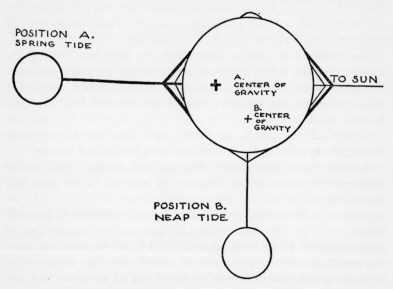

FIG. 7—SPRING TIDE AND NEAP TIDE
(*See pages 31-32*)

as far as Trenton. River tides whose effect is augmented by sea winds
are called *bores*. Frequently when these occur ships take to the middle
of the stream or even to the open seas. Along the Tsientang River of
China the wave is commonly twenty-five feet high. Inland seas and
points along great bays experience little tide. New Orleans, for
example, experiences no tidal rise whatever. Small islands, however,
have currents of great velocity that swirl about the channels separating them.

CHAPTER III

THE ELEMENTS AND THEORY OF CLIMATE

11. Introduction

The elements of physical geography, for purposes of this book, may be classified roughly as *fixed* and *variable*. The most important fixed elements are location, topography, and soils and minerals. The variable elements are climatic: temperature, pressure, winds, humidity, and precipitation.

Geologically, of course, there are few fixed elements, for in the course of thousands of years all the above-mentioned elements are subject to change. But physical geography, upon which the study of social geography is based, confines itself to a very small geological period, the present.

Location is the starting point in any study of regional or local geography. Once the habitat of a social group is known, the student has made immense preliminary strides, for he has at his command a knowledge of environmental controls which, although they may be continental and even terrestrial in scope, are often the decisive environmental influences upon the life of the community. The topography of a place is determined by the configuration of the surface—chiefly the relief and the position of the various water bodies. The soils and mineral deposits are similarly fixed physical features. Every student should, with the aid of an atlas, acquaint himself with the major physiographic features of the earth since a knowledge of the position of the mountains and plains, the rivers and bays, and the soil belts and mineral deposits is indispensable. Further on the environments of certain social groups will be discussed at some length, and in every instance the fixed features, as well as the variable, will constitute the groundwork of the study.

Climatic features are designated as variable because no one of the elements of climate is a fixed quantity. The temperature of a place is constantly changing; the amount of rainfall may vary daily, seasonally, and from year to year, and so with the other elements. Thus the climate of a region may reveal marked changes during the course of a year. Yet it is possible to classify climates roughly into types and to delineate the spatial range of each.

Climate is important because heat and moisture are essential to animal and plant life. Many regions of the earth, though possessing good soil and level terrain, are useless to man and relatively uninhabited because of insufficient rainfall. Some lands of this character have been reclaimed through irrigation, but the proportion is exceedingly small in comparison with their extent. Other regions are barren because of too great or too little heat to sustain plant or human life.

The theory of climate, which underlies the classification of the earth into the socio-physical areas so important for the study of human geography, has its basis in the primary laws of the earth. It should be borne in mind always that light and heat are received from the sun in fixed amounts. In this sense, then, the principles governing climatic conditions are corollary.

12. The Atmosphere

That the atmosphere of the earth has substance every one knows who has encountered a strong wind. Its weight, the amount of pressure which the air exerts, is nearly fifteen pounds to the square inch at sea-level. The atmosphere rotates with the earth and must be considered an essential part of it. Moreover, it is necessary to the sustenance of life for it carries life-giving properties. It acts also as a distributor of moisture and has a marked effect upon temperature.

The atmosphere is composed of a mixture of gases extending several hundred miles in altitude. Air at sea-level is more dense than at higher altitudes, not only because the heavier constituents tend to settle but because the weight of the air is greater. Indeed it is known that nearly three-fourths of the atmosphere by weight lies below the level of the highest mountain, Everest, which attains a height exceeding five miles.

The principal gaseous constituents of the atmosphere are nitrogen, 78 per cent, and oxygen, 21 per cent. Of the minor gaseous substances argon is the most abundant, and carbon dioxide and water vapor are the most important. Dust is an important non-gaseous ingredient.

Nitrogen is not, like oxygen, essential for breathing but seems necessary for both plant and animal life. Both obtain it, for the most part, not directly from the air but in the form of nitrogen compounds. Carbon dioxide, though small in quantity, is important as the chief food of plants. In addition it acts as a blanket to retain some of the heat that is radiated from the land surface into space. If the amount of carbon dioxide in the atmosphere were appreciably increased, the surface temperature would reach a higher level.

The water vapor in the air constitutes less than one per cent of its volume. It varies greatly from place to place and from time to time in the same place. Like carbon dioxide it is constantly leaving and entering the atmosphere. It is evaporated or picked up by winds and deposited on the surface in various forms: rain, snow, dew, frost. As the source of rain its importance can scarcely be exaggerated. Water vapor also acts as a blanket for retaining heat. Dust is omnipresent and is visible in sunbeams. One puff of cigarette smoke liberates 4,000 million granules. The amount of dust is greater over land than sea and greatest in industrial areas. It consists of organic materials, such as pollen, and of all sorts of inorganic substances. Dust particles serve as nuclei about which water vapor condenses.[1] Finally, while slightly decreasing the sharp brilliance of the sun's rays, dust scatters light so as better to illuminate the atmosphere.

13. The Simplified Globe

"Climate is the average succession of weather conditions over a considerable period." The chief elements of climate are temperature, pressure, winds, humidity, and precipitation. A description of these elements at a specific time constitutes the *weather* of a place. The United States government issues a daily weather report which serves many useful purposes. A description of the weather of an area may tell little of its climate, for the weather changes from day to day and from season to season. Climate statistics are based upon daily weather reports over a succession of years. The longer the period of observation, the more authoritative is our knowledge of the climate. We know little of the climatic conditions prevailing in many areas be-

[1] Ions, especially negative ions, also act as nuclei. Thus sunlight as well as smoke may be responsible for the formation of clouds.

cause of the absence of data over a series of years. Meteorologists are of the opinion that observations over a period of thirty-five years are essential for generalizations about climate. A weather report will give little clue to the climate of a region because each of the elements of climate is likely to vary widely from the mean average.

We may, however, speak of *uniform* and *variable* climates. In some regions the weather changes little from day to day, even over a long series of years. The Sahara, experiencing high temperatures and little rainfall from season to season, has a uniform type of climate. The eastern part of the United States, however, has a variable climate since the various atmospheric conditions show a considerable range from day to day and from season to season.

In order to visualize the origin of climatic zones it will be well to observe the conditions set up upon a *simplified globe,* a globe of uniform surface without revolution or inclination. In a world so controlled, day and night do not vary in length, seasons do not exist, and the effects of relief are not operative. Let us examine the atmospheric conditions that arise under such circumstances.

Earthly temperature is the degree of the heat of the surface atmosphere. The sun, a gaseous sphere in mass a million times greater than the earth, is the source of heat. Though the sun has a surface temperature of 10,000° F., and a nuclear temperature of 50,000,000° F., the earth, ninety-three million miles distant, intercepts only 1/2,000,000,000 of the heat radiated by the sun. Part of this solar energy is reflected back into space, part is absorbed by the atmosphere, and only a small portion influences the earth's surface. Upon a simplified globe temperature varies strictly in accordance with latitude. At the equator, where the sun's rays are always falling vertically, the temperatures are highest; at the poles, where the rays are most oblique, temperatures are lowest.

Pressure conditions, however, do not yield to such a simple characterization. Air has weight; as formerly stated, its pressure is nearly fifteen pounds to the square inch at sea-level. Differences in atmospheric pressure are the primary cause of atmospheric currents and winds. On our simplified globe the heated air over the equatorial area expands and bulges. Since air, like water, seeks a common level, this expanded air tends to flow off. It cannot move east or west because pressure conditions there are similar. It therefore flows north and south where isobaric gradients [1] have been set up in the upper atmosphere. In consequence of this loss of air the equatorial region between 10° N. and 10° S. is an area of relatively low pressure. The air that has been displaced settles finally in the high pressure belt, between 25° and 35° in either hemisphere. These regions are, there-

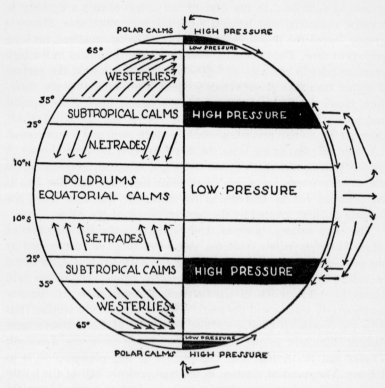

FIG. 8—PRESSURE AND WIND BELTS: SIMPLIFIED GLOBE
(*See pages 37–41*)

fore, areas of high pressure. Four additional pressure belts may be noticed. There is a region extending poleward from each high pressure belt which, in comparison, has a lower pressure. Finally, because of the extremely low temperatures of the polar areas, the pressures there are high because of the contracting of cold air. Hence

[1] An *isobar* is an imaginary line connecting points of equal pressure, and the *isobaric gradient* is a curve revealing the discrepancy among isobars.

on a simplified globe there are seven pressure belts recognizable in the higher levels of the atmosphere.

On the surface, however, because of the unequal pressures set up in higher altitudes, prevailing winds are created. The ascent of air in the equatorial belt gives rise to light variable winds that are known as *doldrums*. In the days of sail it was always a problem to traverse equatorial seas because the winds were unreliable. Mariners greatly feared the heat and the prospect of being becalmed for long periods of time. The system of *planetary winds* originates in the high pressure belts in latitudes 25°–35°. Here the pressure at the surface is higher than that of surrounding areas. The descending air, therefore, blows out in the only possible directions, toward the equator and toward the poles. In each hemisphere on our simplified globe, there are set up two prevailing winds, a north wind and a south wind. (A wind takes its name from the direction *from which* it blows.) A similar system, though moderate in extent, arises in polar areas. On the surface prevailing winds blow from the poles, and the loss is compensated for by currents in the upper air that flow down the isobaric gradient created by the contracting air of the poles.

The earth rotates, however, and in consequence the direction of all the planetary winds is altered. According to a law propounded by the physicist Ferrel, moving bodies in the northern hemisphere tend to deflect to the right and in the southern hemisphere to the left. Hence the north winds of the northern hemisphere tend to become northeasterly winds; and the south winds, southwesterly winds. Thus arise the *Northeast Trades* and the *Westerlies* of the northern hemisphere. Similarly in the southern hemisphere there are *Southeast Trades* and *Westerlies*. The explanation of this phenomenon is as follows. The speed of rotation in the high pressure belt of the northern hemisphere is greater than at latitudes farther north. Hence the eastward velocity of a body moving northward is greater than that further north; consequently the south wind is pointed in the direction of rotation. The north wind, however, has a lesser eastward velocity than the equatorward belt and tends to fall behind, becoming a northeast wind. In the southern hemisphere identical conditions prevail. Since air in the high pressure belts and at the poles is descending, there, too, light variable winds prevail. They are known as *Subtropical* and *Polar Calms* respectively.

Because of unequal pressure conditions, eleven distinct atmospheric belts originate upon the surface of the simplified globe. They are as follows: the Equatorial Low Pressure area, the Northeast and Southeast Trades, Subtropical High Pressure areas in each hemisphere, the Westerlies of each hemisphere, Temperate Low Pressure areas in each hemisphere, and the Polar High Pressure areas.

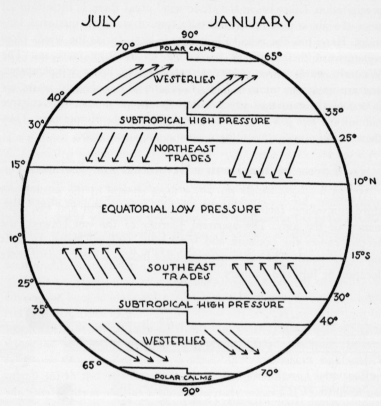

FIG. 9—MIGRATION OF ZONES OWING TO INCLINATION
(*See pages 41-42*)

In introducing water bodies upon our simplified globe we shall be able to describe the fundamental conditions of humidity and precipitation. In equatorial regions because of the high temperature the relative humidity is always high. As air is warmed its capacity to absorb moisture is increased, with the result that the air becomes saturated with moisture. Furthermore, as the air is constantly ascending, there is constantly recurring precipitation. The moisture-laden air cannot retain its water vapor once it becomes rarefied in high altitudes. On the other hand, in the high pressure belts the air is descending and growing warmer under pressure. In consequence, although its capacity for absorbing moisture is increased, there is no precipitation. Likewise in the trade wind areas there is little rainfall since the air is moving horizontally toward warmer equatorial latitudes. Here, too, the relative humidity is high, for as the winds blow equatorward their capacity for taking up moisture increases. The Westerly winds move poleward, encountering lower temperatures, and are unable to retain all their moisture. The cooling of warm air is one of the causes of precipitation. In the polar areas the relative humidity is very low because air so cold cannot absorb moisture. Thus there is little precipitation there upon a simplified globe.

14. Effects of the Earth's Revolution and Inclination

We shall now consider the effect upon climate of the second and third controlling factors—the revolution of the earth and the inclination of the axis. The apparent journey of the sun between the tropics causes the pressure and wind belts, outlined above, to shift north and south. The accompanying table indicates their approximate location in July and January.

	July	January
Polar Calms (N.H.)	70 – 90N.	65 – 90N.
Westerlies (N.H.)	40 – 70N.	35 – 65N.
Subtropical High Pressure (N.H.)	30 – 40N.	25 – 35N.
Northeast Trades	15 – 30N.	10 – 25N.
Equatorial Low Pressure	10S.– 15N.	15S.– 10N.
Southeast Trades	25S.– 10S.	30S.– 15S.
Subtropical High Pressure (S.H.)	35 – 25S.	40 – 30S.
Westerlies (S.H.)	65 – 35S.	70 – 40S.
Polar Calms (S.H.)	90 – 65S.	90 – 70S.

In studying this table it should be noticed, first, that the migration of the zones is not so great as the sun's apparent journey. The rays of the sun are perpendicular at 23° 30′ N., for example, at the summer solstice. The thermal equator, however, never extends beyond 10° N. Secondly, the limits of each zone are reached, not at the time of the solstices, but in January and July. The explanation is as follows. The earth responds slowly to the heating of the sun. Not only is the thermal equator behind the sun, but the seasons lag behind the sun approximately a month. In latitude 40° N., for example, the warmest day does not occur until a month after the June solstice, the longest day.

15. Effect of Land Forms and Water Bodies Upon Temperature and Pressure

The climate of the earth is further modified because its surface is composed of two elements, land and water. They react differently to the sun's heating. Land acquires and loses heat more readily than water does. Water is a reflector of heat and light rays; thus, in comparison, the land absorbs a larger proportion of the heat of the sun's rays. Furthermore, water evaporates and is cooled in the process. On a spring day evaporation may result in cooling the water surface as much as 15°. As water is transparent to heat and light rays, the heat of the sun penetrates several fathoms below the surface. Soil and rock are essentially impenetrable to light and heat rays, thus making for higher temperatures than upon water surfaces. Water is mobile, and for that reason convection currents are set up as soon as the surface begins to heat. This prevents excessive heating at any one point as on the land. Finally, ocean currents transport warm waters hundreds of miles. Hence it is that the distribution of heat on land and water is quite different. The diurnal range of temperature even in equatorial waters rarely exceeds ten degrees, while upon the sands of Sahara the range may be 60°.

Large bodies of water, then, tend to modify the extreme conditions prevailing upon lands. The North Atlantic Ocean, for example, retains the summer's heat long after the rays of the sun are vertical over the Tropic of Cancer, and along the eastern seaboard, seashore bathing is pleasant until late in September. This capacity of the ocean to retain heat also moderates the severity of the winter. Fortunately, too, the ocean maintains its winter coolness far into the summer months, affording some relief to those who live upon its coasts.

In the interior of land masses the moderating influences of large water bodies are negligible. In the interior of North America and, even more strikingly, in Eurasia, the seasonal ranges of temperature are very great. Valencia, on the coast of County Kerry, Ireland, is in

approximately the same latitude as Semipalatinsk, in western Siberia. At Valencia the seasonal range of temperature is only 13°, while at Semipalatinsk, which is a typical rather than an abnormal example of a continental interior, the seasonal range is nearly 75°. Verkhoyansk in northeastern Siberia, latitude 67° 30′ N., is the cold pole of the earth. Here the seasonal range is 120°; in January the mean temperature is – 60°, in July 60°.

Land masses and water bodies also influence atmospheric pressure conditions. In the interior of Asia, for example, where the summer heating is intense, the air ascends, thus setting up an isobaric gradient down which air flows toward the sea. In consequence, the pressure of the interior falls to 29.60″, while that along the Pacific coast rises to 29.80″.[1] In the winter, conditions are reversed. The cold air of the interior contracts, causing air over the Pacific to flow inland. The pressure over the former registers 30.50″; over the ocean, 30.20″. The frequent occurrence of low pressure areas over continents and high pressure areas over oceans in summer and vice versa in winter is especially marked in regions having marked seasonal differences in temperature.

Two permanent areas of low pressure, both in the northern hemisphere, have a remarkable influence upon climate that will be alluded to later. These areas are located just south of the Arctic Circle, one just south of Iceland and the other just south of the Aleutian Islands. They are caused by the presence of large masses of warm water which are carried northward by the Gulf Stream and the Japan Current. Their low pressure (*circa* 29.50″) is most noticeable during the winter.

16. Influence of Land Masses and Water Bodies Upon Winds

As we have seen, the inclination of the earth causes the several temperature belts to shift north and south during the course of the year. The land masses and water bodies are responsible for the irregularity of the earth's isotherms, which are imaginary lines connecting places having equal temperatures, and of the earth's isobars,

---

[1] Approximate mean pressures at sea level: at the equator 29.8″; in the *horse latitudes*, 30.1″ (*circa* lat. 30°); in the temperate zone, 29.7″ (the minimum, lat. 60°).

which connect places having equal pressures. For similar reasons the planetary winds, the Trades and the Westerlies, are shifted three or four degrees out of their normal courses. In Africa, for example, the low pressure prevailing in equatorial regions permits the Northeast Trades to blow far south of their normal course, almost to the equator in July.

There are two classes of winds, other than planetary winds, that exert a great influence upon climate. They are first, *periodic* winds, comprising land and sea breezes, and the monsoons; and secondly, *aperiodic* winds, cyclones and anticyclones. Land and sea breezes are daily in occurrence, while the monsoons are seasonal winds.

A sea breeze is set up when the land in the course of the heating of the day attains so low a pressure that winds from the sea blow in. Land breezes are likely to occur at night, for under conditions of falling temperatures and rising pressure, a breeze arises that can flow only seaward. Land and sea breezes are local phenomena and are felt only a few miles inland. The sea breezes of summer are, in part, responsible for the popularity of the seaside resorts.

Monsoons, however, are the most important periodic winds, and are the life blood of such countries as India and China. Monsoons are intensified and deflected trade winds that blow from sea to land during the summer season. The China monsoon is felt along the east coast of Asia from about 15° N. to 40° N. The Northeast Trades are deflected toward the center of the land mass because of the attraction of the low pressures existing in the interior during the summer. In the winter the movement is outward, for the air is blowing from an area then characterized by very high pressures. The China monsoon begins in May and continues until September.

The India monsoon begins in June and lasts until October. It blows over a wide extent of territory in south Asia from lower Burma to the Indus River region. It, too, is caused by the low pressures of the interior. So great is the influence exerted that the Southeast Trades are drawn clear across the equator toward the heart of Asia. The Northeast Trades, as such, are non-existent in India. The summer monsoon is the great rain-bearer for southern Asia. Without these moisture-laden winds much of India would be as dry and barren as Arabia. From October until March conditions are reversed—the air movement is away from the high pressure areas of the interior toward the low pressure areas of tropical Australia and equatorial

latitudes in the Indian Ocean. In blowing over the Bay of Bengal, however, the winter monsoon brings heavy rains to the southeastern coasts of India. The winter monsoon might be regarded as a greatly intensified Northeast Trade wind that is being deflected toward low

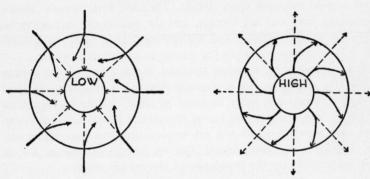

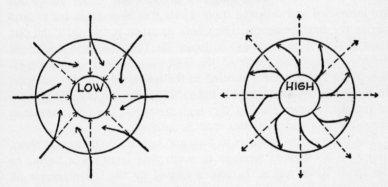

FIG. 10—INFLUENCE OF ROTATION UPON CYCLONES AND ANTICYCLONES
(*See page 46*)

pressure centers. The native trade of this portion of the world formerly was dependent upon the seasonal changes of the monsoon. Thus the winter monsoon carried the Hindu and Arab traders to Africa and the summer monsoon carried them back to India again.

The aperiodic winds are the cyclones, the anticyclones, and, of lesser importance, thunder storms. In the land masses of the temperate zones, particularly, intense heating in summer gives rise to temporary areas of low pressure causing inblowing winds. The direction of such winds is affected by Ferrel's law (see p. 39). Inblowing winds in the northern hemisphere deflect to the right and in the southern hemisphere to the left. Cyclones in the northern hemisphere blow finally in a counter-clockwise direction about the center of the low pressure area. In the southern hemisphere the movement is clockwise. Cyclones are carried along by the prevailing planetary winds. Hence those originating on the northern edge of the subtropical belt of high pressure are carried first to the north and then to the east by the Westerlies. In the southern hemisphere the movement is southward until they are picked up by the Westerlies. Cyclones are most frequent in the zone of the Westerlies, but as they are usually 500 miles in diameter, their outward edges frequently penetrate into the Subtropical Zone of High Pressure. Furthermore, cyclones are more frequent in the northern hemisphere, first, because the great continental land masses are found there, and secondly, because the permanent areas of low pressure of Iceland and the Aleutian Islands give rise to powerful, recurring cyclones, particularly during the winter season. As a rule cyclones are more frequent over the land in summer and over the seas in winter, in conformity with prevailing low pressure conditions. Since cyclones are accompanied by rain, the interior will be benefited during the summer and the windward coasts during the winter.

There are several types of cyclones: tropical, continental tornadoes, and the so-called great cyclones. Tropical cyclones are less frequent than the great cyclones. They are the hurricanes of the West Indies and the typhoons of the East Indies and the Philippines. Their frequency is greatest during the late summer and early fall and September is the danger month in both areas. Tropical cyclones are small in diameter, from 100 to 200 miles. Winds revolve at a terrific speed about a nuclear areas twenty miles broad. A ship meeting a tropical cyclone will encounter fierce winds, a lull, then winds again. Settled areas such as Florida experience great devastation as the result of such cyclones. In 1926 in the Miami district alone, over a hundred lives were lost and property valued at $75,000,000 was destroyed.

Kendrew, the British meteorologist, describes the tropical hurricane as follows:

The local heat and moisture of the Doldrums are predisposing causes. These conditions are present in even greater degree sometimes when the Doldrums lie on the Equator itself, but on the Equator there is not the necessary rotational deflection to set up the whirl which itself tends to increase the violence of the storm by the centrifugal force it generates. Cyclones (i. e. tropical cyclones) are likely to originate in late summer and autumn when the Doldrums lie at their greatest distance from the Equator, in latitudes where the rotational deflection is considerable and the temperature of the ocean still high. The meeting of the north-east and south-east trades (deflected north of the Equator into westerly winds) possibly tends to set up a revolving movement, and may thus assist the formation of the cyclones; probably a marked discontinuity in respect of temperature and especially humidity is always present. Abnormally cold air in the higher atmosphere above the cyclone is probably another necessary condition. The South Atlantic is the only tropical ocean in which cyclones do not occur, and it is noteworthy that the Doldrums never swing south of the Equator here, nor yet do the north-east trades cross the line.

The storms develop in the midst of an extensive area where the barometer is falling, and the winds are weak and irregular and weather sultry. At some spot the fall of the barometer becomes more rapid, and the wind blows in from all sides. The area of rapidly falling barometer is not extensive, and the winds, influenced by rotational deflection, soon form a rapidly rotating whirl around it, anti-clockwise in the northern hemisphere, clockwise in the southern. The weather conditions are almost uniform in all directions from the center. The center itself, the core of the storm, is a small region perhaps 20 miles in diameter, where the pressure is very low, and the winds light and irregular, but the waves are particularly high and dangerous owing to the violent cross seas produced by the winds round about. Sometimes the air is quite calm and the sky clear in the "eye of the storm" as the core is called. Outside the core the winds are revolving with hurricane force, the transition from calm to shrieking hurricane being often extraordinarily sudden, and many a ship has been taken aback. The sky is covered with dense black clouds, and a torrential downpour of rain, often with violent thunder and lightning, completes the tempest.

Many of the most destructive storms ever experienced are the hurricanes of the West Indies and the typhoons of the Philippines and the areas just south of them.

The tornadoes of inland regions in the belt of the Westerlies are equally violent. Originating in areas of unequal heating, they move generally eastward, at the rate of forty miles an hour, and may revolve about the core at a rate of three hundred miles an hour. There are as many as fifty tornadoes a year in the United States, and they are not uncommon in Europe. Their behavior is almost unbelievable. Not only is there a horizontal movement of air but also a vertical one, the result of a powerful indraught of air into the small center of low pressure. This amazing condition within the funnel causes houses to burst outward, corks to explode, and even birds to be plucked of their feathers. In these tornadoes heavy objects such as sheds, tables, horses, cattle and human beings have been swept up and carried as far as a mile. The property damage is, of course, very great.

The great cyclones of the zones of the Westerlies and of the edges of the Subtropical Zone of High Pressure are more frequent and are non-violent in character. They so influence climate that regions subject to them are commonly called *cyclonic regions*. They average from five hundred to one thousand miles in diameter and move eastward at the rate of seven hundred miles a day. Thus they take about four days to cross the United States. One or two are always crossing over the country. They gradually spend their force and disappear over the Atlantic Ocean. Since they are areas of low pressure, the winds blow in and rain results, usually because of falling temperatures at night or because of contact with cooler air.

Anticyclones are temporary areas of high pressure, accompanied by outblowing winds that revolve in accordance with Ferrel's law. In the northern hemisphere the direction of revolution is clockwise and in the southern hemisphere counter-clockwise. The general direction is west to east in the zone of the Westerlies. A glance at a daily weather map will reveal several anticyclones in transit across the United States. Their average size is somewhat larger in diameter than a cyclone and their rate of speed across the country less. They are more frequent over the land masses in winter than in summer. Anticyclones bring clear weather because the air is descending and blowing outward toward areas of lower pressure.

Thunder storms, considered as air currents, are caused apparently by excessive local heating and a rise of air without whirl. Their general direction is with the planetary winds. They are most frequent in the trade wind zones and in lower latitudes of the belt of the Westerlies. They frequently accompany cyclones on their equatorward edges at a considerable distance from the center.

17. Influence of Land Masses and Water Bodies Upon Humidity and Precipitation

Much of this subject has already been discussed, but some generalizations of importance remain. The distribution of land forms and water bodies has a marked effect upon the relative humidity of the atmosphere. Three things should be kept in mind: first, that winds blowing over large bodies of water become very humid; secondly, that winds blowing over land surfaces cannot greatly increase their humidity; and thirdly, that winds originating over lands are likely to be low in humidity.

The condensation of water vapor leads to precipitation in its various forms: rain, snow, and hail. Precipitation occurs when air is cooled below the dew-point.[1] The most common circumstances are as follows: when air is blown poleward or in general from a warmer to a cooler place; when air rises by convection, being cooled and becoming rarer through expansion; when cooler air is brought to warmer air; when air is blown up a cold mountain side.

Sea breezes furnish the moisture of showers that occur along the coasts during the summer. Rain is most likely to result upon hot days when the moist air that has blown in from the sea rises because of convection. At a higher altitude it cannot retain the whole of its moisture. At night, when the temperature is falling, rain may also occur. Monsoon winds blowing from sea to land are very high in humidity. Rainfall sets in as soon as the monsoon reaches the land when the various causes listed above become operative. The great cyclones are responsible in large measure for the rainfall of lands situated in the temperate zones. A cyclone in its course across the United States is usually accompanied by rainfall.

18. Ocean Currents

Ocean currents are caused by the great planetary wind systems which give them their direction of flow. The Trades are most important in this respect, for they are the most steadily blowing winds. In the Atlantic, the Pacific, and the Indian Oceans, they set up great currents which drift gently toward the eastern shores of the continents. These are deflected either north or south until they are picked

[1] The *dew-point* is the temperature at which the amount of water vapor present is all the air can hold.

up by the Westerlies and carried to western continental shores, whence they drift equatorward until they come under the influence of the Trades. In the North Atlantic, for example, the Northeast Trades cause the Canaries Current to drift equatorward and westward until the West Indies are reached. Here, however, the current is joined by part of the South Equatorial Drift which escapes from the main stream owing to the configuration of the Brazilian coast. The entire current then eddies about the West Indies, much of it finding its way into the Gulf of Mexico between Yucatan and Cuba. It then forces its way through a narrow opening, the Florida Straits. At this point the Gulf Stream attains a speed of seven miles an hour. The Gulf Stream moves northward along the Atlantic Coast retaining an unusually high temperature. Off New York it is picked up by the Westerlies and carried toward Europe. Here again it divides, for only a part moves southward to join the Canaries Current. The remainder, as the North Atlantic Drift, passes between Iceland and the British Isles and flows past the North Cape into the Arctic Ocean. The great volume of the Gulf Stream, together with its division off the British Isles, has a profound effect upon the climate of Europe. The Westerlies are warmed as they pass over the Atlantic toward Europe, and since much of Western Europe is a great plain, these warming winds greatly modify the winter temperature of that continent. North America, however, is adversely affected, for the cold Labrador Current drifts through the Davis Strait along its northeastern shores as far south as Maine. Because of this drift, Labrador, which is in the same latitude as Great Britain, is practically uninhabitable. As far south as the Grand Banks of Newfoundland shipping is endangered because the chilled air causes fog and the current carries with it large quantities of pack ice and icebergs.

A careful study of the courses of the ocean currents will reveal similar influences at work in many lands. All currents, save one, are intraoceanic. The West Wind Drift, set up by the Westerlies of the southern hemisphere, encircles the globe. Eastern Japan, the eastern seaboard of the United States, western Europe, and western New Zealand receive the benefit of its warming waters. On the other hand, the cold Peruvian Current, while modifying the equatorial west coast of South America, intensifies the winter of Chile. The cool California Current is responsible for fog and lower winter mean temperatures along the western coast of the United States. The Arctic Drift of

the northeastern coast of Asia renders northeast Siberia as uninhabitable as Labrador.

19. Effect of Mountains and Plains

Altitude has a marked effect upon climate. Temperature decreases
with altitude, about one degree for each 330 feet. Pressure likewise
decreases with altitude because of the heavier weight of air at the
lower level of the atmosphere. High mountains are agents in causing
precipitation for they force strong winds to rise, thus cooling and
condensing their moisture. Frequently lands on the leeward side of
mountains are deserts because they lie in a "rain shadow." Mountains
deflect weaker winds, often protecting large areas from cold winds.
The French and Italian rivieras, famous as winter resorts, owe their
advantages partly to mountain shelter. India is protected by the great
screen of the Himalayas against the cold interior winds which cause
much misery in China. The interior of the United States lacks mountain shelter of this type and suffers throughout the winter from the
cold waves that sweep down from Canada.

Plains are more suitable for human habitation than mountains;
yet in certain regions, the lack of high mountains to intercept the
moisture of the prevailing winds renders the level plain-lands useless
to man. Trade winds, for example, blow equatorward and are constantly increasing their capacity for absorbing moisture. Since none
of the causes of precipitation are operative, vast areas like the Kalahari and the Sahara are deserts.

The effects of altitude upon the world scheme of climatic types are
important and will be discussed in the next chapter. Locally, too,
altitude has important consequences. People dwelling upon equatorward slopes of mountains, for example, are usually better off than
those dwelling upon poleward slopes. Certain crops, such as grapes
and apples, are likely to flourish better upon equatorward slopes than
on the plains below because the sun's rays, especially in higher
latitudes, are more vertical on these slopes.

CHAPTER IV

CLIMATIC TYPES

20. Classification of Types of Climate

The climates of low latitudes are as follows: Equatorial, Sub-equatorial, Trade Wind with Ample Rain, Trade Wind Desert, and Monsoon. The climates of middle latitudes are Mediterranean (Sub-tropical), Maritime, Continental Desert, Steppe, Humid Continental Interior, and Continental with Marine Influence. Climates of high latitudes are either Tundra or Polar.

The various conditions of temperature—pressure, winds, humidity, and precipitation—discussed in the last chapter have the effect of setting up thirteen distinct types of climatic environment. Many of these are found in several of the continents in both the northern and southern hemispheres. A thorough understanding of the physical bases of these types is important since climate is the most significant geographical factor over any large area. Climate frequently determines the habitability of a region and indeed may limit the density of population in a given area. It controls, in many instances, the nature of vegetation which is so important to man. This chapter, in setting forth the climatic characteristics of each environment, is merely re-arranging in a more realistic manner the various elements analyzed in the preceding chapter. The result, however, will have an important practical application, for it will enable us to classify the lands of the earth according to climatic environments.[1]

21. Equatorial Climate

Regions having an Equatorial type of climate are situated in low latitudes, approximately between 10° N. and 10° S. The largest equatorial areas are the Amazon basin, the Congo basin, and the East Indies (including a large part of the Malay Peninsula). Areas of minor economic importance are found in Ceylon and along the coasts

[1] Examine carefully Plate I in reading this chapter.

of the Gulf of Guinea in Africa. The temperatures of the Equatorial type are characterized by remarkable uniformity. Indeed in some regions the twelve monthly means do not vary more than one degree. Typical monthly averages, however, range from 75° to 83°. The pressure is exceedingly low and the winds, the doldrums, are light and variable for the air is ascending. The Trades push in but rarely reach the equator. In sailing days navigators were willing to go a considerable distance in order to cross the doldrums where narrowest in order to escape being becalmed.

The air is high in humidity in the Equatorial environment. Along the African coast the sky is regularly overhung in the afternoon with inky black clouds, the *pot au noir* of the French sailors. The rainfall is uniformly heavy all the year round, and it is largely due to the monotonous temperature and heavy precipitation that this environment is so inhospitable to the white man. There are both hotter and rainier areas on the surface of the earth, but relief is given either in cooler nights or in a dry season. The afternoon shower of equatorial regions is refreshing, but the benefit lasts but a short time.

Annual rainfall varies greatly from place to place, but it is always heavy. The Congo basin has about sixty inches of rainfall, which is about average for the whole equatorial belt. Land and sea everywhere influence precipitation. For example, at the estuary of the Amazon, the rainfall reaches one hundred inches because of onshore winds; in the interior, it is from sixty to eighty inches; in the west, it mounts again, for the Andes force the east winds to ascend. The East Indies have, for the most part, a precipitation heavier than average as they are affected by the monsoon. The heaviest annual rainfall ever recorded in equatorial areas, 412 inches, occurred on the southwest side of Camerun Peak which is exposed to winds that are monsoonal in character.

Typical monthly averages range from one to twenty inches. Normally there are two wet and two dry seasons, though in many places they are not clearly marked because of local conditions. The four seasons are governed by the passage of the sun's vertical rays over a given area. Thus, at Colombo in Ceylon, maximum precipitation is experienced in May (12.1″) and in October (14.4″), while the minimum occurs in February (1.9″) and in August (3.8″). In the East African plateau the annual rainfall is low (30″) because of altitude, yet in places the double maximum is clearly marked. The dry season of the

Equatorial type of climate is but relatively dry since precipitation is at all times plentiful.

22. Subequatorial Climate

The Subequatorial type of climate is transitional between the Equatorial and the Trade Wind types. It is found in latitudes 10° to 17° N. and S.: in southwest Mexico, Central America and South America in the New World and in Africa, Australia, and Indo-China in the Old World. The temperatures are high as in the equatorial areas, but daily and seasonal changes are noticeable at the outer limits of this belt. The pressure is always low because of high temperatures. When the sun is over the tropic, doldrums are encountered in Subequatorial latitudes, but six months later the trades prevail. Rainfall and temperature conditions depend largely upon the sun's position for the rain belt moves northward and southward. Thus each region has a rainy season and a dry season. At the outer limits of the Subequatorial belt the rainy season is short. It increases in duration as the Equatorial belt is approached. At the mouth of the Senegal River, 15° from the equator, there is almost constant rainfall during the three months of July, August, and September.

During the dry season, then, the relative humidity is low and there is little or no precipitation. There is not moisture enough to support the vegetation which becomes brown and withered. The wet season is the period of growth. This type of climate is essentially transitional, a fact which its plant life reveals. At its outer edges the vegetation resembles that of the trade wind desert. As the equatorward edge is approached grasses yield gradually to dense tropical jungle.

23. Trade Wind Climate with Ample Rain

This type of climate occurs where trade winds are forced upward by highlands after having passed over the sea. Eastern Mexico, the east coasts of South America, Africa, and Australia between latitudes 17° to 25° N. and S. have this type of climate. Minor areas are Madagascar, some of the West Indian Islands, the Hawaiian Islands and other islands of the Pacific Ocean.

These regions, many of which are important tropical plantation areas, would be as dry as trade wind deserts were it not for the factor of altitude. The trade winds, as they pass over the oceans equatorward, become warmer and saturated with moisture. Mountains and plateaus force them to ascend to altitudes where, owing to the lower temperatures, they cannot retain all their water vapor. As the trades blow regularly, such regions receive copious rainfall during the whole year. More falls during the summer than during the winter because convection is most active then and the pressures are lower.

An extreme condition is met in the Hawaiian Islands where the mountain barrier in places is as high as thirteen thousand feet. Here the mean daily rainfall is about an inch, and the mean annual precipitation, one of the highest experienced anywhere, exceeds four hundred inches. The East African coast (about 17° S.) has an annual rainfall exceeding forty inches, while the west coast in the trade wind belt has less than ten inches. The same phenomenon occurs in comparing the east and west coasts of Australia and South America in this belt.

Here, then, are favored tropical areas. The temperature ranges are greater than those of Subequatorial regions for they lie in higher latitudes. On islands the temperature is more uniform because of the moderating influences of the ocean. A temperature of 65° in the coolest month and 80° in the warmest month is typical. The cool nights give the planter in the Trade with Ample Rainfall zone an advantage over the equatorial planter and the uniformity of the rainfall renders it an agricultural area superior to many of the Subequatorial regions.

24. Trade Wind Desert Climate

The Trade Wind Desert type of climate occurs in latitudes 17° to 35° north and south in the Subtropical High Pressure Belt (Tropical Calms) or in the zone of the Trade Winds where the land is flat. Such areas are found in southeastern California, southern Arizona and New Mexico, in the northwestern part of Argentina, in Egypt, the Sahara Desert, the Kalahari Desert and the coasts north and south of it, Arabia, Persia and northwest India. Parts of Somaliland and southeastern Abyssinia, and the coast of Peru south of 5° S., though outside the proper latitudes, have this type of climate.

The range of temperature, both daily and annual, is greater than that of any other tropical climate. Typical monthly averages range from 55° to 90°. The most obvious reason for the range is the higher latitude of this belt. As we go north or south we should expect summer and winter to become more pronounced. Yet this factor alone is not sufficient to account for a difference of 40° between day and night. The great range in temperature is due to another factor—the heating and cooling of the land. These lands are barren of vegetation for the surface is composed of rock and sand. Under such circumstances temperature reacts quickly to insolation. The thermometer rises rapidly during the day but at night falls just as rapidly. The land is unable to retain its high temperature since the heat, in an atmosphere of clear skies, drains away quickly.

The furnaces of the earth are found in this environment. In the Australian Desert the temperature has been known to exceed 100° on sixty-four consecutive days. At Azizia, twenty-five miles south of Tripoli, the highest official temperature reading was made, 136.4°. At Death Valley in the California Desert the thermometer has registered 134°. Wadi Halfa in Egypt has the hottest summers on earth. The mean monthly temperatures from April through October average nearly 85°. This means a noonday average of well over 100°. In spite of the intense heat, it is not impossible to live in these areas. The air is exceedingly dry, the wind is brisk, except in the belt of Tropical Calms, and the winters are relatively cool. Most of the trade wind deserts are uninhabitable because there is no rainfall, not because of the heat.

Whether a region lies in the Tropical Calms or in the path of the Trades, there is little precipitation. The average is usually below ten inches for the year. The rainfall is rarely of direct benefit to the inhabitants who depend on oases and artesian wells for their water supply since the whole supply may come in two or three storms. The nature of the soil is such that the rains drain rapidly away. At Doorbaji (Sind), in the Thar Desert, where the mean annual rainfall is five inches, a deluge of thirty-four inches fell in two days. Because of the severity of such storms the French army regulations forbid the overnight encampment of troops in the bottom lands of the Sahara. Otherwise desirable because they are sheltered by steep banks, these lands have been swept by floods which originate from deluges in distant parts of the basin. In regions where roads, bridges, railways and irrigation works have been erected, these sporadic storms cause great property damage.

There is sparse rainfall, then, in areas having the Trade Wind Desert type of climate. In the zone of Tropical Calms there is little precipitation because the air, under high pressure, is being warmed.

In the trade wind zone the movement of air is toward the equator, thus permitting the atmosphere to absorb increasing amounts of moisture. Here only mountains and plateaus can cause rainfall.

25. Monsoon Climate

The regions experiencing the Monsoon type of climate are India, southeast Asia, most of China and parts of Japan. Monsoonlike influences are noticeable in other parts of the world—off the Guinea Gulf in Africa and along the southeastern coast of the United States. The phenomena of the monsoon were explained in the last chapter. In every instance there is a marked seasonal alternation of winds; the moist monsoon blows in the summer toward a continental low pressure area, and dry winds blow in winter from a continental high pressure area.

Temperature in monsoon areas is tropical in general, but it varies greatly because of differences in latitude, altitude, and distance from the sea. The outstanding characteristic of this type of climate is the excessive rainfall of the summer and the lack of it during the other seasons. Hence the monthly average of precipitation show great extremes, from one inch to 110 inches. Unfortunately, however, though the rainfall is plentiful during the growing season, it may vary greatly from year to year in any one place. Thus many communities live in terror of famine caused by the failure of the monsoon to materialize. On the other hand the torrential rains may result in floods causing rivers to burst their dikes, destroying crops and drowning people by the thousands. This happens frequently in China, and the Hwang Ho has been fittingly termed "China's Sorrow."

In India, 85 per cent of the rain falls during the monsoon season, from June to October. In north China, as much as 90 per cent falls during the months from May to September. Bombay has a rainfall of 75.7 inches from June to October and only 0.2 inches from December to March. Much of the rainfall is caused by the ascent of moist air to rarer levels because of the low pressure over the land; but where the rains are torrential, altitude is the dominating factor. The windward side of the Western Ghats in India receives 100 inches of rainfall during the year, while the leeward side has a total of about 20 inches. To the north, west, and east the moisture-laden winds encounter a mountain barrier which they cannot escape. Here the precipitation is heaviest. Cherrapunji, on the south slope of the Khasi Hills of Assam, altitude about 4,500 feet, lies in a mountain funnel. This place has a mean rainfall of 318 inches during the four monsoon months. On a single day forty-one inches of rain fell. This is as much as New York receives during a whole year.

Several monsoon districts have two rainy seasons. In such places the outblowing winds of winter blow over the water before reaching the land. Ceylon and the southeast coast of India have this peculiarity. The coast of Annam, the west coast of Honshu, and the eastern islands of the Philippine group receive their heaviest rainfall from the winter monsoon. South China, also, has a peculiar distribution of rainfall. It has a double maximum—in June just before the monsoon is at its height, and in September at the time of the heavy typhoon rains.

The monsoons permit a density of population that is equaled only in the cyclonic areas of industrial Europe and North America. This is because of the rice crop which is prolific where the rainfall is plentiful and the temperature high. The monsoon changes the whole face of the land when it arrives. Before its coming the surface is hard and parched, the vegetation shriveled, and the air excessively dry. Because of the dust and heat the skies seem grey rather than blue. Little streams of water meander slowly along gigantic river beds. With the monsoon the land is flooded and everywhere luxurious vegetation springs up. River beds that seemed so large a few weeks before can scarcely accommodate their swirling waters. The greatest floods come at the middle and end of the monsoon since the earlier rains are absorbed by the parched surface of the land.

26. Influence of Altitude

In some localities the climate types discussed are greatly modified by altitude. Mountain tops above 16,000 feet in the tropics are normally covered with snow at all seasons. Between latitudes 17° N. and 17° S. altitude has the effect of greatly lowering the temperature and diminishing the rainfall common to such latitudes. The most sizeable area of this kind is the great plateau of East Africa. Just interior from the coast the ascent of the land mass is very marked. The whole of East Africa, from the highlands of Abyssinia to the Drakensberg Mountains is a vast plateau with an altitude varying from 2,000 to 6,000 feet. It is interrupted only by the valley of the Zambezi. In equatorial and subequatorial latitudes, neither the temperature nor the rainfall are capable of sustaining the vegetation common to those climatic types.

27. The Mediterranean or Subtropical Climate

The Mediterranean type of climate, like the Subequatorial, is a transitional type. Regions having this type of climate are located upon the western coasts of continents which fall in the zone of Tropical Calms or Trade Winds in summer; and in that of the Westerlies, cyclones and anticyclones, blowing from sea to land, in the winter. Such areas lie in latitudes 31° to 39° approximately. Southern California, the coast of Chile, southern Portugal, the coasts of the Mediterranean Sea, the coast near Cape Town, the southwest and the southeast corners of Australia on windward coasts, and the northern part of the North Island of New Zealand experience the Subtropical type of climate.

Like all other climate types of middle latitudes, the Subtropical has marked seasonal changes of temperature. The heat of the four summer months is intense. Along the coasts of the Mediterranean Sea the atmospheric conditions are not so unpleasant as in the interior where the warm air of the Tropical Calms is descending under pressure. Strong sea breezes, also, are a daily phenomenon on the coast. Thus the inhabitants do not suffer from the enervating effects of high temperatures. Occasionally, however, there are unbearable days on the coast. At Toulouse, the temperature reached 110° in August of 1923. In the interior the mean monthly temperature is about 80°, fully five degrees higher than along the seaboard. All who can do so take to the nearby mountains during the summer season.

During the winter months, when the sun's rays are vertical south of the equator, the temperature falls considerably. At Athens the mean January temperature is 49°. At night the temperature is frequently below freezing, indeed as low as 15°. In comparison with regions further north the winters are moderate. The noonday temperature is quite high and the skies are unusually clear and sunny.

During the summer most Subtropical regions are under the influence of the Tropical Calms. Islands situated in the ocean, however, may be reached by the trade winds which are particularly extensive over water. The Canary Islands, for example, are under the influence of the Trades though they lie as far north as 29°.

Little rainfall is experienced in the Mediterranean environment during the summer months, but in the winter the Westerlies descend over Subtropical regions bringing cyclonic rains. The winter season, then, is the rainy season. The precipitation is moderate, usually three or four inches a month. Snow and frost are not infrequent, but the snow melts quickly except in plateau regions such as are found in Spain. The peculiar character of Subtropical rainfall is its intermittency. There are only sixty-seven rainy days during the year at Nice, while in the south of England, though the annual amount is the same, about thirty-one inches, there are three times as many rainy days. Even during the rainy season, then, clear and sunny days predominate.

It is obvious why the rivieras of France and Italy are such popular health resorts for Europeans during the winter. The weather is variable and at the same time mild. The resorts are so located that they are sheltered by mountains from the cold blasts of the north. In those places where topographical features permit cold winds to slip through, the winter months are not as pleasant. The Rhone Valley, the head of the Adriatic, the north coasts of the Ægean Sea and of the Black Sea experience cold piercing winds that are intensified because they seep through topographical troughs. Often these winds are violent in character and cause great damage. The *mistral* of the Rhone Valley has been known to upset railway cars. The inhabitants in this area frequently construct their dwellings without windows and doors on the north side. The *bora* of the north Adriatic is a similar wind. The *sirocco* is a wind peculiar to this area, though it is entirely different in character. It occurs most frequently in spring, though it is not uncommon in winter. It is a hot, dusty wind, often cyclonic in character, which blows across the Mediterranean from the Sahara. Wherever it appears, the weather becomes unbearably hot and sultry. The *khamsin* wind in Egypt and the *Santa Ana,* which blows from the hot deserts east of the Sierra Nevada into California, are similar.

The Subtropical environment, then, is hot and dry during the summer and cool and rainy during the winter. The seasonal contrast is quite marked in many ways. During the summer there is no rain, and no growth. The vegetation is shrunken and withered and only hardy evergreens, which adjust themselves to depleted rainfall by growing long roots and hard, thick leaves, thrive. The streams dry up in their channels, and in the remote provinces, men fashion the roofs of their houses so as to catch any rain that might fall. Some escape to the mountains; others depend upon the noonday *siesta* to carry them through the summer. Among progressive peoples irrigation is practised profitably, for the soil is often excellent. In the winter half-year the whole scene changes. The growing season sets in and the products of an intensive agriculture flourish. The Subtropical environment is justly famed for its fruit and nut crops and for its winter cereals.

28. Cyclonic Types of Middle Latitudes

Five types of climate lie wholly within the belt of the Westerly Winds at all times during the year. They are Maritime, Humid Continental Interior, Continental with Marine Influence, Steppe, and Continental Desert. These types are located in regions in latitudes 35° to 65°. All are influenced by cyclones and anticyclones which are borne along in an easterly direction by the prevailing Westerlies.

The outstanding characteristic that all the cyclonic types have in common is variability. Aside from the fact that cyclonic regions lie between polar and tropical zones they have little claim to the title "temperate." Nowhere else in the world are there such sudden changes in temperature and precipitation. Indeed the fluctuations in weather from day to day and from week to week almost deprive mean monthly averages of any significance. Under such circumstances "mean annuals" are really ludicrous, as well as misleading. Let us take an example. New York and Seattle are characterized by ample rainfall during all seasons, but since that of Seattle, unlike New York, is heavier in winter than in summer, marked environmental differences are set up between the two regions. At the root of all the variability in the zone of the Westerlies is the constant passage of cyclones and anticyclones across the continents. Cyclones generally bring cloudiness and rain, while anticyclones presage clear weather. Thus, particularly during the long transitional seasons, spring and fall, in the course of a single week a place may run the whole gamut of weather changes. Variability is very important because it has a beneficial effect upon human health and energy. The prosperity of cyclonic regions is due not a little to the energy stimulated by the abrupt and frequent changes in the weather.

Most of the land areas having cyclonic conditions lie in the northern hemisphere. In the southern hemisphere, only the southern part of South America, the island of Tasmania, and part of New Zealand are subject to cyclonic influences. The cyclonic belt of the southern hemisphere is essentially an oceanic area. Here the "Roaring Forties" sweep around the globe almost without interruption. High winds, high seas, gales, and storms prevail throughout the year, making it perilous for the navigator even in these days of the steamship. Not the least hazardous experience of an Antarctic expedition is the voyage across this tempestuous zone.

In the northern hemisphere, the westerlies, cyclones, and anti-cyclones blow across the great land masses of North America and Eurasia. The degree to which the land masses influence climate is in the main the degree of difference between the various types of climate. Temperature, which varies in accordance with distance from the equator, is greatly modified by distance from the sea. The cold pole of the earth is found in the eastern interior of Siberia, part of the Eurasian land mass. Pressure conditions are dictated by the extremes of summer and winter that arise in the interior of the land masses. The "lows" of midsummer not only establish isobaric gradients that attract the moist air of the oceans, but they set up cyclonic whirls which are borne along by the Westerlies. We have already discussed the part played by the "highs" and "lows" of the Asiatic land mass in creating monsoon conditions. In the northern hemisphere, too, are found the moderating Gulf Stream and the Japan Current, and the low pressure areas of the Atlantic and Pacific, the principal sources of the winter cyclones.

Hence, though all regions situated in latitudes 35° to 65° approximately, are subject to westerlies, cyclones, and anticyclones, the immensity of the land masses has the effect of destroying any uniformity of climate. Land has the property of exerting a radical influence upon temperature, pressure, winds and precipitation. The extent of that influence is the measure of the different types of climate now to be considered.

29. Maritime Climate

The Maritime type of climate is found along windward coasts in the northern and southern hemispheres in latitudes 39° to 65°. The western coast of North America as far as the Aleutian Islands, the coast of Chile south of 38°, the British Islands, the coast of Europe from central Portugal to the North Cape, Tasmania, and New Zealand (excepting the north tip of the North Island) have a Maritime type of climate. The extremes of temperature common to such latitudes are considerably modified by oceanic influences. The annual range of temperature at Olympia, Washington, is only 24°, while at Omaha, Nebraska, in the interior, it is 48°. The pressure is variable with a tendency to high in summer and low in winter. In other words, these areas share oceanic pressure conditions. Westerlies, cyclones and anticyclones are the prevailing winds.

The relative humidity is high because the winds are blowing constantly from sea to land. The annual rainfall exceeds that of any other cyclonic type of climate in amount. It is commonly over sixty inches. It is heavier in winter than in summer because cyclones are more frequent at sea during that season. In addition, the two permanent low pressure areas are the sources of frequent cyclones which are borne to the coasts by the Westerlies. Typical monthly averages range from one to ten inches of rainfall. In localities that are situated on the windward slopes of mountains, the averages may be much higher. Hence in the South Island of New Zealand where the mountains are high and continuous, the higher lands along the windward coasts receive from two hundred to three hundred inches of precipitation yearly. Much of the precipitation falls as snow, and the vast snowfields are drained by great glaciers. The coastal plain of western Europe is the only area where the maritime type of precipitation may be said to run its course without interruption. Yet because of the winter cold and the high pressures of the interior, the line separating the areas of predominant summer and winter rainfall adheres closely to the coast except in western France south of Brittany. Paris, which is considerably less than one hundred miles from the coast, has slightly more rain during the summer than the winter.

30. Continental Desert Climate

This type is next discussed because it is of some value to observe the order in which the cyclonic types of climate appear in crossing the United States. There are two great desert areas in middle latitudes: one in the United States between the Sierra Nevada mountains and the Rocky Mountains, and the other in the heart of Asia. The first is caused by the "rain shadow" of the western mountains, the second because it is so far from the coasts that the winds have lost their humidity before reaching it. It is interesting to note that both great desert areas continue southward in the form of trade wind deserts. The total annual precipitation of the Continental Desert type is less than ten inches, an amount insufficient to support human life. What little precipitation reaches these deserts occurs in summer when continental pressures are lowest, thus permitting an occasional cyclonic indraught to bring them humid air from a great distance.

Records of precipitation in the heart of Asia are rare, but one traveler in the Takla Makan Desert reported after almost a year's stay that it had rained five or six times and snowed three times. At Yarkand,[1] on the western edge of the same desert, half an inch of rain was recorded in the single year that a gauge was maintained. The mean annual precipitation at Kashgar[2] is 3.5 inches, two-thirds of which falls during the summer. Similar conditions, though not as extreme, prevail in parts of Idaho, Utah and Nevada.

The seasonal range of temperature is another meteorological feature of the Continental Desert type. Here, also, the Takla Makan Desert reveals extreme conditions. The mean July and January temperatures at Yarkand are 82° and 21°; at Lukchun, 90° and 13°. The highest recorded temperature at Yarkand is 103°, at Lukchun, 118°. Domestic animals, even camels, cannot withstand the summer heat and must be driven into the mountains. Ellsworth Huntington writes that "according to the Chinese, the summer is so hot that during the day the birds all gather in the shade of the trees beside the rivers. If one of them flies up, he is scorched to a cinder and falls sizzling into the water." Another tale, recorded by Kendrew, affirms that the heat is so great that rice, if not eaten immediately when served, will become so hot as to burn the tongue. The extremes

[1] Soche.
[2] Shufu.

of heat and cold encountered in continental areas are due mainly to the capacity of the barren land to respond immediately to the insolation.

31. Steppe

The Steppe is a type of climate transitional between the desert and types having more favorable precipitation. Regions in middle latitudes with between ten and twenty inches of rainfall are arbitrarily assigned this climatic designation. In the United States the line of twenty-inch rainfall adheres closely to the 98th meridian. In the west, however, though the Steppe boundary corresponds roughly with the Rocky Mountains, there are many districts further west, especially in the high plateau lands, that experience more than 10 inches of rainfall. On the Great Plains, the level, treeless area east of the Rockies, the great cattle kingdom flourished from 1870 to 1880 for the Steppe rainfall was sufficient to support grass. Free grass led to the exploitation and development of this part of the country. The live stock business has been augmented, especially in the north, by the great wheat farms, for it has been found that valuable cereal crops may be supported in this region of sparse rainfall by a system of mechanized agriculture.

There are vast steppe lands in Eurasia, especially in southern Russia and in southern Siberia. In the former region the Soviet government, taking a leaf from the American experience, is planting thousands of acres of wheat on the principle that though the rainfall is unreliable it will never fail throughout that vast area. In this way thousands of acres are being brought under the plow that formerly were of use to none but the nomadic tribes.

It is difficult, as has been intimated, to delineate accurately the bounds of the American steppe. At times it encroaches upon the desert and at times it yields to the Humid Continental Interior type of environment. Farmers dwelling upon the eastern border of the Great Plains are often victims of the vagaries of nature. In the early 'eighties in the United States a large number of farmers settled upon lands where for a number of years the rainfall approximated that of the Continental Humid Interior. In Sherman County, Kansas, the population rose from one person to ten square miles in 1885 to sixty per square mile in 1889. About 1893 precipitation returned to normal, "and every such wave left behind it a mass of human wreckage in the shape of broken fortunes, deserted farms, and ruined homes." The pioneers came from the humid regions of the east and from western Europe. If they had any knowledge of farming whatsoever, it was of farming in a moist climate. In spite of the warnings of the United States weather bureau to the contrary, the conviction still persists in that region that "the country is becoming more seasonable."

32. Humid Continental Interior Climate

The Humid Continental Interior and the Continental with Marine Influence types of climate are exceedingly favorable for farming. The rainfall is plentiful during the long growing season of spring and summer. The limits of the former type in North America include the vast area between the 98th meridian and the Appalachian Mountains. The Great Lowland of Europe, except the coast and a narrow adjacent belt which is classified as Continental with Marine Influence, has this type of climate. It occurs also in southern South America inland from the eastern coast. Like the Steppe type it has marked seasonal contrasts of temperature. The summers are hot and the winters cold. The winters in the United States and Eurasia, for different reasons, are greatly intensified. Central and eastern Europe suffer from proximity to central Asia, whence cold winds blow from the interior area of high pressure. The central portion of the United States, situated between two highlands, is open to cold polar winds which blow down the trough of the Mississippi basin in winter.

The advantage of the Humid Continental Interior type over the Steppe type lies in its additional rainfall. The mean annual precipitation is usually from twenty to forty inches. In the summer season, central United States not only receives moisture from the Atlantic Ocean and from Hudson Bay because of the low pressure indraught but obtains much more from the Gulf of Mexico in the form of cyclonic rains which are picked up by the Westerlies and borne northward. The interposition of the Cascades, Sierras, and Rockies deprives the American interior of the advantage of moisture-laden westerly winds. Europe, because it is open from the west, receives ample moisture from the ocean.

The Humid Continental Interior type, like the Steppe, receives more precipitation during summer than during winter. The reasons for this are that warmer air is capable of absorbing more moisture than the cold air of winter, and that cyclones form more frequently over land during the summer.

33. Continental Climate with Marine Influence

This is the last type of climate of middle latitudes to be discussed. Except in the continent of Europe the Continental with Marine Influence type occurs on the leeward (that is, the east coast) of continents and islands. Its distribution is as follows: the coasts of the United States, roughly from the mouth of the St. Lawrence (Canada) to the Sabine River on the Gulf of Mexico; the Maritime Provinces of Canada; Newfoundland; a zone in South America including northeast Argentina, Uruguay, and the adjacent Brazilian coast; western Europe between the coastal Maritime and the Continental Humid Interior; the east coast of Siberia, Korea, northern and northeastern Japan; the southeast coast of the Union of South Africa; and the southeast coast of Australia.

Its chief climatic characteristic is its tendency toward uniformity. The seasonal range of precipitation and temperature is not as great as that of the continental interior types. Extremes of temperature are moderated because this type shares the temperature characteristics of the adjoining sea. Warm and cold ocean currents, already alluded to, are a further thermal influence.

The precipitation, which averages generally between fifty and sixty inches, is well distributed throughout the year. It differs from the Maritime type in that the greater part of the rainfall occurs during the summer half of the year. The rainfall is well distributed throughout the year because regions having this climate participate in the rainfall of oceanic cyclones as they circle over the coasts. Land breezes cause precipitation, also in winter, when brought into contact with the warmer moist air over the coasts. On the other hand, the precipitation of the summer is greater because, like other continental types, more cyclones originate over the lands then, thus preserving the balance in favor of the summer months. Additional precipitation from showers, caused by sea breezes, helps to swell the summer total.

Before leaving this subject several interesting regional phenomena must be mentioned. In the United States, owing to the great area of low pressure over the interior during the summer, "monsoonlike" winds blow in from the sea over the southeastern states yielding a heavy precipitation. Thus Florida, Alabama, Mississippi, much of Louisiana, and western Georgia enjoy a rainfall which further north is confined to the coastal plain. The British Isles are in the Maritime Climate belt generally, but the eastern part of Great Britain belongs to Continental with Marine Influence because the summer rainfall exceeds that of the winter. London, for example, receives 1.9 inches of rain in January, and 2.4 inches in July. The rainiest month, however, is October, when 2.6 inches fall. The Continental with Marine Influence type in western Europe is confined to a narrow belt, less than one hundred miles wide, where continental conditions are beginning to prevail over marine conditions. Here continental cyclonic influences are just powerful enough to establish a greater rainfall in summer than in winter. Yet, since the continental extremes of temperature do not prevail, and since this belt participates in much of the rainfall of oceanic, particularly winter, cyclones, it undoubtedly belongs to the Continental with Marine Influence type. The central core of this belt would include the coasts of the Gulf of Bothnia, and the Baltic Sea, and would pass southwest through Berlin and Paris. It is an indefinite area because of the variability, seasonally and yearly, of all types within the zone of the Westerlies.

34. Tundra and Polar Climates

Tundra lands lie for the most part just within the Arctic Circle. They are not found in the southern hemisphere because what is not ocean in those latitudes is part of the snow- and ice-covered mass of Antarctica. The climatic feature which distinguishes the Tundra type from the Polar type is that the former has at least one summer month with a temperature between 40° and 50°. July and August might be construed as pleasant months. A midday temperature of 100° has been recorded at Fort Yukon, which is on the Arctic Circle.

This rise in monthly mean temperatures for a few months during summer is sufficient to induce some vegetation. There are over one hundred species of flowers which mature and bloom quickly, and a few tough, hardy perennials. On the other hand the subsoil is permanently frozen, flat surfaces are water-logged in the summer, and strong winds prohibit any tree growth beyond the stunted type.

The northern limit of cereals and trees encroaches beyond the

Arctic Circle in only one region, the northern coast of Norway. This is because of the tempering influence of the North Atlantic Drift, a northerly continuation of the Gulf Stream. On other coasts, however Tundra conditions intrude far to the south. Tundra is characteristic of the Aleutian Islands and the northern part of the Kamchatka Peninsula, both of which are located south of the fifty-fifth parallel. The coast of Labrador is Tundra because of the unfavorable influences of the cold current. The reason for the southerly extension of the Tundra type is that these coasts share oceanic conditions. The seas in high latitudes are little responsive to insolation in summer, retaining for long the winter's cold.

With Polar regions we are not greatly concerned. Their meteorology has never been satisfactorily described, but each expedition adds a little more to our scanty knowledge. It was thought until recently that polar regions were regions of low pressure because of rotational whirl. Now it is certain that the intense cold in Antarctica creates a high pressure area too great to be overcome by the forces of the general circulation. A terrific anticyclonic outblow flows down the slopes of its vast ice-capped plateau. Antarctica is twice the size of Australia, and much of it has an altitude of over eight thousand feet. Scott recorded S., SSE., or SSW. winds for 73 per cent of his observations. It is difficult to understand how precipitation can occur in Antarctica where the temperature is exceedingly low. Yet the presence of huge, slow-moving glaciers and deposits of snow composed of hard, fine spicules of ice cannot be dismissed. Many interesting theories concerning Antarctica precipitation are now before the scientific community. Hobbs' thesis, while not sufficient to account for all the precipitation, holds that "the intense cold is the result of rapid radiation from the snow surface; the air is constantly descending in the anticyclone, and when it reaches the surface contact with the cold snow causes its moisture to be condensed in fine ice particles, or as hoar frost."

Conditions in the Arctic are more complex because of the land masses on the edge of the basin. Pressure at the pole in winter is not as high as that on the land masses, hence the cold pole does not coincide with the north pole. Yet polar pressure is greater than that over the permanent lows of the North Atlantic and Pacific. The result seems to be that strong winds blow into this Arctic divide. Sea ice is carried in a generally northeast direction by winds and current.

Nansen purposely abandoned the *Fram* in the Arctic, northwest of the New Siberian Islands. After three years it reappeared in open waters north of Spitzbergen, after passing to the north of Greenland.

The precipitation of the Arctic polar region is also accounted for by the "hoar frost" theory. But the large amount of snow that falls upon the outer edges of the polar belt, especially along the west coast of Greenland, is probably caused by intruding cyclonic conditions from the south. In the interior of the Arctic basin, however, the high pressure anticyclone is strong enough to resist cyclonic invasion, thus leaving north polar precipitation to be explained in much the same manner as that of Antarctica.

Because of the recent polar expeditions interest in polar meteorology has been greatly stimulated. These areas will remain uninhabited, but the meteorological conditions there have a new importance with the rapid advance of the science of aeronautics.

CHAPTER V

TROPICAL ENVIRONMENTS: NATIVE AFRICA

35. Tropical Areas

The equator passes through the heart of Africa and South America and through the great East Indian archipelago. North and south of the equator lie the tropics. The tropical climatic types are the Equatorial, the Subequatorial, the Trade Wind Desert, and the Trade Wind with Ample Rain. The Mediterranean type is transitional between tropical and temperate, and the Monsoon is a specialized trade wind type. The last two types are treated in later chapters.

Africa is preëminently a tropical continent. The equator divides the continent into two equal parts, each of which lies almost wholly within the tropical and subtropical zones. Africa affords an interesting illustration of the experiences of primitive peoples in adapting themselves to the tropical types of environment. The East Indies provide the best example of the white man's experience in tropical latitudes and will be discussed solely in that light. The tropical regions of the New World are treated in relation to the general background of the culture and mores of Latin America. In any discussion, however, it will be interesting to observe the parallels that arise in areas having the same type of environment; for, viewed objectively, the existence of adaptations arrived at independently is likely to be a measure of the geographical influences upon human culture.

36. Topography of Tropical Africa

That part of Africa lying between the tropics is a vast tableland with an elevation of one thousand feet. For the most part the coastal strip is narrow and hardly worthy of the name of plain. Rivers like the Congo and the Zambezi descend so precipitously to the coast that access to the interior by boat is impossible. Thus sea-going ships are able to penetrate the Congo for a distance of only ninety miles. Beyond Léopoldville, about three hundred miles from the coast, the river is navigable for one thousand miles. It is planned to build a canal from Léopoldville in order to overcome the obstacle imposed by the rapids. The coastlands about the Gulf of Guinea are the only considerable plainlands lying near the sea. This plain penetrates into the interior, entirely surrounding the Guinea Highlands. It is marked by the courses of the Senegal and the Niger rivers. The East African Plateau, however, is the most significant feature in the topography of the continent. It extends north and south through the whole of the tropics. Its average elevation above sea level is three thousand feet, and it is crowned by numerous snow-capped peaks. Here, as in other plateau regions, the prevailing types of environment break down, save along the coastal borders.

37. The Equatorial Environment

Equatorial Africa [1] is confined principally to the Congo basin, and the Guinea coast and valley lands. In the former area the natives dwell largely along the banks of the river and its tributaries, over four thousand miles in extent. These streams provide the only convenient escape from the darkness and the gloom of the "rain forest" whose foliage casts a canopy of shadow over the interior of the continent. Not only man but the flora and fauna, shun the damp, water-logged surfaces. The birds and monkeys live high up in the trees. Bushes and vines, too, are found not on the ground as in the subequatorial jungles but intermingled with the rich foliage of the tree tops. Man, where stream clearings are lacking, builds his shelter among the branches of the huge evergreens. This occurs not alone in Africa, but wherever the equatorial environment prevails.

The natives encounter other obstacles in addition to heat and humidity. The soil is very poor. Even along the stream banks where the clearings are made the incessant rains have leached the soil of many of the chemical ingredients necessary for agriculture. The residue, known as *laterite*, is a porous substance consisting largely of decomposing rock, brownish in color. At best, such soil will support crops for only a season or so, and consequently the tribes are constantly forced to move on and make new clearings. Agriculture is laborious as well as precarious, for the native must engage in a

[1] Examine carefully Plates I, II, III, IV, V in connection with the climate of Africa.

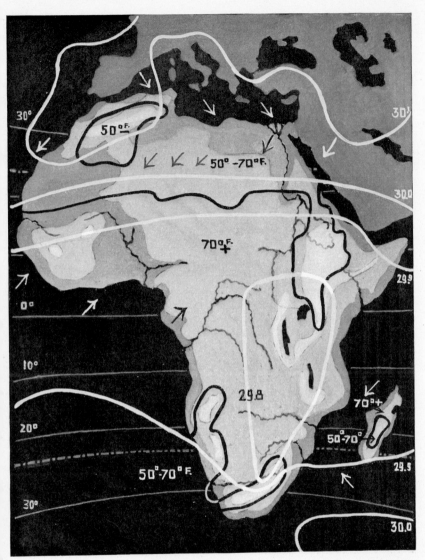

PLATE II.   AFRICA—JANUARY ISOTHERMS, ISOBARS, AND PREVAILING WINDS
(*After Goode*)

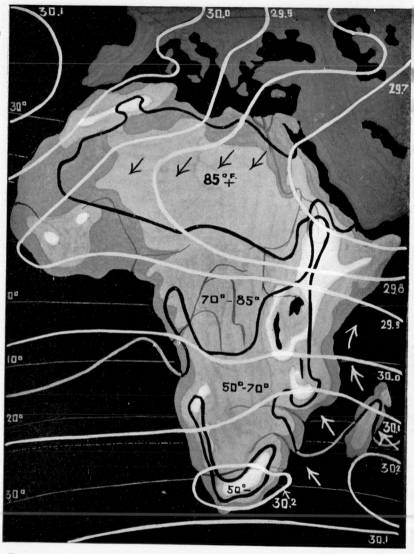

PLATE III. AFRICA—JULY ISOTHERMS, ISOBARS, AND PREVAILING WINDS
(*After Goode*)

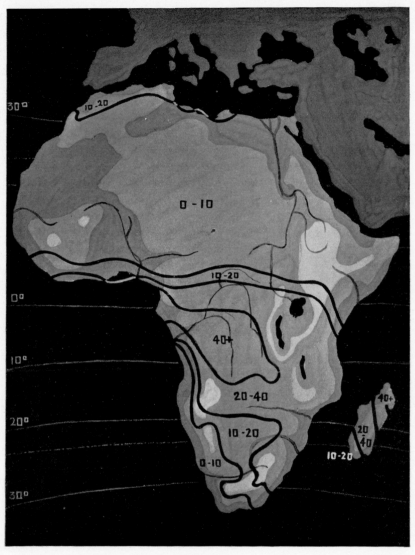

PLATE IV. AFRICA—JANUARY RAINFALL
(*After Goode*)

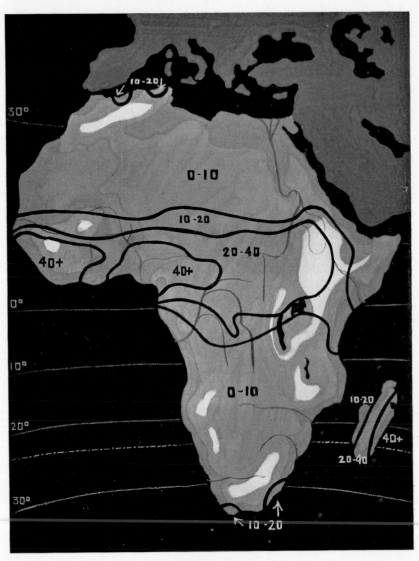

PLATE V. AFRICA—JULY RAINFALL
(*After Goode*)

constant struggle with the wild plant life that threatens to strangle his crops.

The natives of the Congo basin are divisible roughly into the Pygmy and the Bantu tribes. The Pygmies were probably the first comers but were dispossessed by the Bantu who now occupy the choicest spots. Regardless of racial differences, however, all share a culture that is, broadly speaking, homogeneous. Shields, bows, pipes, dress, masks, knives, drums, stringed instruments, ornamentation, and social institutions are repeated with monotonous uniformity throughout the vast Congo area. Moreover "the way of life" of the natives of the Gulf of Guinea is fundamentally the same.

Agriculture, hunting, and fishing are employed in eking out a living. Goats, poultry, and sheep, together with limited quantities of fruits and berries add to the food supply. Milk is tabu but, as it cannot be obtained, no real sacrifice has been indulged. It is impossible to keep cattle not only because of the difficulties encountered in providing pasture and defense from wild beasts but because of disease-bearing insects. The tsetse fly has laid an interdict upon the keeping of cattle in the Congo. Only in the plateau of East Africa where the rainfall is less than sixty inches a year may cattle be raised with impunity. Man, too, is preyed upon by insects that carry typhus, malaria, sleeping sickness, and other fatal diseases.

Among the Bushongo, in the heart of the Congo, the staples of diet are corn and bananas. Iron working is an important function; in fact, iron mongers are relieved of all other duties. This, however, does not represent a division of labor, for there is none. It is an isolated occupation serving a highly specialized function. The Pygmies, by employing a Bantu to make their poisons, relieve themselves of any retribution which might result from the killing of game. This is another illustration of a highly specialized function. Iron is the most valuable form of property, and in the medium of hoes, spades, and lance heads it has become the basis of exchange. The marriage portion which every suitor must pledge is most welcome when offered in ironware. Bark, salt, raphea fabrics, and cowry shells also serve as the media of exchange among Congo peoples.

Among the Bushongo, men and women work together in the patches. Among certain tribes, however, the woman supplies her man with vegetables, while he furnishes the meat or fish. A most unusual arrangement is found in one tribe; the women are allowed to own the fields on condition that they supply the husband and children with food. The social and political unit is the isolated village group. The inhabitants dwell in rectangular houses facing a thoroughfare. The kingship is an hereditary office, carrying with it various functions. In the Bushongo villages, it is the queen mother rather than the queen who is permitted to maintain a court. Land is owned by the village in common but the use of it is permitted to individuals. Property of a personal character passes from father to son. The institution of the dowry is far from peculiar to Congo peoples, but the giving of bark cloth, cowry shells, and the like is not without environmental significance. The prevailing religion is fetichism, while wood carving and a little iron working represent the sole esthetic manifestations.

Under such formidable environmental handicaps, the culture of the inhabitants of the equatorial rain forest could scarcely be anything but low. Much that has been written of environmental determinism is far-fetched, but even the anthropologists, who are prone to minimize the effects of physical environment, concede the limiting influences of the equatorial environment. One familiar with the adaptations of the Congo natives has nothing but admiration for the achievements that have enabled them to survive in the very teeth of their hostile surroundings. Their weapons, their marksmanship, their clever stalking of fish and game are noteworthy manifestations of their capacities. But, at most, they have succeeded only in adjusting themselves to their environment, and however adequate that adaptation may be, their culture pattern lacks the richness and the refinement of the people of more favored environments. The degree of emancipation is very small. The incapacity of the natives has been ascribed to race. Yet when one considers that after five hundred years of contact only fifteen thousand white men, in comparison with nine million blacks, reside in the Congo, one is left with the suspicion that the cause of cultural poverty is not genetic but social.

The rudeness of equatorial cultures is due to poor social environment which, from the nature of things, is but the reflection of the poverty of the physical landscape. It is well-nigh impossible for the greatest cultural agency, diffusion, to operate here. No one will deny that the peoples of equatorial Africa, Oceanica, and America have been exposed to cultural influences from outside. But the traits to which they have been exposed are rarely adaptable to their environment. Even to assert that the natives of the Congo are indifferent to the legal and social adjustments of their neighbors living upon the East African plateau is unjust; the latter presuppose and are directly based upon a cattle economy, a form of wealth that is interdicted in the rain forest. Similarly in South America the culture of the Inca who dwelt in the highlands was not adaptable to the inhabitants of the basin of the Amazon. The inhabitants of the East Indies found themselves able to respond only feebly to the cultural bombardment from India and China, and later from the Moslem and Christian civilizations. Witness to-day the paucity of European adaptations among rain forest dwellers in spite of the century-old efforts made to engraft them. Further, no one will argue that the achievements of the white man in tropical lowlands have been particularly noteworthy.

All equatorial peoples reveal a marked dependence upon the meager equipment afforded by nature. Cultural similarities are remarkable among equatorial peoples the world over. Hardwoods are invariably employed for clubs, tools, and utensils. Bark is commonly used for shelter and clothing unless bamboo is available. In the forest composed of tall trees the blow gun is the favorite weapon because of the ease with which it can be handled. Indeed the blow gun is said "to disappear with the rain forest." Where the bow and arrow are employed they are of the smallest variety for the same reason. Since an arrow of small size is ineffective in attacking large game, the prey is dispatched by dipping the arrow in poison. These adjustments appear in all three rain forest environments and, in the New World at least, were invented independently, not borrowed.

38. The Plateau Environment of East Africa

In Eastern Africa, from Ethiopia to South Africa, altitude rather than latitude plays the rôle of environment arbiter. This huge area over three thousand miles in length and from three to five hundred miles in breadth is from two to five thousand feet above sea level. Here and there, particularly about the equator, snow-capped peaks are to be seen, Mt. Kilimanjaro, for example, rises to a height of nearly twenty thousand feet and ranks among the highest mountains in the world. Numerous streams and rivers cut their way through the massif to the coast, but so precipitous is their flow and so fre-

quent their rapids that they are of little use for purposes of navigation. The white exploiter has had to build railways from the coast
in order to tap the interior.

Conditions of temperature are mitigated for temperature decreases
with altitude. The days are apt to be hot but the nights are cool.
Since the air is rarer, there is little of the sweltering heat that one
encounters in the rain forest. The sharpest contrast with the equatorial lowlands lies in the character of the precipitation. On the Congo
side of the lakes the rainfall everywhere exceeds sixty inches, while
on the Plateau side it falls to ten, twenty, or thirty inches, depending
upon altitude and distance from the sea.

The typical vegetation of the Plateau is not forest but grassland.
Everywhere are vast park-like expanses interspersed with occasional
trees. At higher altitudes in Ethiopia, Kenya, and Tanganyika, and
again in the veldt south of Capricorn, the grasses resemble the steppe
of temperate regions, rather than the tropical savanna. Throughout
East Africa there is much wild life. Herds of deer, giraffe, gnu,
zebra, and similar species feed upon the grasses. In turn the car-
nivores feed upon the herbivores. Kenya and Tanganyika are the
principal homes of the African lion, the foe of man and beast alike.

39. Life in East Africa

In East Africa the physical environment has had a major share
in patterning the culture of the natives. From Ethiopia southward
to the tip of Africa, there is fundamentally but one type of culture,
a cattle culture. Everywhere except in the region between Lakes
Tanganyika and Nyassa where the tsetse fly has made some ingress,
cattle play the most important rôle in the lives of the people. Agriculture, though engaged in by most tribes, is supplementary and is
frequently held in disdain. The possession of cattle lends a prestige
that no amount of acres, hoes, or trinkets can surmount. So esteemed
is every function of the *cattle complex* that the women of the tribe
are forbidden to milk the cows. Milk, which is eaten in a soured
form, is the main article of sustenance. The skin gourd is never
empty for by adding sweet milk at intervals it will sour more readily. Among certain tribes in the north there is a tabu prohibiting the
drinking of milk while vegetables are accessible.

This so-called cattle complex dominates the whole culture. Among the Banyankoli, for example, the chiefs rule over so many cattle rather than so many subjects. Cattle, rather than men, connote wealth and power.

Among the Masai the village is built around the kraal or cattle enclosure. To protect the stock from marauding lions the huts are covered over with dense thorn brush. The people are organized into age classes. The young men, constituting the warrior class, are charged with the sacred duty of protecting the village and the cattle against the attacks of beasts. They live on the pasture and guard the herds. When a lion has killed one of the tribe, it is mandatory upon the warriors to obtain retribution. The procedure is ritualistic in its definiteness. A circle of warriors, step by step, amid much incantation, advances upon the beast. It is utter ruin for the young warrior to take a backward step. When the lion attempts to break through the circle, he is destroyed by the spears of the warriors. The carcass is removed from the spot where it fell and is laid to rest in a ceremony that is as much a tribute to the king of beasts as to the victors. The warriors enjoy many privileges denied other classes in the tribe. The maidens of the tribe live with the warriors and keep them company in their lonely vigil. After his term of service has been rendered, the warrior is permitted to marry and take up his residence with the older men in the village.

Social and economic life among the plateau tribes is based upon the ownership of cattle. The number of wives a man may have is regulated by the number of cattle he owns. Upon a man's death the stock goes to the eldest son of his first wife. A warrior about to marry gives a dowry of cattle to his wife, but where the dowry has not been paid in full the children are held to belong to the wife's family. Transactions among individuals are based upon a valuation reckoned in heads of cattle. Clothing, weapons, and utensils bear the impress of environment. In the northeast and the south, clothing is manufactured of leather; in the northwest, leather is augmented by bark. Iron and wood working occasionally are given the status of specialized occupations. Among some peoples, however, these workers, like the agriculturalists, are treated as pariahs.

Some anthropologists separate Ethiopia culturally from the rest of East Africa. The Galli and Somali who live there have been exposed to the culture of the Arab traders for centuries. Yet both tribes are herders, and although they raise camels, goats, and sheep, their dower and inheritance customs are similar to those of the cattle tribes to the south. Among the Galli the men alone may tend the camels, prized for the excellence of their milk, but the women are entrusted with the care of other varieties of livestock. Even the Somali, who live nearest the coast, do not mix readily with the towns-people who engage in trade and commerce. The folk ways induced by environment tend to survive despite the Arab and, recently, the European influence.

40. The Sudan: A Subequatorial Environment

Between latitudes 10° to 17° north and south of the equator are vast areas with almost identical environments. In the Sudan and in the southern savanna, similar climatic controls are exerted as we have seen. The Sudan is vastly more important to man because it supports a large native population. The southern area, for largely historical reasons, is practically uninhabited by natives. It seems that negro migration in Africa spread from the northeast in two great streams, westward and southward. Both the Sudan and the Eastern Plateau were suitable for the raising of livestock. As a result the remote southern grasslands were never reached. Movements to the south have been less frequent than movements into the Sudan; in fact, some of the Bantu migrations southward through the Plateau have occurred quite recently. Because of the greater importance of the northern savanna, we shall confine our discussion of the African Subequatorial environment to the Sudan.

A Subequatorial region is essentially one of transition from rain forest to desert. As one travels north through the Sudan toward the Sahara, the wet season diminishes in duration. The vegetation responds sensitively to rainfall. On the equatorial side of the belt—especially in the river valleys of the Niger, Benue, and Senegal—the vegetation is dense tropical jungle. It is much less penetrable than the rain forest of equatorial regions because the short dry season permits the soil to dry out, checking the growth of the huge evergreens whose foliage prevents the sunlight from nourishing the lesser growth. Not far to the north, however, the jungle thins out and trees give way to grasses. Here, too, the dominance of rainfall is clearly marked. On the equatorward side of the savanna, where the wet season is of considerable duration, the grasses are very coarse and sometimes attain to a height of twenty feet. As the desert edge is approached, they are shorter, less tough, and make admirable fodder for livestock. At the borderlands of the Sahara the ephemeral grasses coincide with the short, fluctuating, summer rains.

Subequatorial Africa, then, is a region that combines jungle, savanna, and scrub. In many places, too, the natural vegetation resembles that of the pasture lands of the Eastern Plateau though that of the latter is due to altitude rather than latitude. In tropical Africa, then, the grasslands form a great crescent about the equatorial lowlands. Certain similarities, therefore, may be anticipated in the human responses throughout the length and breadth of this great area.

The Sudan extends from the Atlantic to the highlands of Ethiopia, an area of over 3,000 miles in breadth. The main contrast is not between east and west, although there is more jungle in the west because of the depressions of the Senegal and the Niger. The zonation is rather, latitudinal, ranging from tropical jungle, through more or less permanent grasslands, to the desert grasses and scrub. This transition in natural vegetation is reflected in the agriculture practised by the natives. In the jungle lands a type of agriculture is carried on that would be impossible at the desert's edge both in respect to methods and kind of crops. The lack of environmental uniformity has had a far-reaching effect upon the inhabitants of the Sudan. From earliest times, the tribes of the north have traded their products for those of the south. Indeed with one tribe, the Mandingoes, trade became such an important function that its members won the reputation of being the "Jews of the Desert." They are found all over the western Sudan. Town life is another result of this trade. Towns like Kano are not merely local marts but are *entrepôts* of a trade that extends on the one hand to the Mediterranean and on the other to the towns along the Guinea Gulf.

Centuries of contact with the Arabs have aided in raising the Sudan tribes to a cultural level not yet attained by other tropical peoples in Africa. The early culture of the tribes of Nigeria was derived largely from Moorish kingdoms to the north, and, to quote one writer, "Timbuktu was more closely in touch with learning than were many of the northwestern countries of Europe during the early Middle Ages." The great kingdom of Melle, founded probably in the eighth century, extended from the Niger River to the Atlas Mountains. Its prosperity rested upon a great north-south trade. The blacks who accepted the teachings of Islam enjoyed a perfect social equality with their Berber neighbors. About the middle of the fourteenth century the scepter of power passed to the Songhai peoples who lived just east of the Niger. One chronicler tells us that with the downfall of the Melletine capital, Timbuktu, the learned black professors connected with the university were unable to mount the camels provided for their safety, so sleek had they become in times of prosperity. The Songhai Empire at the height of its power extended eastwards as far as Lake Chad. With the rounding of the Cape of Good Hope by Vasco da Gama in 1497 Europeans began to tap the tropical Guinea coastland directly, and the Sudanese kingdoms gradually declined. "A civilization in touch for nearly a thousand years with the most highly cultivated centers of European life was silently buried in the sands of the desert." Enough has been said to show that the Fula peoples who inhabit the interior of the Sudan were able not only to cope with their environment but to utilize their location and resources and, under favorable auspices, to erect a culture whose broader lines have not been totally erased. Racially these tribes show characteristics that set them apart from the blacks along the Gulf. They are handsome, tall, light-skinned hybrids.

41. Life in the Sudan

The Nigerian lowlands, an exceedingly fertile region, coincide with the basins of two streams, the Niger and the Benue, which meet in central Nigeria and flow as one toward the Guinea Gulf. This region may be taken as an excellent illustration of adaptations that have been made to a jungle environment. Here the population is dense. Settlements, five or six miles in length, stretch along the river banks. Agriculture has made some headway. The denizens raise tropical fruits, cane sugar, yams, ground nuts (peanuts), guinea corn, and shea butter.[1] Despite the apparent ease with which these things are produced, for the jungle allows a luxuriant plant life, there are serious disadvantages. The villages are almost at sea level; thus the inhabitants are subjected to higher temperatures and more humid conditions than are those who dwell in the adjacent higher lands. Insect life is little short of terrorizing. The report that British officials keep pet toads to enable them to combat insect pests is

[1] Made from the seed of a species of palm tree.

more than humorous commentary upon the situation. During the long rainy seasons the streams overflow the whole basin for many miles. In places great swamps make an annual appearance and become disease-breeding cesspools that spread plague over the country side. The Subequatorial jungle, then, is anything but a paradise for man.

In the savanna the population is sparser, not over ten per square mile, yet the environment there is essentially more favorable for man. In the southern part of this zone the aspect is park-like with tall, coarse grasses and gnarled trees, while in the north the grasses are tender and shorter. The trees become less frequent and resemble mere coppices. Environment permits varied activities among the Negro tribes. Yams and cotton are grown in the south; millet, tobacco, and peanuts in the north; and a little rice everywhere. In the villages are found guinea fowl, wire-haired sheep, and goats. Tree crops are produced, principally palm oil, palm kernels, kola nuts, wild rubber, and shea butter. The trading town still thrives. At Kano, where the railway from Lagos on the Gulf meets the caravan routes from the Mediterranean regions, the Europeans compete with the Moors for tropical products. This town has been termed the "Manchester of the Sudan" because of its manufactures. Weaving has been known here since the eleventh century. The sandals for half the inhabitants of the Sahara and the Sudan are made in Kano. Its cotton wares and leather goods find markets in Timbuktu and on the Guinea Gulf. Such varied products as cotton, hides, peanuts, and tin find their way to the markets of Europe.

The eastern Sudan, from Lake Chad to the Ethiopian Highlands, is very sparsely inhabited. This region is remote even from the native marts; only wild rubber and ivory, in ever diminishing quantities, find their way to the centers of trade. The natives about Lake Chad plant their crops in February, for during the dry season a belt of fertile soil from five to ten miles wide is exposed along the borders of the lake. To the east is a vast region over one thousand miles broad known as Shari-Chad, which, because of its rich black soil, has been earmarked by its French and English possessors as a potential cotton country. At present it is quite inaccessible. Between the White Nile and the Blue Nile is another uninhabited area, a rich alluvial plain, which, when properly irrigated, is expected to provide three million acres of plantation land for the raising of maize, cotton, and possibly rubber. The native population of the eastern Sudan was decimated owing to Arab slave raids. One tribe, in order to make its women less attractive to the raiders, invented the device (now a custom among them), of hideously distorting the lips of its women. As children, discs were inserted into the lower lip and these were increased in size as the child matured. Under the *pax Britannica* the population is said to be increasing.

Taken as a whole the Sudan is a cattle country. In the west many of the Fulani, a leading pastoral tribe, have settled down in permanent pasture lands far south of their home lands. In the northern part of the Sudan, where the rainy season is shortest, nomadism flourishes. During the dry season many of the Fulani drive their cattle south to the Shari-Chad lowlands, returning with the rains to the healthier highlands. At the desert's edge the press for pasture is often extreme. Such a condition is likely to give rise to raiding, pillaging, and similar forms of lawlessness that are connected with desert life. The nomad Tuaregs are most feared in this respect.

The savanna environment of the Sudan is not without its drawbacks. Epidemics of influenza decrease the population, the rinderpest destroys the cattle, and seasonal drought ruins the crops. In one of the most luxuriant regions in the whole Sudan, near the mouth of the Senegal River, the Fulani tribe in 1917 lost 80 per cent of its cattle through scourge. Provided some means can be found to check the cattle diseases and destroy the insect pests, the Sudan may some day rival the Argentine as a meat-producing region. Indeed some regard the Sudan as a potential India, pouring forth streams of grain, cattle, vegetable oils, fruits, gums, and rubber into the industrial maw of the north temperate countries. Any such realization, however, will require a long and expensive effort, for problems of transportation and organization must be solved. It may turn out that the rainfall of the Sudan will prove too fickle to support such a gigantic capital investment. The white man may be forced to march more slowly, confining his attentions only to such regions as may be worked profitably through irrigation.

42. Transition to Desert

Kano, in British Nigeria, is a busy Sudan trading town of over thirty thousand inhabitants. Zinder, 130 miles north of Kano, is in a much drier region and in consequence supports a much smaller population. The European trading stores characteristic of Hausa towns further south are lacking, and the foreign quarter, principally French military, numbers less than a hundred. Rail transport ceases at Kano; motor transport ends with Zinder; and it is here that camel transport, typical of the desert, begins. Here, too, for the first time one hears rumors of raiding, the table-talk of the desert.

North of Zinder large cultivated areas appear infrequently. Grasslands are rare and the vegetation is that of a dry climate. Bush, varying from twelve feet in height to low scrub, predominates; interspersed are large tracts of barren land consisting of rocky hills and ridges strewn with boulders. Further on the land assumes a desert cloak; sandy tracts appear and on the open downs there is only low scrub and tufted grass. Wild life diminishes; only a few guinea hens and gazelles are seen. Kram-kram, a species of wild grass with tenacious burrs, is everywhere, and the villagers must burn it in order to walk about comfortably. After the short rainy season the natives are subjected to burning heat; while during the winter months the cold is augmented by piercing winds that blow from the desert. During the dry season water becomes scarce—so scarce that in some of the villages the supply is not adequate for a dozen camels.

Tanut, ninety miles north of Zinder (latitude about 15° N.), is at the desert's edge. In fact during the dry season it would be mistaken for a desert settlement. At that time its inhabitants are engaged in tending flocks of goats, sheep, and bullocks. No grain can be purchased. Yet Tanut has a short rainy season every year, and for a few months its inhabitants are agriculturalists producing relatively large stocks of millet, maize, and guinea corn. At harvest the village becomes the grain center of the region. Further north the rainy season is too short or insufficiently reliable for the inhabitants to raise crops. Whatever agriculture is practised depends upon irrigation for water supply, not rainfall.

North of Tanut is a belt retaining a few of the attributes of the savanna climate. The short rainy season fills up shallow depressions with water. Here thickets flourish for a brief time every year. One large belt of bush manages to exist as a sort of challenge to the desert. Here are found large numbers of game—ostrich, giraffe, gazelle, turkey, tortoise, porcupine, and bustard. Yet the region as a whole belongs to the desert. By the end of November the lakes have evaporated, and the nomads have their choice of retreating with the rains to the Sudan or of living a true desert existence—wandering from well to well with their camels, donkeys, goats, and sheep in search of water.

43. The Sahara

Africa north of the Sudan is a vast desert excepting only the Mediterranean coastlands and the valley of the Nile. The Sahara, though parts of it are known under various regional names, extends from the Nile to the Atlantic. In places it is three thousand miles broad and half that distance from north to south. The Sahara must not be thought of as a flat, sandy region for much of it, though barren, is plateau and mountain. The Ahaggar Massif of the central Sahara and the Tibesti Mountains south of the Libyan Desert both contain peaks of ten thousand feet. The little known Aïr Mountains lying midway between Algeria and Nigeria comprise an area of three thousand square miles. From this gloomy, barren plateau rise peaks of six thousand feet or more. The lower slopes of this huge volcanic formation are covered with rough gravel and boulders. A thin line of thorns and bushes mark sandy-bedded water courses that are the paths of occasional run-offs. In the gravel regions at lower levels grow tough scrub, small trees, and the coarsest of grasses. The Aïr region is one of the loneliest in the whole Sahara. Here it is possible to travel for days without meeting a human being. Yet even in these mountain fastnesses there are villages. Iferouane containing three hundred inhabitants and Auderas with two hundred are the largest of the half dozen that exist in the most favored places. There are many rocky and mountainous areas like Aïr in the Sahara.

The deserts experience seasonal variations in temperature unknown to other tropical environments. At In-Salah, an oasis in the south of Algeria (27° 18′ N.), the January temperature is 54° and the July temperature 98°. Here on one occasion the thermometer registered 129°. The barren lands are unable to retain the sun's heat with the result that though at noon it is hot, at night it may be freezing. Only the prevalence of the strongly blowing Northeast Trades makes it possible to move about the desert during the warm season. In the sheltered oases people never venture out of doors at midday. During the dry season the Trades blow into the Sudan causing piercing cold. There the wind is known as the *harmattan*. In the desert it carries with it a fine sand reducing visibility to a few hundred feet and further discomforting the traveler because it gets into his eyes, ears, and, more tragic still, his food. When the *harmattan* is blowing it is impossible to stay upon a camel for more than a few minutes without becoming numb.

The sand storms occur at the beginning of the hot season when the outblowing pressure is greatest. The French, with characteristic linguistic nicety, distinguish between *vent du sable* and *tempête du sable*. The latter type especially is dreaded not only because it blows down everything in its path but because it fills up the wells with sand. Many a man has perished because he arrived at a well with empty water skins only to find it entirely silted-up. The average native, be he Arab, Tuareg, or Negro, rarely carries more than enough water to see him to the next well. When they are asked why they do not make allowance for the possibility of finding none there, the usual fatalistic answer follows: "If Allah wills . . ."

Rainfall is scarce in the desert and this factor, of course, explains the sparseness of life there. One oasis experienced only a single heavy rain in four years, and this is the rule rather than the exception. A single rain will have a remarkable effect. Parched and withered tufts of grass become half green with fresh blades, trees apparently dead spring to life and sprout green foliage, and out of the bare sand spring tiny shoots from wind-scattered seedlings. This revivification, however, is short-lived for years may pass before rain, the life restorer, will fall again. The sun evaporates the moisture and vegetation withers. The French have but one remark regarding the desert: *c'est triste*.

For their water supply the natives rely wholly upon the wells or water-holes which stud the desert. Yet, through mischance, a well may not yield water so that there must be an alternative well in each frequented pasture. The location of these wells is one of the secrets of the nomad. To travel even a short space in the desert is precarious as the French have discovered. No camel corps is permitted to go out without a guide regardless of the knowledge its officer may claim.

44. The Tuaregs: Desert Nomads

The Tuaregs, widespread, yet few in numbers, are the inhabitants of the Sahara. This people, though followers of Islam, roamed the desert long before the appearance of the Arabs in Africa. The pure-blooded Tuaregs are tall and slender with lithe, graceful figures. Their limbs are well shaped; their hands, wrists, and ankles small. The men wear a veil over the face, exposing only the eyes. This custom, reversing that of the Arabs which compels the woman to take the veil, led the latter to dub them opprobriously, "people of the veil." The wearing of the veil has become ritualistic among the Tuaregs; it is retained even when eating and sleeping, and it is considered an act of indecency to remove it in the presence of another. Those who have been photographed without it are men of low class and impure blood. No doubt the veil, which lends a sinister and mysterious appearance to its wearer, has had its effect in terrorizing the sedentary inhabitants of the oases.

Until the advent of the French the Tuaregs reigned supreme in the Sahara. Every oasis paid tribute or was subjected to the cruellest kind of raid. Even to-day large raids are undertaken, but they originate in the Spanish territory of Rio de Oro in the west or in Italian territory in the east. Raiding on a small scale persists in French territory in districts far from the reach of the law. The primary occupation of the Tuaregs is raiding and fighting. Century old inter-tribal feuds are common. The Tuaregs consider it beneath their dignity to lead a sedentary life. Supplying camel transport for caravans is secondary. They are men of extreme opposites. In camp they are lazy and idle and lie about sleeping and dreaming. But on the trail they reveal remarkable traits; they can cover a hundred miles a day existing on a minimum of food and drink. It is common among the Tuaregs to keep themselves alive on long journeys by drinking blood from the veins of the camel's neck. They make war by ambush and sudden attack. Raids are made during the night or at dusk.

Their dress consists of long, loose-fitting gowns of white or indigo blue cotton and long, baggy trousers. The trousers are pulled up when they are at work loading the camel or ascending rocky slopes. Except when they are on camelback, broad sandals are worn. The Tuaregs are armed to the teeth; they carry a long double-edged sword, a dagger, a lance, and a large shield of white oryx. Recently, the rifle, a coveted possession, has displaced the lance. The Tuaregs have social classes—the nobles, the servitors, and the negro slaves. Contrary to the Moslem custom, the women occupy a high place in the tribe. They possess a freedom not yet attained in some of the countries of western Europe. They are permitted to sit in the tribal councils; and descent is traced through the female. They are highly intelligent.

When not engaged in the more spectacular business of pillaging, a Tuareg tribe wanders from well to well and pasture to pasture tending camels, donkeys, and goats. Aside from the prizes of raiding, which are scanty, they depend for existence on milk obtained from camels and goats from which they make a palatable kind of cheese. A little meat from their animals and what grain or dates they can obtain from oases or caravans complete their diet. Because of the French occupation of the greater part of the Sahara, the Tuaregs have been reduced to a purely nomadic type of existence, for the profitable and congenial business of raiding has been forbidden. The erstwhile masters of the desert are now in a sad plight. The impression is gained of a race brooding like an animal in captivity which, by a turn of fate, has been deprived of its freedom. Unable to continue their warlike career, fretting at the uneventful and peaceful nomadic life to which they are condemned and from which they can exact at best only a bare existence, they seem destined to be absorbed into the sedentary population of the oases.

45. Life in the Oases

An *oasis* is a green spot in a desert. Wherever there is green shrub, grass, or the date palm, the nomad knows that a well can be dug and water obtained. His whole life is spent in making the rounds from one well to another. In the far reaches of the Sahara the oases are likely to be small and the wells may fail to yield ground water. Here life is very precarious. Around the larger wells villages grow up, and the size of the village is directly dependent upon the amount of water that can be obtained. In other places, such as certain parts of Algeria, ground water is very abundant. In consequence, a considerable agriculture is carried on, and frequently large exports of dates are made. One oasis in the northern Sahara supports three million date palms. Another exports apricots, figs, quinces, pomegranates, peaches, and pears. The trees are valued as property, not the land. Streams flowing through deserts comprise a second type of oases. The Nile is the greatest "oasis" in the trade wind zones; it supports a dense population of 14,000,000, all of whom live within a few miles of the banks of the river.

Tadjedufat, along the route from Nigeria to Algeria, is a typical Sahara oasis. It is one of the few reliable wells between Tanut and Agadez, a stretch of 250 miles. It has no sedentary inhabitants because the water is insufficient to support agriculture. Yet there are always a large group of nomads in the vicinity of Tadjedufat. Here there is a "very, very old" well, with a diameter almost as great as the well is deep. It is about forty feet across the well and the water is fifty feet below the surface. Three-fourths of the way down it narrows to a width of twelve feet and reaches the water through solid rock. The water is drawn up in leather buckets. At times the nomads throw their buckets over the side and pull up the water for there are only two pulleys. The pulley lines have worn grooves of three or four inches into the solid rock. Because the water supply is dependable there is always a large gathering of natives about the well head. Yet there is always a danger that the well might be silted-up with sand. Certain conventions regarding the use of the water have grown up. The caravans passing to and from Kano are given precedence in using the water, for the nomads respect their desire to travel swiftly. The nomads depend upon the caravans for news of the outside world and often do a little trading with them. It is customary for the nomads in the vicinity to use the smaller wells as long as the water holds out. When it fails, however, they drive their flocks to the neighborhood of Tadjedufat and bring the animals to the well in small batches. It is a slow and tedious process to draw up the water, but time is of no importance to the nomad.

Agadez at the foothills of the Aïr Mountains is a village of two thousand inhabitants. To-day it is ruled by the French, but in former times it was ruled by the black sultan of Aïr. However, the sultan then as now had no real power, for he paid tribute to the Taureg chiefs of the Aïr Mountains. Agadez is the largest permanent non-agricultural settlement in the southern Sahara. For food it depends upon the date palm and the products of herding. Yet, in times past, it was the junction of important caravan routes. There was much trading and an industry grew up which comprised blacksmithing, silversmithing and leather working. To-day, with the decline of caravan trading, the town has an abject air. Its population has decreased and many of the houses on the outskirts have fallen into decay. The dwellings are of red mud with flat roofs. Their featureless appearance is broken only by a pyramid shaped mosque built of mud and palm rafters that rises to a height of eighty feet.

Iferouane, nestled in the heights of the Aïr Mountains, is a true oasis despite its small size. Here irrigation is practised, and the inhabitants find their main support in agriculture. This village is prominent because it is the last human habitation of any kind until Djanet, five hundred miles to the north, is reached. It has managed to survive in spite of the cessation of intercourse with the north. The village lies along a little stream bed in the midst of the mountains. Here are little groups of palms, each surrounded by a small fence-enclosed compound into which goats and sheep are driven at night. In the center of the village are two palm leaf shelters, one of which is used as a mosque, the other as a blacksmith's shop. Between the village and the stream bed are numerous garden plots that are cultivated under the shelter of the palms that line its banks. Water, however, is not obtained from the stream for it rarely rains, but from numerous wells. The garden plots are small and square and are divided by embankments along the top of which run little canals. When water is needed, a breach is made in the wall, and when the field is covered, the breach is sealed up. The gardens are fenced to prevent the sheep and goats from getting in. Millet, wheat, beans, and guinea corn are raised. By the exercise of great toil an annual rotation of four crops can be obtained. The pasture about the village is good, and the inhabitants, a mixture of Tuareg and former negro slaves, engage in herding. As Iferouane is the only agricultural settlement in this part of the Sahara, there is a great demand for its grain. In times of famine caravans will risk the long, dangerous trip from Djanet to purchase grain, and the French, realizing the importance of Iferouane as an oasis, are endeavoring to extend its irrigated area.

Between Iferouane and Warghla in Algeria is a huge barren expanse of 1,300 miles. Permanent settlements, mainly of a military character, exist at Djanet, Ft. Polignac, and Ft. Flatters. The only other human habitations, temporary in character, are found at the well sites. Djanet has about eight hundred inhabitants divided among three villages. Its 140 water holes permit the cultivation by irrigation of corn, beans, tobacco, and dates. Here, however, the fall harvest is insufficient to carry the inhabitants through the winter. By December supplies have become very low and the inhabitants have to resort to a flour made of grinding a mixture of grass, palm tree bark, and old date stones scratched up from the sand. If the native has been provident, he will be able to add a little corn to the mixture. The sultan alone has enough dates to last through the year. These people, like the rest of the desert inhabitants, are lacking in foresight, often trading their meager harvest for cloth, tea, sugar, and utensils brought by the caravans. The French have not been able to do much. They have difficulty in keeping the garrison supplied with food because Djanet is possibly the most inaccessible post in the whole Sahara. Supplies must be brought from Warghla, eight hundred miles to the north. The inhabitants are timid, furtive people, because they have long been prey to the Asgur Tuaregs who levy upon them from time to time, and because of the cruel Tebu raiders who descend upon them from the wastes of southern Tripoli. At the sight of a stranger they scuttle to their windowless huts and lock the door. At Warghla, in southern Algeria, no such hardships are encountered, for this oasis has motor connections with the railway terminus at Tuggart. Settlements like Djanet and Iferouane are far more typical of the Sahara oases than are the prosperous export centers that the tourist visits in northern Africa. It is about such lonely wells far from civilization that the adaptations of man to the desert environment may be seen.

Generally then, the Sahara yields a picture of abject poverty; poverty such as few know it. A handful of people wage an unceasing war against nature and, in the struggle for survival, just barely keep their heads above water. Day after day, year in and year out, a little milk, a few dates, and a very small quantity of grain are squeezed from a harsh environment.

The future of such wastes is not very encouraging. Water will always be difficult to obtain, and a few expensive artesian borings will make little impression upon so great a surface. The French will soon complete a motor route through the Sahara. It is possible to go long distances by motor; In-Salah and even Timbuktu can be reached by automobile. The French dream of reviving the trans-Sahara trade by building a railroad from the Mediterranean to Nigeria. Such a road will never pay dividends; the cost of construction will be enormous and the cost of maintenance even greater. Traffic by sea will absorb the commerce because of its very cheapness. The railway will, however, be of great strategic importance to France, for it will bind together her African dominion and enable her in a military crisis to utilize vast reserves of man power. The Sahara will remain what it has always been—a vast, desolate desert of rock and sand, ravaged unceasingly by wind and sun.

One cannot fail to express admiration for the manner in which a comparative handful of white men, aided by a small number of Arabs and West Africans, have pacified this vast turbulent area and succeeded in maintaining order. That it has been no easy task is impressed upon one by the many little crosses that are seen bearing the inscription *Mort pour la France.*

CHAPTER VI

THE WHITE MAN IN THE TROPICS: JAVA AND OTHER MALAYSIAN LANDS

46. Nature of the Relationship

The white man obtains from the tropics agricultural products that cannot be raised in temperate regions and also metals and minerals that happen to be deposited there in abundance. For purposes of classification the agricultural exports are readily divisible into two types, food crops and industrial crops. A second interest lies in the large potential consuming power of the masses of people who inhabit the most favored of the tropical areas. Since the latter part of the nineteenth century, European states have made efforts to establish political control over tropical lands as the safest method of protecting large capital investments there and as the easiest way of securing a monopoly of the market about to be developed. Recently, however, since political adjustments seem to have crystallized, economic penetration of tropical lands has been adopted as an alternative method of trading with tropical countries. From an investor's point of view many difficulties have arisen from this kind of relationship; principally from the necessity of safeguarding large investments from the caprices of native governments. Many native states are lacking in political experience; in consequence frequent changes are made often with the result that property, both domestic and foreign owned, is in jeopardy of confiscation. Since the investor, under international law, can claim no greater protection for his investments than can the denizens of such a state, the risks of tropical investments are often very great. Yet the stakes are also apt to be high. In consequence European entrepreneurs continue to invest their capital in such enterprises. During times of political strife, various methods for protecting their establishments are adopted—some of them questionable in the eyes of political moralists. The problem to-day is largely one of standardizing the conduct of the various interested parties—of find-

ing a way in which the resources of a region may be developed profitably and peacefully for all directly concerned.

47. "Robber Technique"

Until the latter part of the nineteenth century, methods of dealing
with tropical peoples were exceedingly vicious. Frequently neither
the rights nor the lives of the natives were respected. Both were reck-
lessly exploited, and unfortunately many years elapsed before public
opinion was sufficiently aroused to check the abuse of the raiders.
Even though better times have arrived, there is to-day in many tropical countries a widespread distrust of the European investor. In
some places the scars of exploitation are so deeply graven that re-
quital seems almost impossible.

The operations of King Leopold of Belgium afford a typical illustration of the harm that may be wrought in obtaining what is desired
without heed for either the inhabitants or the resources of the exploited area. In a space of thirty-three years, Leopold succeeded in
wringing about $20,000,000 from the Congo, half of it during the
ten years 1891 to 1900. Despite the fact that the king spent much of
his wealth liberally—in beautifying Brussels, in making Ostend the
most fashionable resort in Europe, and in patronizing arts and letters
—society condemned him for the abuses that arose in the Congo basin. Finally, upon the insistence of the nations of Europe, the territory was placed under the control of the government of Belgium.

A brief examination of the system of "robber technique" as practised in the Congo will reveal not only that the method of "getting
what you want in any way that you can get it" is abusive but also
that in the long run such a system is economically wasteful. The
Congo products most desired were ivory and rubber. The companies
to which this area was parcelled out by Leopold, in return for a fixed
percentage of the proceeds, had of necessity to employ natives to kill
the elephants and to tap the rubber-bearing trees. The natives, however, showed no great enthusiasm for either the rewards or the dignity of labor. This *impasse* led to measures for coercing the natives.
The concessionists adopted various means of forcing them to comply
with their wishes. The most popular method was to assess each village so many pounds of rubber and ivory and compel delivery. Under
this system, in the ten-year period referred to, the annual value of the

rubber obtained rose from 300,000 francs to 40,000,000 francs, and that of the ivory from 2,800,000 francs to 5,300,000 francs. The wastefulness of the system became apparent with the increasing difficulty of obtaining either product. Both the elephants and the rubber supply began to diminish. By 1914, the proceeds from rubber amounted to only 3,500,000 francs.

48. The Model Mine and Plantation System

Wise companies have adopted an entirely different attitude toward native labor in recent years. It must not be supposed that conditions of labor in the tropics to-day are everywhere ideal, yet the most enterprising developers of tropical lands show a solicitude for the natives that was totally lacking only a generation ago. An effort is being made to reward the native in accordance with his own standard of values. To do this properly has involved the study of primitive cultures with a view to encouraging not only the preservation of the native industries and arts but of those customs and institutions that are worthy of perpetuation. No longer is the endeavor made to force upon native races those things in our own civilization—education, religion, and so on—that are entirely foreign to their way of thinking. The thoughtful manager, with the coöperation of his company, spends large sums upon improving sanitary conditions. Model villages are erected and a premium is put upon cleanliness. The education of children is undertaken with the aim of better enabling the boy or girl to fit into the scheme of things about him. The boys are trained in the occupations likely to be open to them, and the girls in the domestic arts customary to the community. Many of the arts of weaving and designing that constitute part of the cultural heritage of any people have been preserved by keeping out the cheap and gaudy cotton products of the Western factory.

49. The Plantation System

The modern plantation system is a business enterprise that requires a maximum of skill and foresight, for in the realm of both food and industrial crops, the competition is likely to be severe. It is now realized that only the most efficient producers in the tropics can survive. The reasons are largely geographical. Most tropical crops require two things: heat and dependable ample rainfall. Numerous areas throughout the tropics satisfy both requirements. Rubber, copra, and similar products can be raised in any of several tropical environments. Equatorial regions like the Dutch East Indies, Subequatorial regions like the Niger basin, Monsoon regions in low latitudes like southern India, and Trade Wind with Ample Rain regions like Cuba, all stand ready to enter the field when a new tropical money crop appears.

Plantation agriculture is scientific. Many of the plantations maintain large experimental stations which are constantly seeking to domesticate a wild crop, to obtain a better variety of plant, or to transplant a variety that has been successfully cultivated in some other tropical region. The efforts of the Firestone Corporation to plant rubber in Liberia, and those of Mr. Ford to create rubber plantations in Brazil, in an endeavor to break foreign control of the rubber market are among the more spectacular illustrations of tropical plant adaptation. The persistence and the patience exerted by the white entrepreneur to mold the tropics to his uses—indeed to the uses of mankind—is one of the finest achievements in the "conquest" of environment. It is a subject more worthy of the historian of the human race than the petty squabbles of states over jurisdiction in tropical regions.

A statement from the official catechism of the Dutch entrepreneurs of East Coast Sumatra, a prosperous plantation area, will give an inkling of the difficulties and financial risks encountered before success was finally attained.

Ever since 1878 serious experiments have been made with cocoa-nuts, and years before that with nutmegs, the cultivation of which had to be abandoned, owing to the export duty imposed since 1876, it thus being rendered impossible to make any profit on them. Experiments were made with madder (used in dyeing), which came to nothing. In 1870 a specially trained worker was sent out for the cultivation and preparation of indigo, the experiments meeting, however, with no success. Various coffee estates, moreover, were planted in the tobacco territory, but the coffee cultivation was given up on account of the berries not ripening, but rotting on the trees, so that there was no chance of making this cultivation pay. The cultivation of cocoa, quinine, and "rameh" (fiber)—the latter seeming to be very promising—was tried. All these attempts had to be abandoned, after having cost very large sums of money. It has become evident, after all those years, that alone with tobacco, with re-afforestation of the harvested land, in a cycle of many years—often eight—can a product be obtained, capable of capturing and maintaining a good name in the world market and of giving in the long run a suitable profit. Not only the Deli Company, but nearly all the tobacco companies have, to their detriment, at some time or other tried other cultivation on the tobacco land. The experience has been gained and profited by; on this special land, with this special climate, this special crop offers the planter the best guarantee for a paying crop in the long run. . . . It may suffice to mention here that, since the commencement of the tobacco cultivation to the present time, 129 companies have gone into liquidation or abandoned the tobacco industry, while there are at present fourteen still remaining, with seventy estates in exploitation. The vision floating before the eyes of some outsiders, of Deli having been right from the start a place where everything always went smoothly in a kind of El Dorado, where, from every scattered grain, gold-bearing trees sprang up, will have been sufficiently dissipated by now.

To operate in the tropics, large capital must be available whether the exploitation is in mining or agriculture. Many tropical areas remain undeveloped because of the lack of capital or rather because it is too risky to invest capital there. Equatorial Brazil offers immense possibilities to the rubber planter, yet comparatively little capital has been invested in Brazilian rubber plantations. Furthermore, a corporation cannot afford to invest huge sums in establishing railways when coastlands are accessible. Most of the tropical developments are to be found in close communication with the coasts. Finally the areas opened up must have an adequate supply of labor. The lack of a labor supply is perhaps the paramount reason for the slowness in opening up the vast tropical reserves in South America and Africa.

In British Guiana, for example, where sugar is the chief crop, the labor situation has gone through many ramifications. The natives, as in the West India islands, early proved unfit for plantation labor, and were replaced by negro slaves. With the emancipation of the slaves in 1834, Chinese labor was imported. After 1867, Hindus and East Indians were brought in. The latter groups can endure the sultry, hot climate and get along with rice as the principal article of diet. One of the reasons why the plantation system of Guiana has difficulty in competing with the Cuban plantations is the lack of a mobile supply of labor. In the Dutch plantation region of East Sumatra, alluded to above, the cost involved in obtaining a satisfactory labor supply has been a great charge upon the investment. During the seven years, 1920–1927, over $5,000,000 were expended by the government. The native labor supply was insufficient and delinquent, and

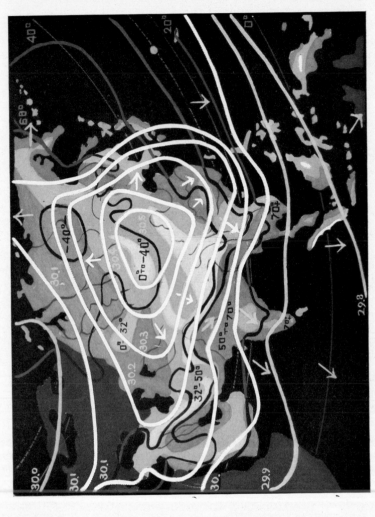

PLATE VI. ASIA—JANUARY ISOTHERMS, ISOBARS, AND PREVAILING WINDS

(*After Goode*)

the attempt to employ Malays from the mainland failed because the Malay proved himself a lazy and unwilling worker. Finally the owners had to turn to China for their supply. In recent years Javan labor, which is now abundant, has been imported because it is less expensive to transport than Chinese labor. So long as this territory continues to expand heavy initial labor costs must be met.

50. Java: The Successful Venture

Java is regarded by all nations interested in opening up tropical lands as the plantation that has been preëminently successful. Since 1880 the population of Java and Madura, its satellite, has increased from twenty to forty millions. The density of population is 750 per square mile, making Java the most densely populated land in the world. Java produces a larger proportion of the world's supply of tropical goods than any other colony. In addition to a long list of "money crops" that includes sugar, coffee, tea, cocoa, indigo, spices, cinchona, tobacco, rubber, copra, and others, Java possesses large timber and mineral resources. Tin, gold, coal, and petroleum are being exploited, but the deposits of copper, silver, zinc, lead, and nickel, known to exist, are practically untouched. During 1930 Java produced nearly forty million barrels of petroleum, an amount exceeded by only five other countries. In Java, as elsewhere in the tropics, the white man plays the rôle of exploiter, not of settler. To-day only 170,000 white men live there, and the great majority are engaged in the work of estate management.

Java and Madura [1] experience an equatorial type of rainfall; yet because of the land forms and location, the two islands escape the enervating effects of such an environment. Hills and high ranges afford relief from the heat, while an excellent system of natural drainage mitigates the worst effects of the equatorial dampness. Many of the estates are located along the coasts where they are subject to the moderating influences of the ocean. The laterite soils, normal to water-logged equatorial regions, are absent not only because of the drainage but also because much of Java is composed of a recently decomposed volcanic ash, rich in the essential mineral properties of a good soil. The other islands of the East Indies are not so well endowed with respect to drainage and soil. Borneo, an island

[1] Examine carefully Plates I, VI, VII, VIII, IX.

four times as large as Java, supports a population of less than two hundred thousand. A recent United States consular report states that there is not a cultivated tract in all Borneo worthy of being called a farm. In fact, the only other promising East India area, the east coast of Sumatra, has a volcanic soil.

Since the Dutch occupation, great care has been exercised in seeing that the natives have a sufficiency of land upon which to raise a food supply. Fortunately the staple food is rice, a commodity that is capable of supporting a population of two thousand per square mile. Recently, however, there have been importations of rice into Java. To provide a balanced menu, maize and cassava, which yields a tapioca flour, both native American products, have been successfully introduced. Soya beans, high in albumen content, peanuts, cane sugar, tobacco, and cotton, complete the list of essentials for feeding and clothing the huge labor element. The Malay race throughout the East has a reputation for laziness and shiftlessness, but the Dutch have demonstrated that these qualities are not innate. In fact, in the other East Indian plantations Javan labor is preferred, and the Javan worker is not thought of as a Malay. The name, Malay, is reserved for his shiftless relative upon the mainland.

In addition to favorable environment and excellent labor conditions, the Dutch have provided the *sine qua non* of the plantation system, a good administration. After centuries of probing into all phases of the plantation relationship, the Dutch have erected a system of jurisdiction calculated to safeguard not only labor but the land as well. Every lease of estate land is examined thoroughly. Soil exhaustion is stringently guarded against in the terms of the lease. No reckless speculative enterprises are permitted. In the case of sugar lands, for example, cultivation is limited in accordance with the capacity of the mill. The same piece of land is planted in sugar but once in three years. Moreover, the Dutch have been in the van in regulating living and sanitary conditions among the estate workers. Their regulations are used as models throughout the tropical plantation world. The Dutch also inaugurated the system of education among tropical peoples formerly termed, in derision, "the ostrich policy" because it had the appearance of withholding from the tropical denizen the intellectual fruits of a higher civilization. To-day it is recognized that the social heritage of such peoples is likely to represent a better adaptation to the tropical environment than the imposition of an entirely new set of mores.

The Dutch system is sound because it is the product of centuries of experience. The Dutch began with a system of "robber technique" that was rectified only after it was realized that it was a policy as harmful and wasteful to themselves as to the natives. Their earliest quest was for the highly valued spices of the island. A Malay chieftain was made responsible for bringing in a quota of spices at fixed periods. Even in the early days of the plantation system the lesson had not been wholly learned. The natives were compelled to plant a thousand coffee trees per family. Two-fifths of the crop was charged to taxation, and the rest sold to the government at its own price. The roads to be built were allotted among the native chiefs, and failure to complete a stretch of road was punished by hanging the delinquent. Later the "culture system," a modification of the prevailing method of exploitation, was adopted. The natives cultivated a fifth of their lands for the government and expended upon them a fifth of their labor. After 1878 the system of free labor was introduced. All restraints upon labor were removed except a poll tax, whose object was to induce the natives to hire their labor upon the estates. Lands in Java were thrown open to entrepreneurs of the various European countries, and the competition for labor among the various estate owners, Dutch and others, has worked in favor of the natives.

51. Plantation Food Crops

Cane sugar makes no stringent demands in its cultivation. It needs a warm climate, from 75° to 80°, and a heavy rainfall, from sixty to eighty inches per annum. These requirements are present in many places in the tropical world. Sugar has been preëminently successful in Cuba, Porto Rico, and with the American tariff exemption, in Hawaii and in the Philippines. Cuba, producing a fourth of the world's sugar, is Java's chief rival for the market. There, where three-fourths of the plantations are under American control, sugar thrives so luxuriantly that little scientific agricultural control is necessary to produce the most astonishing crops. Nurturing the soil is unnecessary since only a fourteenth of the potential sugar lands are in actual use. Yet, Java, a land of many staple crops, produces a sixth of the world's supply, and if India, which consumes its own crop, be disregarded, Java ranks second among sugar-producing lands. Sugar to the amount of three million tons is annually produced in Java by scientifically cropping the lands; preventing soil exhaustion by regularly rotating sugar with beans, corn, and rice. Java's exports go principally to the great markets of the East: China, Japan, and India. There is a market also in England, and, when the beet-sugar crop does not fulfill expectation, in continental Europe. It is interesting to note that the United States relied on the Javan crop during the Spanish-American War. In 1898 a cargo of sugar reached San Francisco from Java every two days. Sugar, despite Cuban competition, is the leading "money crop" of Java.

In the raising of coffee the Dutch exhibit the high degree of patience that has characterized all their plantation efforts. Coffee thrives best on hills at an altitude of one thousand to two thousand feet where the land is well drained. It needs heavy rainfall, from 75 to 120 inches. Coffee has had a shifting career. Indigenous to Abyssinia, it was introduced into Arabia during the eleventh century; thence it moved eastward to India and Java, and finally to South America. Brazil, with a limitless area of excellently drained highlands, dominates the world market, producing 80 per cent of the world's supply. Here is one of the few instances where the New World has usurped an Old World product.

The Dutch have encountered many difficulties and misfortunes in their experiences with coffee. First of all, a leaf blight attacked the species (Arabica) that had been cultivated in Java from earliest times. It became necessary to import a new variety from Liberia. This experiment proved unsuccessful with the consequence that in 1901 it was necessary to begin anew. Another foreign variety, Robusta Africa, was introduced successfully only to confront the overwhelming competition of Brazilian coffee. Brazil, by a systematic policy of price-fixing, was able to clear the field of all rivals except Java. Coffee-raising in India and Ceylon had practically disappeared owing to blight, but Brazil was able by her policy to oust Paraguay, Hawaii, and Nyasaland from the picture. Java coffee survives not only because the grade is good but because the planters raise it as a "catch crop" with rubber. There are about 370 coffee plantations in the Dutch East Indies, and all but ninety are situated in Java. Practically all the others are on East Coast Sumatra.

Tea-growing in Java is more recent than the growing of coffee. Tea is also a tropical hill crop, but it is confined largely to the tropics of the Far East. Tea was first consumed in China and Japan, where it was customary in early times to use a little of it to improve the taste of the water which had to be boiled as a sanitary precaution. About the middle of the seventeenth century Chinese tea was introduced into the European market where it had an immediate vogue. The early tea trade was most lucrative. In 1665 tea fetched £15 per pound in the London market. The Chinese, however, were unable to retain the European market in the face of the plantation system that was inaugurated successfully in Assam and in Ceylon. Chinese exports fell from three hundred million pounds in 1881 to a quarter of that amount forty years later. The tea plantations of Ceylon at present furnish employment for half-a-million workers. In 1905 the Chinese sent a government commission to India to study the plantation system which had all but destroyed their garden-grown tea industry. The Japanese introduced the plantation system on a large scale in Formosa, where "oolong," reputed to be the best quality tea in the world, is grown. Java, with less land to spare than the other tea-growing regions, began to invade the trade. Only methods of intensive agriculture have enabled Java to rise to the rank of fifth among the tea-producing lands. Lacking the land for a further extension of plantations, the Dutch are encouraging the natives to raise tea upon the lands set aside for their gardens at the same time instructing them how to obtain the largest yield. This tea is bought up by the estates owners and by Chinese manufacturers who compete with them. Over a third of the total crop is produced in this manner.

The cacao bean from which our cocoa and chocolate are produced is a potential rival of tea and coffee for drinking purposes. It has the same stimulating effect and is an extremely nutritious food substance. Cocoa has a food value twice as great as either eggs or beef. This bean is the product of the cacao tree, which is native to the river basins of equatorial South America, the Amazon and the Orinoco. The Spanish and the Portuguese found it in the New World and quickly introduced it into the Philippines, whence it spread to suitable places throughout the Old World. The tree is of medium height and will flourish only under the most exacting conditions. It requires more heat than coffee, yet it must stand in the shade of larger trees, for the direct rays of the tropical sun are detrimental to it. Therefore, it thrives best in the lowland rain forest. It does not flourish in regions directly exposed to the Trades for the heavy pods attached to the trunk and the larger branches would be severed by the wind long before the kernel ripened. The cultivation of the cacao crop is restricted by these requirements to the environment of the equatorial calms. For a time Java toyed with the idea of competing with the American product, for it was found an excellent grade of cacao could be produced. At present, however, the industry is declining. The reason for the withdrawal of the Dutch is to be found in the rise of the vast cacao plantations along the Gold Coast during the past twenty-five years. In this equatorial lowland, where rice for the Negro workers can be raised in conjunction with cacao, the industry has not only far outstripped its Old World competitors but is gradually destroying the dominance of the scattered plantations of tropical America. In 1905 only six thousand tons were marketed; to-day 230,000 tons are produced in a very compact area. The Gold Coast export, representing half of the world's supply, is worth $40,000,000 a year.

Quinine, of great use in combating malaria and other disorders, is manufactured from the bark of the cinchona tree. The tree is native to the slopes of the eastern Andes in South America, where for several centuries it was laboriously collected. In 1854 it was introduced into Java, where, amid the humid slopes and valleys, it flourished so extensively that within thirty years the Dutch had practically gained a monopoly of the market. The cultivated tree of Java produces more than twice the amount of the wild variety. Late in the nineteenth century it appeared that the European buyers had established a price monopoly that threatened to curtail any further expansion of the industry. In 1898, however, the Dutch established their own factories for making quinine and "in this way," cryptically states their official account, "a satisfactory commercial arrangement was obtained for the industry." This is but another of many examples of their patience and shrewdness.

52. Rubber

In 1930, the tropics produced 860,000 tons of rubber; all but thirty thousand tons was plantation rubber. Furthermore, the production of plantation rubber was practically confined to the tropical

Far East: the Dutch East Indies, Malaya, Borneo, Ceylon, and India. The development of the industry is one of the most interesting stories of environmental adaptation. Before the beginning of the present century the natives in South America and Africa went about tapping rubber-yielding trees and collecting the sap, latex, which by smoking was coagulated upon paddles or sticks. The use of the product has had a long history. Because an English chemist had discovered, about 1750, that it could be used for erasing pencil marks, it was given the name "rubber." Later Dr. MacIntosh, a Scotsman, utilized it in rubber-proofing cloth. His process, however, was not very satisfactory because in warm weather the rubber became sticky and in cold, it cracked. In 1842 an American named Goodyear found that in mixing sulphur with rubber, in a process known as vulcanizing, these faults were remedied. The demand for rubber received an impetus with the advent of the rubber boot and shoe industry inaugurated by Goodyear. About 1890 came the bicycle tire, and shortly after, the automobile tire. Meanwhile Brazil, Ecuador, and Peru were producing half the world's supply. Before the coming of the automobile fifty thousand tons a year sufficed to meet the world demand.

There is a large variety of rubber-bearing plants, but all are native to regions combining relatively low altitude, heavy rainfall (90 to 120 inches), and a high temperature (75° to 90° F.). In 1876, seventy thousand seeds of *hevea brasiliensis,* the best rubber yielding species, were taken to the Kew Gardens in London for experimentation. Several thousand seedlings survived, and they in turn were sent out to botanical gardens in Ceylon. Transplantings were made in Ceylon and in British Malaya. At the time, however, the rubber stream from equatorial Africa was beginning to flow, and it was difficult to persuade planters in the Far East that such a crop would be valuable. In 1900 only four tons of plantation rubber reached the market in comparison with 54,000 tons of wild rubber. But by 1913 plantation rubber equaled wild rubber in amount, and to-day it constitutes 95 per cent of the world's supply.

The demand occasioned by the rubber tire business was providential for the British in Malaya. Here was a region of virgin land where *hevea* would grow as rapidly as sixty feet in three years. Owing to the uniform climate, it was possible to obtain latex the whole year round. Thousands of acres were cleared by burning the forests. The huge stumps could not be uprooted, so they were left in the soil to rot. To protect the rubber lands against the rapid weed growth, cover crops were planted. Usually one hundred rubber trees are planted to the acre but only fifty are permitted to mature. In Malaya in 1905, forty thousand acres were planted in rubber; to-day the estates embrace over 2,500,000 acres. Plantations were established also in the extreme southwest of India, in Ceylon, and latterly in British Borneo. Second place, however, was attained by the Dutch.

At about 1876 *hevea* was also introduced into Java where it received but scanty attention until the beginning of the boom in 1900. Since that time estates rubber has spread widely in Java and has had a phenomenal growth on the Sumatra East Coast. Now, about 1,500,000 acres are in plantation rubber in the Dutch Islands, and more than half of it in the "outer islands." Java, because of a lack of suitable lowland and because of the competition of other crops, has not made so rapid a progress as Sumatra. None the less, Java has kept to the front by very shrewd measures; first by planting rubber in her reserved forest lands, and secondly by encouraging the production of native rubber under estate supervision.

About 1902 *hevea* was introduced in East Coast Sumatra by British entrepreneurs from Malaya. The two regions, separated only by the narrow Strait of Malacca, are similar in their suitability for estates rubber. Moreover, the Dutch on the East Coast have always boasted, with good reason, of the regularity of their labor arrangements which, apparently, are better than those of Malaya. The Sumatran plantations afford much better physical conditions for growth than Java, for the East Coast is low in altitude and the rains are uniform the year round. The intrusion of rubber into the East Coast economy necessitated readjustments which were undertaken with great skill. Tobacco and coffee lands that were not first class were converted into rubber estates. At the present time practically all the profitable coffee plantations operate upon the basis of rubber with coffee as a "catch crop." Fifty per cent of Dutch East Indies rubber is grown on the Sumatra East Coast. The Dutch have encouraged foreign investment in their territories. Taking the East Coast rubber industry as an example, we find that the Dutch interest amounts to 33 per cent, the British 32 per cent, the American 15 per cent, and the Franco-Belgian 13 per cent.

In 1919 the bottom fell out of the rubber market. The price

dropped to twenty-five cents a pound, a sixth of its former value. The causes were to be found in world-wide depression, and in under-consumption explained by general improvements in the tire industry and the utilization of reclaimed rubber. In 1922 Malaya and Ceylon, producing two-thirds of the world supply, accepted the Stevenson plan for curtailing production. Meanwhile, the Dutch, unaffected by the restriction went ahead with their plantings, so that when the demand was restored in 1925 they were prepared to take advantage of the situation. In 1929 their huge plantings of 1923 matured and they were able to meet the British output almost pound for pound. At the present time, again threatened by over-production, it is probable that British and Dutch will combine to restrict the output.

America uses almost two-thirds of the world's rubber, yet our investors control only 3 per cent of the rubber holdings. In 1923 when we were in the toils of the Stevenson curtailment, the sky was rent with the protests of American consumers. It was at this time that Ford and Firestone became interested in Brazil and Liberia. Other investors, however, foreseeing the advantages of the East Coast Sumatra area, began to buy holdings there. To-day the American investment on the East Coast exceeds $21,000,000.

53. Other Industrial Crops

The coco palm, which yields copra and coconut oil, is found throughout the tropics from Ceylon to the far islands of the Pacific. In fact many of the Polynesian islands are economically valueless save for the possibilities of expansion in these products. Coconuts have a food and an industrial value. Half the meat of the nut is fat or oil, and the nut possesses the unusual quality of keeping for months without turning rancid. It was found that in combining hydrogen with the oil it could be converted into a white tallow-like substance which when properly colored provided a substitute for butter. In all the ports of western Europe margarine factories were set up. By 1912 the trade in this product exceeded the international traffic in butter. The war greatly stimulated the manufacture of this substitute. Margarine, like butter, contains the food essentials of fat, protein, and vitamins.

About 1920 the demand fell off owing to the restoration of the dairy industry and the insistence of that interest for protection against such a ruthless competitor. Concurrently, however, there rose a demand for coconut oil for industrial purposes. Of all the vegetable oils used in soap making—there are half a dozen important varieties—coconut oil is most highly esteemed because of saponifiable properties that render it suitable for cold process soaps, and because it alone will yield a soap that will lather in salt water (marine soaps). Its high percentage of glycerine gives the oil a special value. In spite of the artificial limitation of coconut oil for food purposes, its total export from the tropics tends to increase. The Philippines have gone into its production extensively upon a plantation basis which has proved profitable. In 1928, yielding almost $50,000,000, coconut oil equaled sugar as the leading Philippine export. In Ceylon, Malaya, the Dutch Indies, and the South Sea Islands, the nuts are bought from the natives who collect them as the demand appears. In the Dutch East Indies there are hardly five hundred copra plantations, and only a third of them are in Java. Yet in 1917 before the product became important a rough census showed the existence of over one hundred million coconut trees in the East Indies. In the *Handbook of British Malaya,* another potential coconut area, an opinion is voiced which corresponds with that of the Javan estate owner: "While coconut planting is unlikely to prove a highly remunerative speculation, yet it may be looked upon as a sound investment, yielding at present prices from 10 to 20 per cent. on the capital outlay." When margarine returns to its former status as an acceptable substitute for butter, which it is likely to do because of its cheapness, the estates owners of Java and elsewhere will be ready to undertake its cultivation upon a large scale. At present there are too many other remunerative products competing for the land in Java.

The plantation managers in the Far East are at present more interested in the oil palm (indigenous to West Africa) than in the coconut. The reason is largely one of better financial return. It is estimated that a ton of palm oil is worth twice as much as a ton of coconut oil. Both the nut and the kernel yield an oil that is being widely used in the manufacture of soaps and candles in western Europe and the United States. Such an opportunity could not be overlooked by the planters of the Far East. In Malaya the government reserved 100,000 acres for the cultivation of the oil palm. East

Coast Sumatra began to experiment in 1911, growing the oil palm in combination with coffee. The enterprise was so successful that coffee was abandoned on many of the estates. Java, more conservative, has also plantations of oil palms, but coffee is more often retained as a "catch crop."

Java has made advance in fiber products; in one she enjoys almost a monopoly of the market. This is kapok which is grown all over the island. The plantation yield, however, is insignificant in comparison with the native output. Kapok is the most satisfactory filler for pillows and mattresses, and because of its buoyancy is becoming more and more important in life-saving apparatus. The seed yields oil that is of value commercially. Java also has plantations of sisal and cantala hemp. At present, however, the sisal of Yucatan and the abaca or Manila hemp of the Philippines seem to have a secure hold upon the markets for these products.

Another illustration of the patience and ingenuity of the Dutch in Java is in connection with the development of *gutta percha*. This product of the gutta tree proved useful in the manufacture of submarine cables. In 1884 the Dutch began to domesticate the tree. The tapping of the tree proved difficult and harmful to the tree. After years of experimentation a method was found of extracting gutta percha from the leaves and twigs. The tree was successfully reduced to a large bush. Just as success was achieved the wireless development occurred with the result that the gutta percha industry was depleted. New uses were found, however, and the culture not only revived but became more extensive. Gutta percha has replaced balata because it serves better for purposes of insulation. It is widely employed in the making of chemical valves, and acid containing bottles and also in the manufacture of golf balls. The Dutch control the market for gutta percha.

54. Tobacco

The tropics compete with the temperate zones in the production of tobacco as in the case of cotton. This indigenous American crop can be grown in both belts providing the soil is rich and the rainfall moderate and dependable. The United States exports the largest amount of tobacco. The Dutch East Indies are second, although more is actually grown in Japan than in the East Indies. In the East Indies tobacco planting is confined to Java and the Sumatra East Coast. It is a plantation crop in both areas.

Sumatra tobacco is especially valuable, like the Cuban, because its thinness and elasticity give it a preëminence as a wrapper for cigars. In Sumatra the Dutch cleared a long belt parallel to the east coast of the island and from five to ten miles inland. There the soil, a decomposed lava, is extremely good. An estates system was set up that was almost without an equal in the plantation world. The various planters, for the regulation of the labor supply and for purposes of marketing, formed an association that has stood the test of time. In the vast acreage devoted to tobacco raising there are seventy estates with a total European personnel of only seven hundred persons. Under their control 74,000 work folk are employed under strictly enforced coolie ordinances. The large majority are Chinese and Javans. Tobacco grows rapidly and as soon as the "money crop" is harvested the lands are planted with the rice and maize necessary to feed the work people. The tobacco crop is much in demand by the dealers of Amsterdam who act as its distributors throughout continental Europe. Dividends as high as 75 per cent per annum have been paid. Some stigma has been laid to the Deli Association's operations since the death rate among the workers during the decade from 1912 to 1921 ranged from 11 to 25 per cent per year. During the last decade, however, the average has fallen to 7 per cent.

55. The White Race and the Tropics

The experience of the Dutch in Java during the past three centuries is sufficient to enable us to draw certain conclusions concerning the relationship of the white man and his culture to the tropical areas. That the products of the tropics are valuable to our highly mechanized civilization there can be no doubt. Without the rubber supplies that such regions yield our industrial régime would be seriously impaired. Despite the fact that we could possibly get along without their vegetable oils, sugar, tobacco, tea, coffee, cocoa, and a host of other products, their contributions to our food and industrial supplies are far from insignificant. Their agricultural exports are far from being a luxury trade. From these regions, too, we obtain large amounts of essential minerals and metals. Malaya alone produces

40 per cent of the world's supply of tin each year. The resources of the tropics, agricultural and mineral, have only been tapped. The development of the tropics lies for the most part in the future.

That the white man will never settle in large numbers in tropical lands seem also to be an established fact. What is true for India and Java is true of every important area in the tropics. In Jamaica, under British administration for several centuries, the white population is slowly decreasing. There are hardly fifteen thousand whites in comparison with a colored population of eight hundred thousand. The Negro population in Jamaica has increased over 25 per cent since the beginning of the twentieth century. The whites have had to resort to various artificial arrangements to cope with the heat and moisture of tropical regions. They must take long leaves of absence, or retire to the hill country, in order to recuperate. The era of white settlement in the tropics may never dawn; in fact it seems likely that our racial characteristics are such as to prohibit our making the necessary climatological adaptation.

The white man plays an essential rôle. He is the exploiter, the entrepreneur, and the ruler. In the past he has made mistakes, but he has benefited by his experiences. A study of any one region will lead to no other conclusion. Robber technique has not only been outlawed but is not practised in the most successful tropical ventures. Not only public opinion, which is increasingly articulate, but the entrepreneurs themselves, are interested in minimizing abuse and injustice. Avarice and greed are no more likely to reveal themselves in the dealings of whites with natives than in the dealings of our factory owners with their labor. To speak of curtailing development in the tropics is a purely negative attitude and in a broad sense vicious because compliance with such dogma is equivalent to setting bounds to the conquest of man over his environment. The white man has assumed leadership in this struggle, and if he is to maintain his hegemony, he must realize that leadership has its duties as well as its privileges. Fortunately, business interest and ethics tend to coincide in the desire to treat native labor fairly.

The Dutch have worked from the inside out rather than from the outside in. Their prosperity rests upon their capacity for adapting not one, but many crops, to the environment of Java. Their awareness and their willingness to experiment have rewarded them richly. Their plantations produce practically every "money crop" known to tropical lands. Others have followed their example, particularly where virgin lands are being opened up. The British in Malaya might well rest content with their produce of tin and rubber. Yet there, as in Java, we find experimental stations, public as well as private, seeking always opportunities for undertaking a new culture. Java supports a population of nearly forty millions. Her export trade amounts to about $600,000,000 a year. The native population has attained a scale of living that could not possibly be approximated through any efforts of its own. But even more important to the natives of the tropics is the boon of a secure life. Against famine, against the ravages of disease, against infant mortality, against the raids of predatory neighbors, they are reasonably safeguarded. These are the blessings that are valuable to those who must struggle for existence against a hostile physical environment.

CHAPTER VII

INDIA: A MONSOON ENVIRONMENT

56. Geographical Unity

India is about the same size as China proper. Its population is estimated at 350,000,000, and the density per square mile at 175; somewhat less than China's in both respects. Like China, India is a geographical unit. Europe, elevated to the rank of a continent because of its importance, has always been more accessible geographically than India. Only the Urals separate Europe and Asia, yet they are a paper barrier in comparison to the Himalayas, a mountain wall with an altitude of from ten to twenty thousand feet. This lofty chain is about 2,500 miles from east to west and along its whole extent there are only seven gaps. The Khyber Pass in the northwest is regarded as the only really vulnerable entry from a military standpoint. The passes through Burma are equally difficult because dense jungles must be traversed before India proper can be reached.

India has, too, a climatic unity. Despite the fact that the Tropic of Cancer divides its latitudinal extent fairly in two, India is a tropical country, wholly under the influence of monsoonal winds which bring it rains during the growing season. Like China, India depends upon the summer monsoon both for the amount and distribution of its rainfall. Latitude is a relatively unimportant factor. Throughout India the distribution of crops is governed by the amount of rainfall rather than by distance from the equator. Identical crops, in consequence, are likely to appear both in the north and the south.

This geographical isolation and interior unity has had its influence upon the civilization of India. Notwithstanding the fact that several of the larger linguistic families are represented, the manners, customs, and occupations of the people are remarkably uniform. The caste system, for example, has not only cut athwart linguistic barriers but has won adoption among the most diverse religious groups. Many of the followers of Islam in India have adopted this ancient social system and are grouped in castes. Since the early Aryan occupation, India has been overrun several times by foreign invaders, but these have had small influence upon the culture of the country. The conquering peoples, as in China, were silently absorbed. Isolation, we believe, has had a dominant rôle in the formation of races. So homogeneous have become the genetic characteristics of the great body of people that ethnologists are agreed that, except for the aberrant hill tribes, there is but one race in India to-day, the Hindu or dark white. The uniform social environment so necessary to racial formation was to a large degree induced by geographical particularity.

57. Land Forms and Rivers

The chief topographical divisions of India are six in number. Four belong to India proper: the mountain wall, the Desert of India, the fertile plain of Hindustan, and the Deccan plateau. Ceylon and Burma may be added because they, too, are under monsoonal control and because they are part of the Empire of India. The Himalayas extend southeasterly from the mountain knot, the Pamirs. They constitute the highest range in the world and include three peaks over 28,000 feet in height. The mountains are unimportant as a human habitation but are most important in their climatic effects. On the southern edge, facing India, their abruptness is remarkable. The Thar or the Indian Desert is likewise uninhabitable. It is situated in northwest India east of the Indus River and is several thousand square miles in area. Here the rainfall, less than 10 inches per year, is too sparse and irregular to permit human habitation. The density is four per square mile and the population shifts from season to season as the wells fail. Caravans traverse the Thar to Delhi, but through its heart there is neither road nor railway.

The fertile plain of Hindustan lies to the east of Thar Desert. In relief it is an extension of the desert and it preserves a remarkable flatness until the Khasi Hills of Assam, far east of the Ganges, are reached. For hundreds of miles there is not so much as a mound to disturb the monotonous surface of the plain. A thousand miles from its mouth the Ganges is hardly five hundred feet above sea level. The Hindustan Plain, exclusive of the Thar Desert, is over a thousand miles from west to east and several hundred miles broad. It includes most of the drainage basin of the Ganges and is a fertile

PLATE VII. ASIA—JULY ISOTHERMS, ISOBARS, AND PREVAILING WINDS

(After Goode)

agricultural region. In its eastern parts the population is the densest in India, over five hundred per square mile.

The Deccan plateau comprises roughly the southern half of India proper. Several parallel ranges running from west to east have served as a barrier between Aryan- and Dravidian-speaking India. The whole plateau averages over two thousand feet above sea level. The Western Ghats rise rather abruptly near the western coast limiting narrowly the long plain that terminates in the Malabar Coast. The plateau is rather rugged than otherwise, and generally speaking, it slopes eastward from the west and the south. The Eastern Ghats lack the abruptness of rise of the western mountains, permitting a broader coastal area. The southern rivers are not useful for navigation. Those on the western side fall too precipitously, and those flowing eastward are characterized by rapids.

The rivers of the north, the Indus, Ganges, and Brahmaputra, differ radically in character from those of the Deccan. Along their courses water flows during the whole year, for they rely not only upon the monsoonal rains but upon the melting snows of the Himalayas. Many of the streams of the Deccan, on the other hand, dry up entirely during the dry season. As roads have always been impractical in India, the streams were utilized for transportation. The luxurious vegetation, the seasonal rains that transform vast areas into swamp, and the absence of stone in regions needing roads have discouraged their building. In recent times, however, the rivers have been needed for irrigation so that they are being used less and less in navigation. This situation has led to extensive railway building in India. Only the delta of the Ganges and the Brahmaputra to its eastern bend sustain river traffic. The Indus has never been a reliable carrier for it pursues a shifting course.

58. Climate

The winter temperatures of India greatly resemble the summer temperatures of Europe.[1] The mean monthly averages at this season vary in accordance with latitude; from 55° in January in the Punjab to 75° in the southern Deccan. During the rest of the year, however, all atmospheric conditions are part of the phenomena of the monsoons. In the spring, about the middle of March, the so-called hot

[1] Examine carefully Plates I, VI, VII, VIII, IX.

season of India begins. The sun moves up from the equator over the Tropic of Cancer and the land mass of India heats up rapidly. The heated air ascends but there is no rainfall, for the relative humidity is very low. A great low pressure area forms over the northern part of the Deccan and especially over the Thar Desert. In May, the hottest month, the isotherms radiate like concentric circles from this area. The mean monthly temperature for the low pressure center is 95°. The greater part of India has a monthly mean of over 85°. During this hot season, "man and beast," writes a witness, "languish and gasp for air, while even in the house, the thermometer stands day and night between 98° and 115°. Little by little the European loses appetite and sleep; all power and energy forsake him. Vegetation suffers equally; almost all green things wither; the grass seems burnt up to the roots; bushes and trees seem moribund; the earth is as hard as a paved highway; the ground is seamed with cracks; and the whole landscape wears an aspect of barrenness and sadness." At a temperature greater than blood heat all things feel warm to the touch, and during the day one can neither read nor sleep. "It is possible to reach at times a curious state of coma when the mind is a perfect blank."

During June the monsoon arrives. Its appearance is remarkably regular from year to year. It reaches Bombay usually on June 5, Bengal on June 15, and the Punjab on July 1. In most parts of India, it remains until about October 15. The Indian monsoon is a seasonal wind blowing day and night with great regularity at something less than twenty miles an hour. The heating up of the land mass, particularly in the northwest, creates a zone of such low pressure that winds from south of the Equator are attracted to India. Normally at a latitude of 15° S. the Southeast Trades would blow toward the African coast. These, however, flow down an isobaric gradient toward India and after crossing the equator come under the influence of right-handed rotational deflection and are southwest winds on reaching India. They blow strongest along the west coast and across the Bay of Bengal into the Ganges basin. Here they are deflected by the mountain wall and become easterly winds.

The monsoon is a moist wind blowing from the ocean and from it India derives about 85 per cent of its annual rainfall. Monsoon rain is unfortunately not as constant as monsoon wind; in consequence though the greater part of India receives ample rainfall for agriculture, it is not well distributed during the season. Bombay, for example, once received half of its annual rainfall in two tremendous showers of ten and twelve inches each. In many places the rainfall from year to year is likely to vary widely, creating the problem of how best to preserve and distribute the monsoonal rainfall.

In October the monsoon ceases to blow and the whole of India experiences sultry, uncomfortable weather. Large areas become water-logged. Decaying vegetation at high temperature induces miasma with the result that fever, dysentery, and frequently cholera, are rife. Toward the end of October the transition period is over; the sky is clear and the weather delightful. Very gradually the winter monsoon sets in. An area of relatively high pressure develops in the northwest part of India, and winds begin to blow outward toward equatorial regions. As these winds originate over land there is very little rainfall in India proper. The Punjab fortunately receives during the winter months enough rainfall to maintain such winter crops as wheat and barley. This rainfall, however, is cyclonic in character and is thought to come via the Mediterranean which is under the influence of the Westerlies from November till March. These cyclones, however, fail to reach the Ganges.

The winter monsoon is not as strong as the summer monsoon. In many places its rate does not exceed two or three miles an hour and is insufficient to propel windmills. The winter monsoon is not, as was formerly thought, governed entirely by the high pressure areas formed over the interior of Asia. The monsoon, as a surface wind, is not forceful enough to surmount the barrier of the Himalayas. India does not receive the intense cold spells that blow into China proper during the winter season. As they leave India, the outblowing winds are generally northeast winds, intensified Northeast Trades. The winters are extremely pleasant for Europeans, but the natives appear to suffer acutely when the thermometer approaches freezing during the night. The winter monsoon in blowing over the Bay of Bengal brings considerable rainfall to the southeast coast of India and to the island of Ceylon.

59. Conservation of Rainfall

Monsoon rainfall is plentiful but sporadic in character. Unless methods of conserving and distributing it during the growing season were employed, agriculture could hardly flourish in many regions now very productive. A sketch map of the annual rainfall will aid in

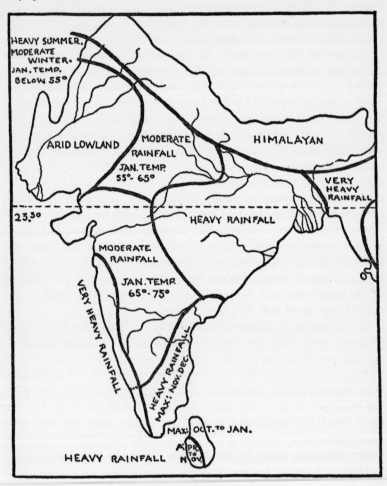

FIG. 11—INDIA: CLIMATIC SUBDIVISIONS
(*After Stamp*)

revealing the full extent of the problem. The southwest coast receives a heavy monsoonal rainfall, over eighty inches on the narrow coastal plain, and from forty to eighty inches along the windward slopes of the Western Ghats. Beyond the Western Ghats is a large area

that receives from twenty to forty inches rainfall, irregularly distributed from year to year. In the Deccan this belt extends almost to
the eastern coast. It continues northward into the western part of
the Great Plain, forming a rather broad belt about the eastern side
of the Thar Desert. The inhabitants have adopted various methods
of conserving the rain water. In the eastern Deccan tanks (dams)
are widely employed to prevent the streams from draining-off their
waters during flood season. Over seven million acres of land rely
upon a regular supply of water from this source. In the north, along
the southern edges of the Great Plain from Delhi to Benares, the
people protect their fields against drought by digging wells. The
water table may be pierced at depths varying from ten to fifty feet
below the surface. From this source over fourteen million acres
are assured of sufficient moisture.

Northeastern India has heavy rainfall. The west coast of Burma,
the delta of the Ganges, and the northern edge of the Great Plain
where the mountain wall intercepts the moisture-laden winds have an
amount exceeding eighty inches. The remainder of the plain and
much of the rest of northeast India receive from forty to eighty
inches. There is a resemblance, therefore, between the precipitation
of the southwest and the northeast, which manifests itself in the
natural vegetation and the planted crops.

In addition to the native system of wells and canals the British government, since 1885, has undertaken the task of creating a vast irrigation system in India. Almost £100,000,000 have been invested in
various projects, with the result that nearly 30,000,000 acres have
been brought under irrigation. Nearly 70 per cent of the work
has been carried on in the drier regions of the Great Plain, Punjab,
the United Provinces, and Sind. The Madras area has also been
greatly improved. Almost a fifth of the cultivated land of India is
under irrigation. Great Britain in fifty years has added ten Egypts
to India and the work goes silently on. It is by far the greatest boon
that Britain has given India. In vast areas the haunting possibility
of famine has been destroyed, and thousands of acres of new land
have been opened for settlement.

The English first experimented with the native system of inundation canals. These canals are fed by rivers during the flood season
only. They are unsatisfactory over any large area because even during the rainy season they are likely to remain unfilled when most

needed, and furthermore they dry up entirely during the dry season. In some regions, like the Madras area where the whole water supply depends on monsoonal rains, they must of necessity be used, but in other parts of India wherever possible the system of perennial canals has been introduced. Many of the tributaries of the Indus and the Ganges do not depend entirely upon monsoonal rains for their supply of water. They flow regularly all year round because of the melting snows of the Himalaya Mountains. Along these rivers vast canal works have been instituted. In the Peshawar region of the Indus nearly one million acres have been reclaimed, and in the Punjab three million acres. The Sutlej Valley system in the Punjab will add over five million acres more. With the completion of the Sukkar Dam project in Sind, the waters of the Indus will be completely harnessed for agricultural purposes and another five million acres of land opened to cultivation. The Sukkar Barrage project is one of the greatest irrigation schemes in the world and when complete will have cost almost £20,000,000. These works present a major example of the way in which modern civilization is able to force the physical environment to serve its purposes. Power projects will follow in the wake of irrigation works, as industry supplements agriculture.

60. Agriculture

Agriculture, including stock raising, is by far the chief occupation of the people of India. Nearly three-fourths of the inhabitants engage in it, while industry occupies little more than 10 per cent and trade 5 per cent. Agriculture in India is primitive and crop yields are low in comparison with those of other countries. Rice, for example, has a yield of less than one thousand pounds per acre in India, while in Japan the yield is 3,200 pounds. Cotton yields about ninety pounds per acre; in the United States the yield is over 150 pounds. Canadians obtain twenty bushels from an acre of wheat; in India the yield is twelve bushels.

Indian agriculture has never been a business; the Western conception of "the money crop" is just becoming known. The Hindu farmer is satisfied in producing enough food to provide for his family and domestic animals. As in China, the farms are very small. In Bengal, for example, where there are eleven million farmers, the average holding is less than two and a quarter acres. Statistics for the whole of India are lacking, but at most the farm rarely exceeds five acres in size. This limitation of size is a detriment to the farmer who wishes to market his crop. This condition is aggravated by the practices of subdivision and fragmentation. The first refers to the custom of dividing the holding equally among the male heirs, a usage that is sanctioned both in Hindu and Mohammedan law. Fragmentation is the division of a patch of land among several owners. The waste of time in going from one strip to another is ruinous for the cultivator. The rapid increase of population in India adds to the distressing economic situation. A better form of tenure prevails where proprietary brotherhoods work large fields in common. But as long as the average holding continues to diminish in size, agriculture will never attain the status of a business.

The land is rarely replenished with fertilizer. In China dung is used for this purpose, but in India it is used for fuel instead. In addition India has begun to export oil-bearing seed crops which might be used to replenish the soil with nitrogen. The result of all these circumstances is impoverishment. At present only one-fifth of Indian farmers are free of debt.

The Indian farmer, unlike the Chinese farmer, employs domestic animals in farming. Where the Chinaman relies almost entirely upon his own labor there are in India two oxen or buffaloes for every plow. In fact it is said that there are more domestic animals than there are plows and that the latter, not the former, must be shared. In the north, oxen are employed, as a rule, and in the south and other wet rice-growing regions, the buffalo fills the need. Oxen are not used for beef in India for the bull is sacred to the Hindu. Dairying has never developed as an industry, and in the large cities milk is more expensive and of poorer quality than in any city of Europe. Goats are found everywhere but are valued only for their skins. Horses, donkeys, and camels are employed in travel and in transportation.

61. Life in Agricultural India

Faridpur, a county of the province of Bengal, contains over two million people and has a density exceeding nine hundred per square mile. It is entirely agricultural; the urban population of the two towns in the district does not exceed twenty thousand. Faridpur illustrates perfectly the physical nature of lands lying in the Ganges

Delta. In one part the land is still below flood level and countless streams are still building up their banks; in another part the rivers are flanked by large strips of land that have only recently emerged from the marsh; in a third part the land is generally above flood level. People live in all three areas. In the southeast where the land is increasing at the expense of the rivers the dwellings are new and orchards are few, for the streams are ever changing their courses. In the southwestern part of the district, an area of seven hundred square miles, the population is eight hundred to the square mile, yet the whole area is a vast marsh. For eight months during the year the inhabitants live clustered in villages that have been created by raising earth elevations above flood level. In the flood season they resemble small islands in a huge lake; during the dry season, they look like craters. For four months during the year large parts of the marsh dry up sufficiently to enable the planting of crops. The soil, like all delta soil, is extremely fertile. The northern part of the district, a thousand square miles in extent, is drier and consists of a series of sandy plains interspersed with countless ancient water courses. Villages, some of them century-old, are found along these former stream banks. Trees and orchards are abundant, giving the whole region a settled appearance though the filling up of depressions in flood season is a reminder of an earlier age.

These Hindu villages hardly resemble our villages at all. They have no streets and are merely clusters of dwellings grouped about a large pond from which earth has been collected, or arranged in a long line that follows the firm bank of some old stream bed. From house to house there is only the faintest semblance of a foot path. There are no rows of houses; no church, for worship is a family affair; and no shops. The homestead, consisting of a house and several appurtenances, occupies about a quarter acre of ground. It is erected always by the lessee, never by the landlord. Despite this fact there is little individuality, for the home has become institutionalized. The dwelling consists of a group of huts, the more prosperous having from four to six, the poorer always two or three. These huts face upon an open courtyard. The largest serves as a parlor where guests are received, while the smaller ones serve as bedrooms. The kitchen is lodged in a separate hut. The huts are not constructed of stone as the landlord will not permit it. Preferably they are made of mats because they solve the problem of ventilation. The walls are made of coarse grass mats, the roofs of thatch or corrugated iron or tin where possible, and the floor of hardened liquid mud. A metal roof is insurance against fire during the hot dry season. Sleeping huts, cattle sheds, and a kitchen are essentials in every Hindu homestead. The necessity of erecting the huts upon a mound of earth has made the family pond a feature of the homestead. The pond is used for washing dishes, pots and pans, and clothes; for drinking water; and finally for bathing. The Bengali are scrupulously clean, each member of the family indulging in a bath a day even in the chilliest weather. The house garden is important for the raising of vegetables and tobacco, and wherever possible, fruit trees and bamboo.

The interior of a Bengali dwelling would strike us as being singularly barren. Usually there is no table, no chair, no bedstead, no chest, no carpet. The walls are bare of decoration and there is no ceiling. Windows are rare. A Bengali eats from a mat placed upon the floor as he squats upon his haunches. He will not eat from a table, and if he chooses to sit, it will not be upon a chair, but upon a low stool, for chairs tire him. The bedding is made up on the floor, for there is no greater discomfort than sleeping upon a cheap stead which is all he could afford. The kitchen hut is the most furnished part of the domicile. A fireplace of baked clay, brass pots for cooking, large earthen jars for storing food, and miscellaneous culinary utensils are always in evidence. Often the parlor is used to store the jars containing rice. Here too, the family fishing rods are kept, for every Bengali is of necessity a fisherman. The parlor is used for other purposes foreign to us. One shelf holds the family linen and bed clothing; another supports a mirror and contains combs, brushes, and often paper and ink. One writer states that the most characteristic piece of furnishing is the fishing rod and adds that the fewer the food jars, the poorer the family.

A high caste Hindu lives little better than his more humble neighbor. His homestead costs more to erect because more earth had to be scooped up to give a foundation for his more numerous huts. There is the usual bewildering display of earthen jars and brass containers, for the Bengali buys his annual supply of rice and other foodstuffs when the price is lowest. In one household sixty-five earthenware jars and forty brass jars were counted, in addition to twelve baskets for holding fresh vegetables, fruits, and fish. There were seventeen members in this family. In the main room were two long benches for visitors, for it is a Bengal custom for people to drop in upon the well-to-do and pass the time of day. Materials for smoking and chewing the betel nut were at hand. Five hookahs or smoking bottles were reserved for visitors; two for the Brahmin caste, two for lower caste Hindus, and one for Mohammedan guests. Good form demands that the guest be offered a smoke from his own particular hookah, or served with a leaf containing betel nut and lime. Another feature of Hindu hospitality is a row of shoes and sandals which are offered for the use of the guests.

Under normal circumstances the life of a Bengal cultivator is likely to be a happy one. Nature is bountiful; both soil and climate are excellent for crops; and the farmer is able to supply food for his family without excessive labor and sell enough to accumulate a little money. Rice is the principal crop; it is sown in the spring and harvested in the autumn. Where jute can be grown the farmer will, in addition to three months' hard work in the rice fields, devote six weeks' work in July and August to steeping and stripping jute fiber. But there are always more idle than work months during the year.

During the months of really hard work—March, April and May —the farmer rises at five in the morning, takes a few puffs from his hookah, and goes out to his fields with his oxen. His morning's ploughing is interrupted by his children who bring him breakfast at about ten o'clock. His food consists of a mixture of rice and green pepper cooked the night before. At midday he ceases work, goes off to the pond to bathe, then returns to the house to eat. This meal consists of rice mixed with a dressing made of pulses and a curry made of vegetables and fish. After napping for an hour or so, he returns to the fields for harrowing or weeding. At dark his labor is finished, and after bathing again he will spend time gossiping with his neighbors. About eight he takes his evening meal, which is identical with that of noonday. Then he retires, sleeping upon the blanket or sheet which has been spread upon the floor.

At harvest, whether of jute or rice, the farmer is assisted in the fields by his children or hired hands. Harvesting is usually completed in the course of a week. The laborers are provided with breakfast, with hookah, and a sixth part of the crop. They work from sunrise until early afternoon. The farmer in the late afternoon occupies himself in thrashing the paddy in the courtyard. The oxen are tied to a stout stake in the center of the threshing floor about which the paddy is piled, and they are driven round and round until the ear is separated from the stalk. The ears are given to the women to husk. Often the Faridpur cultivator finds it profitable to leave the harvest to the hired men and go off to richer districts and hire out as a laborer. In Nadia the crop is richer than in his own district and the pay is high; one-fifth of the crop. His wages far outweigh the portion of his own crop that is paid out for labor.

The remainder of the winter is passed in comparative idleness. Odd jobs are indulged in: fishing tackle is repaired, houses are re-thatched, and walls renovated. The market is a great attraction and draws large throngs from nearby villages. The rest of the time is consumed in smoking and gossiping.

The dismal period during the height of the rains is another relatively dull time. Lakes abound and rivers and streams overflow. All the men go fishing at this time of the year. The fish are easily caught, for they swim out over the shallow fields. Fishing is an art and great skill is shown in spearing fish from a boat. Traps, nets, and baskets are employed, however, when food is really needed. Once a week during the rains several villagers will go off to the marshes to gather grass for the cattle. These wet grasses are succulent and nourishing. The cattle have great difficulty in feeding themselves during this season.

Visiting friends in other villages is a favorite pastime during the rainy season. A cabin boat is built for the purpose, capable of accommodating the whole family. When relatives are being visited, it is customary for the guests to eat and sleep with the host; but where the host is merely a friend, only the meals are taken with him and his family. To attend the market on market days is the chief recreation of the farmer. Probably ten or twelve markets are held within boating or walking distance of his home and each is visited in turn. Even during the busy season he attends two a week, and in the dull season he finds time to attend four or five. No women go to market in Bengal; the farmer is attended by his sons or neighbors. Ordinarily he never buys anything, nor does he eat or drink anything. His time is spent in smoking and gossiping with old acquaintances. He will show a great interest in the cattle dealing and is an expert upon breeds and prices. At the market disputes between neighbors are gone into and often adjudicated. At harvest time, however, he will spread himself a little, carrying home sweetmeats, a melon, or a fish or two for the women folk.

The women work all the year round. No woman is supposed to be idle at any time while husband, father, or brother is in the house. Nor is any woman allowed to eat while a male remains unfed, even the smallest boy. In this part of India women are not permitted to labor in the fields; the only part they take in agricultural work is in husking rice or stripping jute fiber, always on the premises. On the whole they lead a dull life in comparison with their Western sisters. They are not permitted to engage in the conversation of the men; and they can only gossip with women friends when washing pots or bathing in the public stream. Custom alone makes their lot bearable for they do not know the charm of a fuller, freer life.

The children have an easy time. The father is fond of his sons, and the close relationship continues long after the son has married and has a family. He is always happiest when his boys are about him in the fields or fishing. The boys perform many small tasks such as tending cattle, and fetching food. At the age of fourteen the son is considered able to take his place as a laborer in the field. There is little schooling, for the people believe that too much schooling will lead the lads to despise the occupations of their fathers. The education of the girl consists in serving an apprenticeship about the house.

62. Agricultural Regions

Any division of India into agricultural regions must have its basis in differences of rainfall rather than in differences of soil. On the whole, the soil of India, though of several varieties, is rich; furthermore, there is much less waste land in India than in China. In the Great Plain of Hindustan the soil is of a transported variety, alluvial in type. It is very fertile, though in the Ganges delta the contour of the surface is likely to change much from year to year because of the silting that takes place during the flood season. The great "black cotton soil" area, east of Bombay, is composed of ancient lava deposits and contains the usual ingredients of a good soil. The soils of the Malabar Coast are derived from decayed vegetation and belong to the class of loamy soil that contains a high percentage of humus. Everything grows in such a soil; hence the farmer must contend with luxurious wild plant life. The Deccan, especially in the south, in addition to being quite rugged has a red soil that is poor in comparison with the others.

In those regions where the rainfall is heaviest, over eighty inches, the wet rice crop predominates. Famine because of drought is rare; yet in certain places, like the delta of the Rangoon in Burma, precaution against destruction by flood is necessary. In the districts receiving from forty to eighty inches of rainfall rice also predominates. Since both wet and dry crops are possible, there is likely to be considerable diversity. In both areas of heavy rainfall, as in all parts of India where possible, two crops are planted and harvested, though the second crop may be simply a "catch" or secondary crop upon which less labor is bestowed. Irrigation works are not necessary in these districts.

The twenty to forty inch rainfall belt is the region of danger in India. Here lie the great famine zones. Precipitation is likely to be insufficient during any year and is likely to be poorly distributed during the growing season. In this zone both primitive and modern irrigation are employed. These are regions of dry farming, and the crops are the hard grains, millet and more recently wheat. Wet zone crops, such as rice, can only be grown where there are irrigation canals. Where the rainfall is less than twenty inches no crops are possible without irrigation.

63. Food Crops

Food crops comprise 80 per cent of the total. The principal grains are rice, 25 per cent, millet of various types, 20 per cent, and wheat, 10 per cent. The chief non-food crops are cotton, 7 per cent, oil seeds, 6 per cent, and jute, small in bulk but very valuable.

Rice is the staple of life, indeed the only food crop, in the wet areas. There are many varieties of rice, and though the government has for years been trying to prevail upon the inhabitants of certain districts to give up less productive varieties, it has encountered a resistance that is rooted in intense conservatism. The natives are loath to change their manner of living so that it differs from that of their forefathers. Rice occupies one-third of the cultivated acreage of India. Swamp rice, which requires level flooded fields, is much more important than hill rice which is grown upon terraced slopes.

In India, as in China, the modern method of cultivation is not employed. The seeds are first planted in a "nursery" field. When the seedlings are six inches tall, they are laboriously transplanted in rows in the flooded fields. Rice grows best in the deltas where an impervious layer just below the surface aids in keeping the fields flooded. The young plants grow rapidly, sometimes from six to nine inches in a day. In tropical areas where the plantation method has been introduced, it is possible to grow as many as six crops during the year. In India, however, only a single crop is harvested. It is grown as a summer crop, planted toward the end of the rains and harvested early in winter. The methods of planting and the reaping are very primitive. The former is done with the aid of the buffalo which drags a wooden plow through the ground. Burma alone is able to produce rice for export. Much of it goes to other parts of India to make up local deficits, while the remainder is sent to Germany, Japan, and Malaysia.

Millet has the importance of rice in the drier regions of India. It can be grown without irrigation in places where the rainfall is as low as twenty inches. With the extension of the system of perennial canals wheat is gradually extending into millet areas. Millet is used only for domestic consumption, but wheat is likely to command a sale in the world market. Wheat, a relatively new adaptation in India, has risen to third place in the food crop list. Millet prevails in the drier regions of the Deccan and wheat is particularly associated with the new agricultural development in the northwest. Along the Indus and its tributaries, wheat is grown as a winter crop and is almost independent of monsoonal rains. It is planted in the fall after the rainy season and harvested before the spring season reaches its maximum heating. Wheat lands are watered by tapping streams that receive their waters from the melting snows of the mountains and from the occasional, but never failing, cyclonic rains that reach the Punjab from the west. The surplus wheat of the Indus is important as a protection against famine in other parts of India. Barley, maize and gram are grown extensively. Pulses, the edible seeds of the pea and bean families, serve as an important variant to rice and millet.

Some of the most characteristic Indian food crops do not appear among the leaders. Sugar culture tends to increase very slowly because, though climate and soil are eminently suitable to the raising of cane, it cannot compete with the more efficient plantation agriculture carried on in other tropical regions. A leading Indian crop until 1890, it has gradually given way in face of Javan competition. Spices such as pepper, ginger, cloves, and nutmegs have been associated with Indian commerce from earliest times. Europe, during the period of exploration and discovery, set a high value upon Indian spices. Vasco da Gama reaped a profit of 6,000 per cent upon a single cargo. The trade, however, was precarious because of the dangers of navigation and the ravages of pirates. The British East India Company from 1601 to 1620 sent out eighty-six ships, of which only thirty-six returned. The best pepper in the world is still grown along the moist, hot, Malabar coast. Many of the fruits familiar to us, together with tropical varieties, are grown in India. Although the fruits are very meaty, they lack the acidity of the temperate varieties. The mango is esteemed by the British colony in India but as yet there is no demand for it outside the tropics. Nor has its introduction into the United States from the West Indies been successful. The "mango showers" which fall with great heaviness along southern coasts just before the monsoon take their name from the fruit which ripens at that time.

Coffee was early introduced in the Deccan and in Ceylon and flourished successfully until a fungus growth, resulting in leaf rust, attacked the plants. The industry was practically destroyed, and most of the plantations turned to tea growing. Tea is a hardy plant, but requires, above all, ample rain and excellent drainage. Waterlogged land is ruinous to the crop. Recently cleared forest land yields the best crop. Such lands were found along the Brahmaputra in Assam and in Ceylon. Here the plantation system was introduced with the result that Indian tea has rapidly supplanted Chinese tea. Assam provides over half the world's supply. Again the superiority of the plantation over domestic agriculture is seen. China has three or four pickings during the season, while Assam has as many as sixteen and Ceylon more. The tea plant in its wild state resembles a tree, but the crop variety, constantly pruned, attains a bush form.

Opium was once a rich and extensive Indian crop. Commercial opium is the dried juice of the seed of the poppy. The capsules are punctured at sundown and the juice, a milky substance, changes by morning to a brownish substance. Opium products, like morphia, which produces sleep and insensibility to pain, are valuable to the medical profession. Opium smoking, however, is very injurious. The Chinese were very fond of opium smoking and a lucrative trade with India resulted. When the harmful consequences of opium smoking became known, steps were taken to obliterate the traffic. Poppy cultivation in India was taken over by the government and sales restricted to the medical profession. The acreage decreased from 615,000 in 1906 to sixty thousand twenty years later. Tobacco growing has been introduced in India and smoking has become universal. Although India ranks second to the United States in production, there is no foreign market for Indian tobacco. The methods of curing do not suit the European taste.

64. Industrial Crops

The United States is the world's chief cotton grower producing roughly sixteen million bales yearly. India, however, occupies second place with an annual production approaching six million bales. In pre-war years the land under cotton never exceeded fourteen million acres. To-day twenty-five million acres are planted in cotton. Cotton has been grown for centuries in India, particularly in the vast hinterland of central India lying just beyond the Western Ghats. Here the rainfall is not so heavy as along the west coast, and the region is adaptable for cotton raising, despite the tendency to drought. The black lava soil is very spongy and holds the moisture after the monsoonal rains flood the land. Furthermore, this soil is exceedingly fertile and long years of single cropping fail to exhaust it. Some care, however, must be exercised, for the seed must be planted in the short interval between the first rains in May and the terrific monsoonal downpour that follows shortly after. From March to May the soil has been baked dry and is too hard to seed. Relying upon the unusual fertility of the soil, the Hindu farmer sows his seed broadcast like the American farmer sows wheat.

Cotton has for a long time been one of the few money crops in India. The Chinese and more recently the Japanese have absorbed most of the export. In view of its importance the British government has inaugurated many improvements in cotton growing. It has, as with other crops, endeavored to correct wasteful methods of agriculture for the yield is very low, less than one hundred pounds per acre. In addition, prolonged efforts have been made to obtain types best suited to the particular soil conditions. Cambodia cotton is firmly established in Madras, Egyptian cotton is planted in Sind, and

American grades are being experimented with. The Government Agricultural Department has expended much money in improving the native varieties, but the conservative Hindu farmer has short patience with new grades or methods.

In the opening up of newly irrigated lands in the northwest, however, the government has had a free hand. When the task of irrigation has been completed, cotton production in the Indus-Punjab area will be trebled. This cotton will be of sufficient quality to meet the demands of the Lancashire manufacturers or of newly established Indian factories.

Oil seeds rival cotton in importance. Rape and mustard, sesamum, peanuts, and linseed head the list, while castor oil and coconut oil are not unimportant. Almost half of the oil crops are exported from India. Rape (colza oil), before the advent of mineral oil, was the favorite lamp fuel. It is commercially important in lubrication and soap manufacture. Sesamum oil is widely used in India for cooking, and anointing the body. Commercially it is valuable in soap-making and in the manufacture of the best quality of oleomargarine. Linseed, as in China, is grown not for its fiber but for the oil which its seeds yield. It is valuable in the manufacture of varnishes and paints. None of these crops flourish in the wettest parts of India. The ground nut, known variously as the monkey nut or peanut, has recently come to the fore as a money crop. In America, peanuts are used as food, but the Hindus utilize the crop in the manufacture of oleomargarine. Commercially the peanut is important in the manufacture of soap. It will grow in the light sandy soils of dry regions where no other crop can be raised. In consequence, this crop, which before the war was too unimportant to be recorded, now occupies an area of nearly four million acres. Ground nut crops are regarded as one of the great triumphs of the Government Agricultural Department. Cotton seed oil is a valuable by-product in cotton growing areas. The residue of all the oil seeds is used for cattle food, not, as in China, to replenish the soil.

Castor oil is important because of its peculiar medicinal properties and is a great favorite with the natives. In addition it has an important commercial use. Castor oil is valuable as a lubricant in low temperatures since it does not freeze, and is widely employed in the aviation industry. The coconut palm flourishes along the wet coastlands of the Malabar region. Its general importance in tropical economy has been mentioned. In India, as elsewhere, the oil obtained from copra is valued in cooking and in anointing the body. The export is used in the manufacture of soap and candles.

Although hemp and kapok are grown in India, jute is the most important of the fibers. It has an interesting history. Originally jute was used by the peasants of Bengal for making clothing. In 1832 a merchant of Dundee, Scotland, discovered that it could be used as a substitute for hemp. As the "brown paper of the wholesale trade" it furnishes sack cloth for coffee, wheat, cotton, and wool. The Ganges delta supplies over 90 per cent of commercial jute, while half the crop is consumed, as formerly, in the making of "gunny cloth" for the native population of Bengal. Dundee has always been the center of jute manufacturing in the Western world. The jute seed is sown before the rains in March and is ready for cutting in September. It reaches a height of ten to fourteen feet. The fiber is separated from the stalk by soaking in stagnant water. Then the fibers are separated from the plant material by beating the stem upon the surface of the water in which the laborer stands. It is washed, then dried in the shade, before being sorted and baled.

Indigo has been manufactured in India from earliest times. It is thought that the blue threads of the ancient Egyptian mummy cloth were dyed with indigo produced in India. Yet, because man succeeded in making a better adaptation, indigo-growing in India has all but ceased. The German synthetic method of manufacturing this dyestuff from the retorts of coal tar has all but destroyed the value of the Hindu crop. It is interesting to note that during the World War when German dyes could not be obtained indigo growing revived temporarily. To-day the indigo acreage is less than a tenth of that at the beginning of the century.

65. Mineral Resources

India, contrary to popular opinion, has no great mineral wealth although a variety of deposits are present. If Burma oil and lead be excluded, the only really valuable products are coal, gold, and manganese ore. Less than 2 per cent of the workers are engaged in mining, most of them in mining coal. India since the war has produced about twenty million tons a year, and almost all of it comes from the northeastern provinces of Bengal, Bihar, and Orissa. The

United States produces twenty-five times as much. There are large fields of lignite and brown coal, as yet undeveloped, in Burma, Assam, and the Punjab.

Manganese is an important adjunct to the steel industry; each ton of steel requiring about fifteen pounds of manganese. India has been a chief competitor of Russia in the export of manganese ore, but with the dislocation of industry in Russia, production in the Caucasus has been impaired. To-day India is producing as much as Russia and exporting more. Most of it is worked in open quarries in the hillsides in the Central Provinces. The manganese exports are said to be good indicators of India's industrial prosperity. India is also a large producer of mica. A moderate output of gold is maintained, practically all of it coming from a single district in Mysore.

Special interest attaches to production in iron, mineral oil, and lead—three necessities in the world of industry. There are large deposits of iron ore of excellent grade and two million tons a year are being mined, five times as much as in pre-war years. The possibilities of iron ore have greatly encouraged those who believe that the economic salvation of India lies in supplementing agriculture with manufacturing. Lead and oil are Burmese products—of far greater value than the famed rubies and sapphires of that land. It is of interest to note that the company which mined for precious stones there is now defunct. Burma has maintained a production of about eight million barrels of oil since the World War. Small fields are operated in Assam and the Punjab. There is a possibility of obtaining oil in Baluchistan but very little in other parts of India. The exhaustion of the present fields in the near future will greatly reduce the value of India's mineral production. The lead mines of Burma are important also for the silver, zinc, copper, tin, and tungsten that are found in the ore.

66. Manufacturing and Commerce

Approximately 12 per cent of the workers in India are engaged in manufacturing and 6 per cent in commerce. In spite of the relative smallness of these pursuits they have tended thus far to aggravate rather than alleviate the problem of poverty in India. British enterprise in improving agricultural methods and in opening new lands for occupation has tended toward a solution of the distress arising from drought and congestion. Possibly these measures of amelioration may eventually result in raising the standard of living. On the other hand, it is difficult to see any immediate relief in the prevailing status of foreign trade and especially that of manufacturing. Many believe the solution of the problem of poverty lies in the exchange of Indian raw products for English manufactured goods; others think that more is to be gained by establishing a modern industrial plant in India. At present, both systems have made headway; yet both have been instrumental in causing dislocation in a country where the margin of subsistence is too small to permit tampering with the economic balance.

India ships grain, cotton, jute, tea, and oils to England, Japan, the United States, and several countries in western Europe. In return for these goods she receives sugar from Java, cotton manufactures, iron, coal, and machinery from England, the United States, and Germany. England is her principal customer, taking 25 per cent of her products and providing 60 per cent of her imports. The inundation of cheap cottons and metal products from the Western world, and their more recent manufacture in India under European supervision has had the effect of destroying the domestic system of manufacture in India. The native cottage system entailed not only the spinning and weaving of cloth for the immediate family but frequently the production of a surplus of such stuffs, as well as the making of fine muslins, carpets, and hand-wrought iron for local sale. The coming of the cheaper products of the Western world has not only discouraged the handicraft industries but has thrown the whole population back upon the soil. At present the establishment of the factory system in India has not proceeded far enough to utilize the huge labor supply that it has indirectly released. The resultant hardship has given rise to widespread political discontent.

Calcutta and Bombay are the chief manufacturing and trading towns of India. Over 80 per cent of the commerce flows through these two ports. Calcutta drains a vast agricultural hinterland and is the seat of the jute manufactures. It does not have an excellent harbor because of a tendency to silt up. Four times since the founding of Calcutta in 1686, it has been necessary to change the location of the harbor. Bombay controls the vast hinterland of western India. It is the successor of the Portuguese Braganza and the Dutch Surat. Bombay is built upon an island, has an excellent natural harbor which faces toward Europe, and commands the passes to the large hinterland lying beyond the Western Ghats. It is destined to be the industrial metropolis of India. The cotton products of the immediate hinterland as well as those of the newly developing plantations of the Indus and the Punjab will flow toward Bombay. Karachi, the outlet of the Indus region, will never become a manufacturing center because the air there is too dry to permit cotton spinning. Undoubtedly the development of the water power resources of the Western Ghats will augment the industrial supremacy of Bombay. Madras, on the east coast of the Deccan, is losing its importance as a trade center. The port is ill-fitted for the requirements of modern commerce. To-day it has only a sixth as much commerce as its ancient rival, Bombay. Karachi, near the mouth of the Indus, has risen rapidly to the position of the third port of India. It has become the *entrepôt* of the huge agricultural crops that are produced in the irrigated lands of the Indus and its tributaries. It affords an excellent illustration of the manner in which a newly developing hinterland will demand a port for its goods.

CHAPTER VIII

CHINA: THE LAND OF INERTIA

67. Greater China

Monsoonal environments, as well as the cyclonic areas of higher latitudes, are exceedingly favorable as human habitats. Nearly a third of the earth's inhabitants are concentrated in regions under the influence of monsoons. China and India, each with populations exceeding 350,-000,000 souls; Japan with nearly ninety million including twenty million Koreans and four million Malays in Formosa; the Philippine archipelago with twelve million; and southeast Asia with twenty million people under the French flag and half as many in the native state of Siam—all these comprise a vast agglomeration whose habits of living are regulated by the great seasonal wind currents that blow in and out of Asia.

China, while sharing with the other great communities of the Far East a monsoonal setting, has like India and Japan a quality of unity that is distinctive. This "oneness" expresses itself in many forms: genetically in a separate race, linguistically as the stock branch of the Sinitic family, historically as a congeries of provinces with a concrete domain, and culturally as a social group participating in a set of adaptations manifest in every sphere of human activity. The essence of this unity, however, is geographic.

China proper, comprising the eighteen historic provinces, contains fully nine-tenths of the inhabitants of Greater China.[1] It is preeminently the region visited by the monsoonal rains; indeed its very limits seem circumscribed by the monsoon. Beyond lie the dry steppes, flanked by the endless mountains and great plateaus of the interior. Within the eighteen provinces much land is unfit for cultivation, possibly only a third is arable; nevertheless it supports a population of two hundred to the square mile. In the fertile valleys and plainlands the density of population is comparable to that of the huge

[1] Examine carefully Plates I, VI, VII, VIII, IX.

134

metropolitan areas of the West. The province of Kiangsu on the
coastal plain, 39,000 miles in extent, has a population density of nine
hundred per square mile.

China proper comprises but a fourth of Greater China. From the
northwest possibly six thousand years ago came the first Chinese
migrants. Since then, as agriculturalists, they have been moving eastward and southward, displacing and absorbing those who were unable to make the best of their geographical advantages. To-day they
are penetrating Malaysia in much the same manner. Outside the
eighteen provinces lie the three great desert areas, Tibet, Sinkiang
(Turkestan), and Mongolia. These regions receive little rainfall, less
than ten inches a year, and are therefore practically uninhabitable.
Each supports a population of two million or less, small in proportion
to the great size of the region. The inhabitants are principally desert
nomads who follow their flocks from one patch of grass to another.
All three marginal areas are closely linked to China, for the topography of the land points to the east. Their market for wool and
livestock has always been in China, and from the Chinese they have
learned what little they know of agriculture and irrigation. In times
past these restless nomads have raided and even conquered the Chinese, who neglected to develop the arts of war. But, like the scant
moisture of their desert rains, the conquerors were rapidly and silently
absorbed.

Tibet is a huge plateau with an average altitude exceeding ten
thousand feet. Along the lofty pathways that lead from China little
villages have grown up, which have prospered because of the historic Chinese trade with India. Cultural influences from these remote lands have given a picturesque touch to the nomadic pattern
of the Tibetans. The Dalai-Lama, who regards himself as a rein-
carnation of Buddha, governs these nomads politically and spiritually.
Their religion is a curious blend of Buddhism and native shaman-
ism. Remoteness has permitted the patriarch of the "forbidden city,"
Lhasa, to rule more or less undisturbed for centuries. Sinkiang sur-
rounds the Takla Makan Desert. In sheltered places and along disappearing desert streams, a mixed population of Turki and Chinese
rear flocks of sheep, collect jade, and by means of irrigation raise a
few fruits and vegetables. Mongolia is another great waste surrounding the Desert of Gobi. Here, too, are towns, for the old trade routes
to the West skirt the desert's edge. From Urga to Kalgan, located

just beyond the Great Wall, come horses, sheep, and camels to the Chinese market. For centuries the Chinese were forbidden to venture beyond the Great Wall, but recently sturdy peasants from Hopei (Chihli) and Shansi have been turning the grasslands of Inner Mongolia to the plow. A frontier movement, similar to that experienced in the American West, is now under way. The Mongolian frontier is being advanced about a mile a year. Agriculture is rather precarious for the growing season is very short. The crop of grain or beans must be planted and harvested between the time of thawing, late in spring, and the end of the rainy spell in August. Unlike most of China proper, no second crop is possible as insurance against failure, but the desire to own land is a strong incentive to boldness. To-day parts of Inner Mongolia are rather thickly settled.

Manchuria, too, for centuries lay "beyond the Great Wall" remote from the beaten paths of migration and settlement. In the basins of the Amur and the Liao, however, are great stretches of fertile land with a sufficient rainfall for agriculture. Though the average amount hardly exceeds twenty inches, it is monsoonal in character, falling almost entirely during the three summer months. As in Inner Mongolia, the growing season is just long enough to provide a harvest, but the character of the rainfall is more reliable. In recent years Koreans and Chinese have colonized Manchuria in great numbers. Chinese estimates are not to be trusted, but the population in 1915 was believed to be ten million. To-day it is fully double that number.

In addition to millet, maize, and sorghum, which support the population, there is a money crop in the soya bean. Over twenty million acres are planted annually in this crop and the yield is about five million tons. The soya bean is employed both for food and industrial purposes. The people use it as a sauce (soy), as a food paste, and as a bean curd. The beans are eaten as a vegetable or ground into flour. The oil of the bean takes the place of lard in cooking. Bean cake and refuse is fed to the pigs or used as fertilizer which is scarce. The industrial uses of the soya bean are many. It is important as a lubricant, as a varnish for water-proofing, and as an oil in lighting. From it are made also salad oil, paint oil, a substitute for coffee, a kind of condensed milk, and soaps and other toilet articles. In large, it is the staple of the new agricultural area.

The Japanese, through various devices, have obtained a virtual suzerainty over Manchuria (Manchukuo). They have not settled there in any great numbers for they cannot compete with the lower standard of living of the Chinese and Koreans. Scarcely 250,000 Japanese reside in Manchuria. Their capital investment, however, is huge—almost three-quarters of a billion dollars. They have invested large sums in industrial developments such as mining and transportation. Japan lacks especially coal and shale oils, which can be obtained in limited amounts, at least, in Manchuria. The iron ore deposits are large but the ore is of low grade. The Japanese, aside from directing industrial enterprises, are engaged as skilled workmen in the mining, transportation, and commercial activities, but very few are farmers.

68. Climate of China Proper

In a land which measures from north to south 2,500 miles and which extends nearly three thousand miles inland one would expect great climatic diversity. Broadly speaking the great interior land mass exerts a unifying influence upon all phases of the climate. Temperatures are continental in character, hot in summer and cold in winter. In July, the mean monthly temperature for most of China proper is over 80°. Even in Manchuria, which lies north of the 40th parallel, it is above 70°. In winter the cold is severe; in the north the January mean is as low as – 10°, while the greater part of China experiences temperatures below freezing. In the south, near the Tropic of Cancer, the January mean is highest, 60°, yet even here, because of outblowing winds, severe cold spells are not infrequent. Frost and snow are not unknown at Canton.

The monsoon, since it controls the amount and seasonal distribution of the precipitation, is a more important climatic factor in China proper than latitude. The high temperature of the interior in summer and the extreme low temperature of winter are instrumental in setting up strong winds. During the winter the air contracts and, under higher pressure, winds sweep over China proper continuously from October until April. Day and night, month in and month out, they move seaward at a speed of about fifteen miles an hour. During the summer the heated air of the interior ascends, establishing an unusually low pressure régime. A steep isobaric gradient results and from May until August there is a strong monsoonal indraught. As the humidity of the monsoon is very high, rainfall is plentiful in the plains and lower ranges.

Monsoon rains correspond with the growing season. Over 80 per cent of the precipitation occurs during the three summer months. The year's total is high, about sixty inches in China proper; greater in amount than New York City receives. In the west and southwest a transitional belt from wet to dry, such as occurs in Manchuria, is prohibited by the abrupt rise of mountains and plateaus.

The peculiarities of monsoonal rainfall have for the inhabitants a sinister aspect. These rains frequently take the form of very heavy showers and often wash away the crops, especially on the terraced hillsides. Hong Kong, for example, has repeatedly experienced twenty inches of rain in a single day. Such heavy rains do no real good, for they drain away quickly and are likely to be followed by dry spells. It has been estimated that during a period of a thousand years, from 620 to 1620, drought occurred in 610 seasons. In North China, in Shensi and Shansi especially, flood rains have caused great destruction. The forests have been stripped from the mountain sides leaving the terraced fields below unprotected. The lowlands suffer even more severely for the rain waters rush into the valleys and plains unarrested. The Yangtze rises one hundred feet during the rainy season. Tungting Lake, a great marsh in the winter, is converted into a lake four thousand square miles in extent during the summer. The waterways overflow, the dikes burst, and the fields are flooded. The Hwang Ho (Yellow River) frequently changes its course. In 1887 it emptied into the Yellow Sea; two years later it emptied into the Gulf of Chihli (Pohai), causing great destruction and the loss of a million lives. Severe floods are a normal occurrence; in 1926, 1931, and in 1933 they caused widespread catastrophe. The fields were drowned, the people rendered homeless, and thousands died of starvation because facilities for relief were totally lacking in many areas. The social effects of drought and flood are vividly portrayed in Pearl Buck's novel, *The Good Earth*.

69. Land Forms and Soils

China proper may be divided into five major topographical areas, The Great Plain, North China (Upper Hwang), the Middle Yangtze, the Upper Yangtze (Szechwan), and the Si Kiang region. These are the chief agricultural areas of China, in contrast to the barren lands of Tibet, Sinkiang, and the other outer provinces.

The Great Plain extends along the coast roughly from Peiping (Peking) to the Yangtze, excluding the Shantung Peninsula. It is about 750 miles long and 350 miles wide. The relief is gentle and most of the lands are drained by the lower tributaries of the Hwang. The soil is alluvial in character and is constantly renewed by the rivers. In addition it benefits greatly from loess deposits that are carried by the winter winds. Loess is fine desert dust, yellowish in color, which adds greatly to the fertility of the soil. During the winter the loess is actually visible at Peiping and elsewhere in North China. The poor visibility occasioned by the loess-laden winds has caused many shipwrecks in the Yellow Sea.

The Upper Hwang region is a rugged area composed of mountains and valleys. Here the rainfall is likely to be plentiful for the land rises rapidly to great heights. It is drained by many streams, yet because of the deforestation the drainage is not good. Terracing is a feature of the agriculture. The soil is unusually fertile because of the loess deposits. This region suffers much from drought and floods, and life is rendered precarious because of these catastrophes. Too heavy rains wash away the loess, yet the soil requires plentiful rainfall for loess soil is porous. On the whole, however, the Upper Hwang is very productive agriculturally.

The Middle and Upper Yangtze are transitional belts between the north and south. Topographically they afford a great contrast. The Middle Yangtze, centering about Hankow, is a region of hilly relief and alluvial soil. Like the basin of the lower Hwang it is in danger of flood, but as the terrain is somewhat higher, the Yangtze is a more stable river. The Upper Yangtze or Szechwan region, though mountainous, is well drained and receives abundant rainfall. The soil, a decomposing sandstone, is reddish in color and extremely fertile.

The Si Kiang region in southeast China is another rich agricultural province. Here the soil is alluvial and high in humus content. The relief, aside from the coastal plain, is very rugged, but the valleys are well drained by the numerous tributaries of the Si Kiang. The natural vegetation is tropical and luxurious, and although it retards advance into the interior, this covering is insurance against the flood ravages so frequent in the other parts of monsoonal China.

70. Agriculture

Agriculture, like every form of human activity in China, has become institutionalized. Its methods have changed but little through the long period of Chinese history. It is now as always the main occupation of the people and naturally has had a dominant influence upon all social relationships. The people live close to the soil; and land, the birthright of the peasant, is valued above all else. Each family holds tenaciously to its plot; yet because of family subdivisions the holdings grow smaller and smaller in size. More than half the "farms" are less than an acre and a half in extent. Even the most conservative estimates hold that five acres are needed for the average-sized family of seven. In the more fecund south two acres would suffice, but that section is already overpopulated.

Agriculture in China is of necessity "gardening" rather than farming in our sense. Every nook and cranny of the field is worked, every stalk is given individual attention, and every plant is fully exploited. Only the family burying ground escapes the hoe. Western critics are fond of dwelling upon the folly of reserving two square yards in perpetuity for each deceased, especially where the custom interferes with mining and transport operations. The Chinese, however, regard the family as sacred in all its aspects and willingly yield this land to consecrate its memory.

The Chinese use the hoe and not the plow in their farming. The plow requires the aid of a domestic animal, and the farmers cannot support horses or oxen on their small plots. Nor does dairying exist, for there is no pasture land for cattle. Human labor, because of the low standard of living, is cheaper than animal work. There is no need of fences or hedges, and where we would have a road there is usually a foot path. The Chinese keep pigs upon every habitation. In fact, the character for home consists of the symbol for *roof* with the symbol for *pig* just below it. Pigs and chickens subsist upon refuse that they garner along the roads and about the villages. To the children is delegated the task of keeping them out of mischief. The more prosperous in the north possess an ox or a horse, and in the south a water buffalo, an animal particularly fitted to work in the wet rice fields. Donkeys and camels are used as pack animals in the north, while human carriage prevails in the south.

There is little waste in Chinese agriculture. What the peasant does not consume or sell is turned over to the pigs and chickens. Sticks and grass are used as cooking fuel and the ashes are returned to the soil. Fuel famines are frequent and actually occur in places underlaid with extensive coal deposits. Dung is prized as fertilizer and the canals are scoured for refuse. Waste vegetable products such as leaves and stems are made into a compost and returned to the land. The soil is called upon to bear a heavy burden and must be carefully husbanded. In the monsoon areas it is customary to raise two crops, a summer and a winter crop. Winter wheat, harvested in early summer and followed by a crop of millet or beans, is most common. In south China a four-crop system is possible; winter wheat is interplanted with peas, and during the summer cotton and turnips are grown. To guard against soil exhaustion, one crop in every six is a legume. Irrigation as well as soil restoration is well understood and has been practised since the earliest times. The legendary inventor of the irrigation dike is held in sacred esteem by the people. The methods of irrigating are singularly simple. Where the river is above the level of the plain the dikes are opened and the fields flooded. More widespread, as the river is usually below plain level, is the "swinging" method whereby a basket of water is swung sideways and upward by two men using a wooden propeller. Along terraced slopes gravity, of course, simplifies the distribution of water.

71. Agricultural Regions and Crops

In North China, comprising the Upper Hwang and the Great Plain, the staple crops are wheat and kaoliang.[1] This is a loess-covered area and one where dry farming is practised. The Upper Hwang, including the provinces of Kansu, Shansi, and northern Shensi, where loess erosion is very rapid, resembles in places a series of miniature plateaus. From these treeless barrens the subsoil is washed down and may render the arable fields at lower levels utterly useless. The Great Plain is also a region of hard grains, but because of its location it affords a greater diversity in agriculture. Rice, for example, is grown as far north as Peiping. During the growing season this gently rolling country is covered with green crops. When the Hwang overflows all is turned a yellow brown and is useless for the time being. Shantung is mountainous and only the lower loess-covered slopes are cul-

[1] A tall species of millet.

tivable. Millet is the principal crop here as in other parts of North China. Shantung and the region around Peiping are noted fruit-growing districts. Peaches, thought to be indigenous to China, apples, and pears are the principal fruits. Buckwheat and barley replace wheat and millet in those parts of North China where the altitude is high. Maize, dubbed by the Japanese "the southern barbarian millet," was brought to China from America by the Portuguese and is growing in favor because of its hardiness. The soya bean is the most popular legume, for it is one of the few money crops in this part of China. The peanut is important for the same reason. It has an oil content of nearly 50 per cent, and can be grown in sandy wastes where nothing else can be cultivated.

The agriculture of Middle China (Middle and Upper Yangtze) resembles that of more southerly regions. Rice, tea, and sugar predominate. Water transport replaces that of the donkey and the mule. Szechwan "of the Four Rivers and the Red Basin" is an extremely fertile province. Rice is the principal crop both on the hills and in the valleys. Tea and silk make their appearance and, along with tung oil, are the most valuable products of the district. The Chengtu region, located in the Red Basin of Szechwan, is one of the most densely populated areas in all China. The Middle Yangtze, centering about Hankow, is similarly a transitional area with rice as the principal crop and the mulberry an important one. Here the hard grains of the north are raised along with cotton in the more sandy soils. Cane sugar and tea are widely cultivated but beans, oil plants, and sweet potatoes are also grown in this more southerly latitude.

Rice is one of the six legendary grains and is mentioned in the ceremonial plantings of the Emperor Shen Hung who lived about 2800 B. C. It is the "meal" of China and the most popular food. Some provinces cannot raise enough for their own use and must import it from Hunan, Kiangsi, and Anhwei. It is raised wherever physically possible. In the north it is largely a dry crop, but in most parts of China it is a wet crop. Within certain well-defined limits rice is both a hardy and a prodigious crop. For the wet crop five months of an average temperature of 70° and abundant moisture are required. Rice grows best in the slowly draining fields of the terraced river bottoms. The young shoots are sprouted upon sunny slopes and then are laboriously transferred to fields ten times the size of the original bed. The water buffalo with its broad flat hoofs and tremendous strength is of great assistance in the planting. During the growing season the chief tasks are to keep off the birds and prevent the weeds from choking the young crop. From Szechwan to the Yangtze delta and in the Si Valley as far west as Yunnan, rice is the staple food. The alluvial flats of the Middle Yangtze produce so much rice that the people have literally too much to eat. Here the diet consists of three bowls of rice three times a day, and each portion is in reality two bowls, for a second bowl is always pressed down over the first. Without rice China could hardly support such a huge mass of human beings. Like bamboo and the soya bean, rice serves many purposes: it furnishes a strong drink and it provides medicine; the straw is used as fodder; paper, sandals, thatch, and other wares are additional products.

The leguminous plants are of great importance to China because of the absence of animal foods. In the Western world they are of value in the production of nitrogen bacteria, but in China they constitute an important portion of the actual food supply. Vetches, pulses, beans, and peas have a wide distribution. The soya bean, discussed in connection with Manchuria, along with sesamum and rape, afford valuable substitutes for animal fats. Vegetable oils of all sorts comprise one of the chief articles of Chinese commerce. From Szechwan, Kweichow, and Hunan come tung oil and the seeds of the wood oil which are marketed at Hankow. These oils are used in waterproofing and painting. Tea oil is used in hair dressing; castor oil, mustard oil, and flax oil serve many purposes. Latex, an oily substance extracted by tapping the lacquer tree, forms the basis of an old hereditary industry. Finally the tallow tree yields a seed oil that makes a highly desirable commercial wax.

Tea plays an important part in the lives of the Chinese. First used only for medicinal purposes, it was adopted more than a thousand years ago as a substitute for water which came to be avoided as unclean. Now it occupies a place in the social ceremonial comparable to that of wine in the Mediterranean countries or whiskey and soda in Great Britain. The tea-growing areas correspond roughly with the wet rice areas with this important difference: that tea thrives best on the hills and the drier slopes. Grown wild the plant is a tree, but under cultivation it is a bush, maturing in from six to ten years and flourishing for ten to fifteen years thereafter. There are three pickings a year, April, May, and August. The first picking, undertaken when the leaves are still covered with down, yields the pekoe variety. Green and black tea are the result of different methods of treatment, and are not different varieties of leaf. Green tea, which has a high tannin content, is made from leaves that are permitted to dry out quickly, while black tea is attained by fermentation which alters the chlorophyl. The tea plantation has not developed in China. Commonly tea is a household crop, grown in patches that will not conveniently support rice, and is cared for by the women and children. During the seventeenth century, under the auspices of the Dutch East India Company, tea entered into the commerce of the Western world. Foochow early became a great export center, and the tea trade became the certain road to wealth. The trade reached its zenith about 1878 when eighty million pounds of tea were exported from Foochow. Just prior to this time an Englishman, Robert Fortune, in the employ of the British East India Company found it profitable to grow tea in India. Owing to the rapid spread of the plantation system there, the Chinese were undersold and the Foochow market slowly declined. For a time Hankow, better situated to care for the overland trade with Russia, the principal customer, was preëminent in the export trade. The limitation of tea imports into Britain during the war, the subsequent impoverishment of the Russian tea-drinking classes, and the present preference of Americans for Ceylon and Assam rather than China teas have seriously crippled this historic trade. The domestic consumption, however, is enormous. It is alleged that the per capita consumption of tea in China is five pounds a year.

The cultivation of sugar cane is very ancient in China, and the plant is thought to be indigenous there despite the fact that cane can be grown only in tropical regions. To-day it is planted widely in the southern provinces and in the western districts of Yunnan and Szechwan. Like other crops that are admirably suited to plantation culture, sugar growing has never gotten beyond the status of "family" cultivation in China. Possibly it is for this reason that domestic sugar is unable to supply more than 10 per cent of the needs of the people. In many districts sugar is a real luxury and has acquired the same status as candy with us.

The sweet potato was diffused from America via the Philippines as late as the middle of the eighteenth century. Even to-day, though widely cultivated, it is not popular. The upper classes regard it as

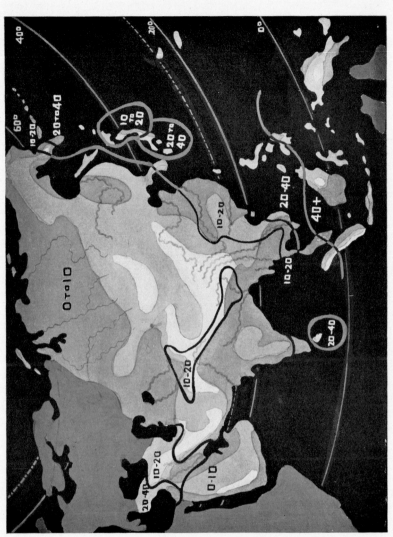

PLATE VIII. ASIA—JANUARY RAINFALL

(*After Goode*)

food fit for coolies, and the latter in time of plenty regard it as proper food for pigs. But, like any convenient source of food, it cannot be disregarded by the Chinese and this has been a determining factor in its consistent spread and use.

Opium is still a source of great profit in parts of China where the authorities are not too vigilant. The poppy from which it is extracted is planted in North China as a winter crop and is harvested in June or July. In the south it is planted in the rice fields in early autumn and is harvested earlier than in the north. The opium is obtained by pressing the milky latex from the ripe seed. In congealing it is transformed into a thick brown substance resembling molasses. For smoking, careful preparation is necessary. Frequently it is mixed with other ingredients. Professor Buxton speaks of a genuine "gasper," a cigarette made of opium, tobacco, and hemp. Opium is not indigenous to China but was diffused from Java through Formosa, and from the records of Chinese literature appears to have been used medicinally as early as the twelfth century. Since the seventeenth century, efforts have been made to prohibit its use in smoking, but only since 1917 has it been legally ostracized in both domestic and foreign trade. The India government refused to certify cargoes earmarked for China, and by 1920 all importations in Chinese jurisdictions presumably had ceased. But the poppy still flourishes in remote districts, although some of the war lords have made commendable efforts to discourage its cultivation.

In time tobacco will entirely replace opium as it is being cultivated in every one of the eighteen provinces. This product, like maize, was diffused to China from America by way of the Philippines. Tobacco in the south is grown as a winter crop because of the mildness of the season but in the north it must be planted as a summer crop. Although there is an immense local traffic in tobacco and although there is a considerable export, the industry suffers from lack of standardization. As a result the Western brand of cigarette enjoys a considerable market in China in spite of the fact that the Chinese could easily raise enough for their wants. For the most part, however, pipe smoking is popular. In using the water pipe one or two puffs of a strong mixture of tobacco and sesame oil suffices the smoker. Tobacco is now the national luxury of the peasant, and in the majority of cases it constitutes the sole luxury.

Ginseng is highly valued as the people believe it will cure any number of ills. The root from which it comes takes about six years to mature. Liquorice and rhubarb also are widely used for medicinal purposes. Camphor is a marketable commodity, although about twenty years ago the industry almost perished because the planting of new trees was neglected. In Yunnan, however, there are large forests of wild camphor which, because of their inaccessibility, have never been exploited. To obtain the oil, the tree is felled, the wood cut into very small rectangular pieces, and the oil extracted. Considerable ingenuity was shown by the Chinese in overcoming the difficulty of distilling a liquid that is apt to solidify and clog the pipes in the course of the process.

China raises a number of textile crops and their capacity for extension is almost unlimited as they do not, with the possible exception of the mulberry, demand a sacrifice of food production. This is a fortunate condition for China's food requirements are so great as practically to preclude any considerable export of food crops. Moreover, if China lacked the capacity for raising industrial crops, it is not likely that she would ever be a serious competitor in the young industry of the Far East.

Of the industrial crops, hemp has the widest distribution, giving rise to the view that it was the earliest textile crop. The plant is both prolific and tough; in Kiangsi, for example, it is capable of yielding three times a year. Because of the ease with which it can be raised, it makes a convenient summer crop in many districts. It will grow in latitudes where cotton does not. It is valuable, also because of its byproducts; the seeds yield an excellent oil which has a low freezing point, and which is widely used as a luminant.

Cotton was introduced into China from Khotan about the twelfth century. It is grown most successfully in the loess areas of North China but appears almost everywhere because of its popularity as a secondary crop. Cotton is also a "family" crop, but where transport facilities exist, there is a ready market for the surplus in Japan. Only eight of the provinces participate in this trade. The fact that to-day almost as much raw cotton is imported as exported is a sad commentary upon the vagaries of transportation and distribution within China. To compete successfully with India, however, it will be necessary for China to improve the grade of her cotton, for a large part of it is of such short staple that it cannot be accommodated by the looms of modern industry. The home market affords a priceless opportunity for the industrialization of cotton in China, for coarse cotton goods are worn by nearly 400,000,000 people.

Sericulture, which appears in the ceremonials of the earliest dynasties, is very ancient in China. While the emperor went out to plow the first furrow at the planting season, the empress worshipped at the shrine of the silk goddess. The desire for silk in the West was responsible for the maintenance of one of the most ancient trade routes in the world, the overland route. Alexander the Great presented a silken robe from China to his tutor, Aristotle. In the sixth century, two Nestorian missionaries carried to the Emperor Justinian at Constantinople a hollow bamboo containing silk worms. These worms were fed on the leaf of the mulberry and survived. From this source originated the great Mediterranean silk industry.

Silk cultivation is widespread in China; indeed there is hardly a district in China proper that is not engaged in it. The methods of caring for the eggs are traditional and primitive. They are sealed in jars or simply laid upon paper and stowed in the rafters. In some parts of China the women wear these papers next to their bodies to induce hatching. In other places, warm water is sprinkled upon the eggs to procure their maturation. Some of the Canton variety produce six generations a year. The natural food of the larvæ is the leaf of the mulberry tree which reaches maturity at about twenty years when it produces about two hundred pounds of leaves. The larvæ are difficult to raise, the mortality being about 50 per cent. The survivors consume vast quantities of food. It has been estimated that to mature the larvæ from one ounce of eggs, 1,500 pounds of leaves are required.

The reeling of silk, like the raising of the larvæ, is done at home, usually by the women. The cocoons are killed by scalding, and the skein is unwound by permitting the twisted threadlets to pass through an eyelet. The single thread is then wound upon a wooden reel and sold "by the reel." The use of machinery would probably double the production of raw silk; still the total is immense, reaching twenty million pounds in 1930, a fifth of the world's supply. Silk is the principal article of the Chinese export trade, and if the industry were organized upon a business basis, the markets would be China's almost for the asking. Even in its present sluggish condition, Chinese sericulture is responsible for the largest quantity of the finest grade of raw silk. Sericulture is most important in the south where the favorable temperatures make it possible for production to go on all year round. The care of the worms and the various processes in the production of raw silk have the aspects of religious rites and a national significance. Silk culture is an integral part of Chinese civilization.

China, in summary, is the world's largest producer of rice, soya beans, tea, and tung oil, and is exceeded only by Japan in the production of raw silk. It ranks third or fourth among the nations as a producer of cotton, and is an important raiser of corn, peanuts, kaoliang, and tobacco. Four-fifths of the population, at least, is engaged in agriculture and the crop yield per acre probably averages higher than in the United States. Yet China accounts for a smaller proportion of the world's agricultural exports than do little Holland or sparsely inhabited Australia. In fact, food ranks high in a trade where imports exceed exports. Annually, owing to famine and flood, China is forced to import large stores of dried fish, wheat flour, and even rice for those who cannot be reached by the wretched interprovincial agencies of transportation.

Beans, principally the soya bean, and raw silk constitute China's chief exports at present, and these far outrank her minor exports— dried eggs, tung oil, cotton, and tobacco. Tea ranks relatively low for reasons that have already been explained. Total tea exports to the United States fell from 8.7 million pounds in 1928 to 5.3 million pounds in 1929. Chinese agriculture is ill adapted to the needs of modern trade. Household agriculture is a fundamental drawback for its products cannot be standardized, let alone adapted to meet the demands of a changing and fickle market. Facilities for collecting and transporting the product are generally inadequate. Until the tempo of Chinese agriculture is developed in harmony with that of the needs of the market, it is unlikely that China—for better or for worse—will be influenced more than superficially by the civilization of the Western world.

72. Rivers and Roads

The rivers, like the climate and land forms, are of greatest importance both geographically and economically. Geographically they distribute the rains and the soils, sometimes too lavishly, and economically they not only aid in making the land productive, but they are the mainstay of the transportation system.

The Hwang Ho dominates northern China. Rising among the plateau heights of Tibet, it pursues an S-shaped course emptying, after a journey of 2,300 miles, into the Gulf of Chihli. In northwestern China the Hwang makes its way through steep mountain corridors and loess plateaus. Entering China Proper at Kansu it falls from an altitude of eight thousand feet to 5,200 feet in 150 miles. Lanchow is the point at which the river becomes navigable for small craft. From Lanchow to Tungkwan, the "Eastern Gate," where the river receives its main tributary, the Wei, the fall is only four feet to the mile, yet navigation is precarious even for the skilled boatmen as the course is strewn with rapids and gorges. Yet this precarious agency must be used if Shansi coal is to have an outlet. At Tungkwan, the meeting place of west and east China, the river turns eastward and flows through the heart of North China into the Great Plain. The Wei tributary waters the loess areas of Shensi and contributes to the productive capacities of that province. The Chinese are thought to have entered China proper in following this stream eastward. The vagaries of the Hwang Ho after it enters the Great Plain have been commented upon. The chief difficulty is that the river flows on the plain, not in it. The Chinese have built dikes but have never deepened the stream bed. Unfortunately, the coöperation necessary for stringent control of the dikes is lacking. As the beds of silt become higher and higher, the floods penetrate further and further into the plain. At present the northern portion of the Great Plain is at the mercy of the river; at times it is converted into a vast inland sea.

The Yangtze basin, at the southern extremity of the Great Plain, experiences the same ravages to a minor degree. The Yangtze and its tributaries are the mainstays of navigation in Middle China. In the basin region, canals (dominated by the historic Grand Canal) appear everywhere, yet their importance to navigation is small, for the Chinese in all their canal building never discovered the principle of the lock. The expense attached to frequent changes of bulk rendered dependence upon long carriage by canal out of the question. The canal, for purposes of commercial traffic, has been superseded by the railway.

The Yangtze is one of the great inland waterways of the world; it is three thousand miles in length and possesses, according to geographers, all the properties of the perfect navigable river. Ocean going ships are able to ascend to Hankow, a distance of 680 miles; while

Ichang, one thousand miles from the sea, is served by easy junk traffic. The large junks make the trip from Ichang in from four to ten days but the return journey takes from forty to fifty days. The river above Ichang is navigated with difficulty because it encounters rapids for several hundred miles in flowing through the Wushan Gorge. In going downstream these rapids are shot by the skilled boatmen, but in going upstream the boats must be towed or "tracked" by large gangs of coolies. Though the upper Yangtze furnishes the means of local transportation in many districts yet, it has one insuperable defect: the rich Red Basin of Szechwan is cut off from the rest of China. Until a railway is built, the rich productivity of this province cannot be fully realized. Even the commerce from Ichang to the sea is limited to the capacities of junk commerce. It is essentially a "package" trade, for in spite of the fact that it engages five thousand vessels, the total annual carriage is no more than 125,-000 tons. China stands in dire need of the great resources of the western provinces: cotton, silk, food, and minerals.

The Si Kiang rises in the tablelands of southwest China and pursues a generally eastward course through rugged lands. Though this river and its tributaries are important in draining southeast China, the river traffic for the most part comes to an end at Wuchow. The whole area, considered economically, can be classed as the hinterland of Canton. Trade, however, that has an international significance, is practically forced to proceed through Hong Kong.

Nowhere is the decadence of Chinese culture more apparent than in the system of transportation and communications. The roads, once the glory of the Empire, are in a sad state. Trade follows the same channels as of old, save that it does not run on the imperial highways but alongside them in muddy paths worn by men and beasts. The canals have scarcely fared better. The Imperial Canal has fallen into disuse. Even in the south, where most of the traffic is by water, transport is primitive. Many canals are kept open because the peasants have use for the silt and débris that obstruct them. Thus, much of the canal system serves agriculture rather than transportation.

Various domestic animals are employed in the carriage of goods; camels in the desert borderlands, yaks in the mountains, and buffalo and oxen on the plains. The chief carrier, however, is man. Through the whole country, inns and rest places mark the "day's journey" of the coolie. Its length is dependent more upon topography than upon distance. Where the coolie does not travel with the pack strapped to his back, he pushes a wheelbarrow which supports the load directly over a solid wooden wheel. In using the wheelbarrow, the coolie can underbid the other pack animals for he can push along a burden of three hundred pounds, needs no caretaker, and consumes less food than any of the beasts. On the level plains great carts with heavy, solid wheels cut into the road and chew it up. Until recently good roads and motor vehicles were confined to the immediate proximity of the foreign towns. Since the motor bus has proved a military necessity, there has been more interest in good roads. It is reported that the military bus has found its way as far as Szechwan.

At Kalgan, Sian, Lanchow, and Suchow, the products of inner and outer China, principally tea, rice, tobacco, hides, and wool, are exchanged. At these inland trading towns the great caravans assemble for seasonal journeys to Lhasa, Kashgar, and the more remote Bukhara and Darjeeling. Their roads are trails through the deserts and plateaus. In China proper they are not much better at present, though at one time six Imperial Highways reached out in all directions from Peiping. The Ambassadors Road from Peiping to Canton is a famous historic highway. The road from Hankow to Lake Zeisan measured 2,580 miles. Roads are less frequent in south China, where water transportation is employed wherever possible. The roads of China are heavily trafficked but poorly improved.

The railways of China, about ten thousand miles in extent, run north and south, while traffic is largely east and west. Peiping is the center of the rail communications, with trunk lines running northwest to connect with the Mongolian trade routes, north to tap the Manchurian development and link up with the Siberian system, and south to the Yangtze basin. Spurs run into the various treaty ports, and branch lines to the accessible coal fields. South of the Yangtze, railways are few because of engineering difficulties. The projected extension from Hankow and Wuchang to Canton and Hong Kong has never been completed. The present civil disorders have rendered the railroads practically useless for commercial purposes. Inadequate as the system is, it has cast in sharper lines the economic development of certain regions. The line into Manchuria has given Peiping a real hinterland which, of course, the recently established Japanese influence may destroy. Kalgan, at the Great Wall, has been transformed from a frontier post to a frontier city. Railway penetration has been a large factor in extending the Chinese frontier far into Inner Mongolia, and without its service such a settlement as Tatung, combining resources of coal and wool, would be impossible. Where the planning has been wise, the roads have paid richly and to the geographer, here as elsewhere, have demonstrated their assistance in enabling man to make a finer type of adjustment to the physical environment. The Peiping-Hankow system has the greatest potentialities for it will facilitate the industrialization of a densely inhabited region. The Middle Yangtze is eminently suitable for cotton production; it lies also within easy reach of large coal deposits. It is not too much to expect that the cotton industry, which has made an appreciable beginning, will develop into a major industry. Hankow may well become the nucleus of an industrialized China. At present, however, the means of communication for industrial purposes are practically nil in the potentially rich Yangtze Valley. Though the road traffic is forty times as great as the river traffic, both types are essentially "package" trade. The south is worse off. The silk and cotton production of the Si Kiang valley is increasing, but Canton is forced to obtain coal and iron from abroad. So long as this condition exists, Hong Kong can with ease retain the commercial and industrial hegemony of South China.

73. Industries

Compared with what it might become in view of its various resources, China's industry is at a low ebb. Yet the prevalent cottage system and the workshop industry are the means through which China maintains a high degree of economic self-sufficiency. We do not know with certainty how many people are engaged in these domestic types of manufacturing, nor do we know the quantity or value of the goods produced. We do know, however, that thousands of people are engaged in the making of iron and copper cooking utensils, braided reed mats, felt mats for beds, oiled boots, baskets, carts, wheelbarrows, adobe and burned bricks, cheap silver jewelry, cotton cloth, hosiery, and simple implements such as plowshares and scythes. Thousands are employed in the salt industry, and in North China porcelain-making and rug-making provide goods for export as well as for domestic use.

There has been a beginning of modern industry in China. The

iron smelting plants centering about Hankow and Wuchang in Middle China have attained a producing capacity of nearly one million tons. Cotton-spinning and weaving, silk-weaving, tobacco manufacture, and flour-milling constitute sizeable industrial enterprises. The larger part of this industry is centered about Shanghai. More than half of the cotton spindles are located there and an even greater proportion of other manufacturing equipment. Much of this enterprise is due to foreign impetus and direction. The Japanese alone control over 40 per cent of the cotton spindles and 35 per cent of the looms. There is, in addition, considerable mining activity in China. The production of coal and iron has only a local importance, but China enjoys a unique position in exporting 75 per cent of the world's antimony. She also ranks second in the production of tungsten and fourth in the production of tin. In exchange for her metals, raw silk, and soya beans, China, in addition to large supplies of sugar, rice and other foodstuffs, is receiving materials necessary for equipping modern industrial plants. With the increasing importation of machinery, electrical supplies, and chemicals, her purchases of cotton piece-goods are certain to diminish. At present, however, the amount of piece goods imported is more than double in value that of raw cotton and cotton yarns.

Much has been written of the industrial future of China and the temptation to pursue that theme is great. Geographically the picture is rather roseate, but of what avail are all her splendid resources in the face of such besetting evils as poverty, ignorance, disease, corruption, and disorder? These ills and others only too frequently sweep the land, spreading chaos and paralysing hope. Estimates of China's coal reserves vary from 23,000,000 tons to 996,000,000 tons. Every one of the eighteen provinces is known to contain some coal. In South Shansi alone there is a bed of anthracite covering 13,500 square miles, while the provinces of Honan, Szechwan, and Yunnan are thought to be one huge field of coal. China's reserves are equal to those of any country in the world. From 20 to 40 per cent of the coal is anthracite. On the other hand, though the anthracite may be used as metallurgical fuel, it is not as efficient as coking coal. At present only 25,000,000 tons are mined annually, and development is likely to proceed slowly. Much of the coal is situated so far inland that the transport charges may be prohibitive when the beds are opened. Largely for this reason Japan cannot look with certainty to China to alleviate her coal shortage; but China may develop industries that will seriously rival those of Japan.

Many legends have arisen concerning the immense iron ore deposits in China. The whole of China Proper exhibits huge heaps of slag, the refuse of centuries of domestic iron working. Unfortunately these appearances are but a superficial index. Though the ore has a wide distribution, the deposits, with few exceptions, are small in bulk and low in quality. This type of deposit is capable of supplying small domestic plants that can be shifted from deposit to deposit. China's ore, however, is of no value to modern industry with its large scale smelting units, expensively equipped and requiring assured reserves of ore for long periods. Approximately four-fifths of the ore lies in Manchuria and northern Chihli. Of poor grade, low in iron content (estimated *circa* 35 per cent), and high in silica, the deposits are useless without preliminary concentration. Even if the ore were of high quality, the entire reserve would be exhausted in a country like the United States, where the consumption is over sixty millions tons annually, in from ten to fifteen years.

In spite of all that has been said, an economic regeneration would be of great benefit to China where pressure upon the land is beginning to be felt. The migrations to Malaysia and elsewhere afford little hope of permanent relief. Granted good government and a reasonable degree of stability, China is not lacking in resources, labor, and the other essentials of a more complex economic system. One indeed may visualize a greater China with its industrial nucleus situated at Hankow in Middle China, with a system of transportation that will unite the rawstuffs of the north and the south and those of the east and the west. Given the initial direction, even the fifty treaty ports will cause little inconvenience, for though they may tap the hinterland of China they are not rooted in it.

CHAPTER IX

JAPAN: A STRUGGLE AGAINST ENVIRONMENTAL LIMITATIONS

74. Size and Population

Japan is confronted with the problem of overpopulation in a more acute form than any other country. Japan proper, as we shall show, has about reached the saturation point, and the other areas in the Empire are ill suited to absorb a population that is increasing at the rate of nearly a million a year. Few Occidentals realize what a precarious state the Japanese are in, but the present disturbances in the Far East are bound to draw the attention of the world to their plight. A study of the geography of Japan will make clear the nature of the problem. Here is a country with hardly a single resource capable of caring for the wants of the population. The Japanese have utilized every weapon known to man to overcome the limitations of their environment but the fight is going against them. For them there are but two possible remedies, to check the growth of population or to add new territory.

The whole Japanese Empire is hardly equal in size to the state of Texas, whereas the area of Japan proper falls far short of that of California. The Empire includes Korea, Taiwan (Formosa), Karafuto (South Sakhalin), together with Kwangtung (leased territory in Manchuria), and a mandate which though embracing three million square miles of the Pacific north of the equator amounts to only eight hundred square miles of land. The grand population of the Empire is something less than ninety million. Japan proper, comprising 56 per cent of the land area, supports over 70 per cent of the population. The density of the population is over four hundred per square mile. Speaking broadly, the outer belt is supposed to produce the raw materials which Japan proper will transform into manufactured wares. The outer belt, however, is far from

155

meeting its specifications, and there is much that is wanting in the industrial structure of the inner belt.

75. Japan Proper

Japan proper lies off the coast of Asia between latitudes 30° N. and 45°N. It does not include the more recent additions in the archipelago, such as Karafuto, which extends as far north as 50°N. or Formosa which is crossed by the Tropic of Cancer. Japan is an empire comprising over 1,700 islands but there are only four of any size in Japan proper: Hokkaido (Yezo), lying off the Russian Maritime Provinces; Honshu, the largest, separated from Korea by the Sea of Japan; and Shikoku and Kyushu, two relatively small islands separated from southern Honshu by the waters of the Inland Sea. All four islands lie closely together and geologically represent a single formation. From north to south through them run two mountain chains, in places indistinct. One hugs the western coast; and the other, the eastern. The depression of the Inland Sea marks most clearly the inland divide. Elsewhere the central valley is obscured by great volcanic masses which appear to run at right angles to the mountain ranges. The midland valley is completely obliterated in the central portions of Honshu, whence arises a cluster of peaks, "the Japanese Alps," eight thousand feet in height. In central Hokkaido, where transverse mountains intersect the range that forms the Kurile archipelago, a similar formation occurs.

76. Land Forms and Water Bodies

The location and configuration of Japan's land mass directly limit its agricultural possibilities and influence its climate. First of all, much of the land is too rugged and too barren to permit cultivation even of the most painful variety. More than three-fourths of the surface is inclined at an angle exceeding 10°. The arable lands of Japan, which constitute only 15.5 per cent of the whole, lie between the ranges and the coasts, along the stream banks, and up the slopes as far as cultivation is humanly possible. The great plain of Honshu surrounding Tokyo is hardly more than one hundred miles broad in any direction. With all the devices of man, it will be exceedingly difficult to increase further the proportion of arable land in Japan. Reclamation and irrigation are being carried on, but there is little land of any value that has not already been utilized during the thousands of years of occupation. Many a terrace has been won from a mountain by stubbornly advancing foot by foot during the course of centuries.

Unfortunately Japan lies along one of the earth's tetrahedral edges. The high mountains of eastern and southern Japan are in close juxtaposition to great ocean depths. The earthquake belt lies along this line of weakness. The exposed regions experience 1,500 sensible shocks every year; in Tokyo there is a shock every three days. Since many of the disturbances take place under the sea, fatalities from tidal waves frequently exceed deaths from earthquakes. Japanese history records many disasters: in 1498, twenty thousand perished; in 1792, fifteen thousand were killed or drowned; in 1844, twelve thousand perished; in 1855, seven thousand were killed at Tokyo; in 1891, a like number died; and in 1896, over 27,000 were drowned in the Sanrika district by the tidal waves. The great earthquake of September 1, 1923, is without parallel in recorded history. The earthquake and the resulting fires completely demolished Yokohama and destroyed half of Tokyo. Half a million dwellings were razed to the ground and 91,000 people were killed. Although some of the earthquakes are associated with volcanic eruptions, it is a curious fact that the volcanos act as safety valves, for earthquakes are rarely experienced in their immediate vicinity. Yet, because the farmers are forced to brave the volcanic slopes in their quest for land, any disturbance is likely to give rise to famine and suffering.

The rivers of Japan are of little use for navigation; they are too short and too swift. They are, however, of importance for purposes of irrigation and as a source of water power. Because of insularity Japan has many good harbors. They are especially satisfactory because of the great depth of the sea floor. Kobe and Yokohama are preëminently the ports of Japan, each enjoying about 40 per cent of the foreign trade.

77. Mineral Resources

Coal and iron are the sinews of modern industry, but Japan is lacking in both. Although Japan has a sufficiency of manganese, limestone, chromium, and other necessary ferro-alloys, her poverty in the essentials prohibits her from becoming a rival of modern industrial states like Great Britain, Germany, and the United States. The Imperial

Geological Survey after exhaustive study has set the total iron ore reserves at eighty million tons. Only half of this amount is of sufficient quality to be useful in industry. Japan's whole reserve would hardly meet the requirements of the blast furnaces of the United States during a single year. Only two iron ore deposits are workable under present conditions, one on the Honshu east coast and the other in Hokkaido. The average output of ore, in spite of the increased demand, does not exceed that of the prewar period. In view of this scarcity Japan is forced to import from western Europe and the United States. In order to conserve fuel, Japan imports scrap iron rather than ore. From 60 to 70 per cent of Japan's pig iron is manufactured from scrap. It has been estimated that three million tons of ore would be required annually to manufacture the iron and steel now consumed in Japan. Since the actual production is in the neighborhood of 160,000 tons, Japan's interest in the adjacent mainland is readily understood.

The coal reserve seems large for it exceeds nine billion tons. Yet over 90 per cent of the coal is insufficient in quality to yield a satisfactory metallurgical coke. In proportion to her population the Japanese coal reserve is smaller than that of any modern nation except Italy's. Japan has about 120 tons per capita in comparison with the four thousand tons for the United Kingdom or Germany, and 27,500 tons for the United States. Germany would exhaust Japan's coal reserves in about forty years. At the present rate of production Japan will run through her coal resources in about two hundred years. Since the cost of mining will increase as the existing mines become deeper and the veins thinner, Japan must import coal or the high fuel prices will demolish her industries. In spite of frugal consumption Japan is at present importing from China, Manchukuo, and Indo-China. Kyushu and Hokkaido each possesses about 35 per cent of the total reserve, but the former produces 67 per cent of the output and the latter only 17 per cent. The Kyushu deposits are situated in an area of dense population and lie near the coast. Low transportation costs and nearness to the industrial centers have made this district the leading coal center. The Hokkaido mines have been opened only recently, but since they are inland and in sparsely inhabited territory exploitation has not proceeded rapidly. Sakhalin and northern Formosa with moderate reserves of coal will not assist greatly in meeting the deficiency. Japan will never be able to overcome the lack

of coking coal. The cost of coke per ton in Japan is $7.50; in the
United States, $3.50. The coke product of some mines is too porous
to support the charge of ore and flux in the blast furnaces; in other
cases there is too much sulphur content in the coal to permit its use
in the smelting of iron. Coal must therefore be imported from China
(Tientsin) and mixed, one part in four, with Japanese coal. The
low wages of the Japanese miner are more than offset by his meager
output of coal. The American miner, with the aid of mechanical
devices, produces four and a half tons per day; the Japanese miner
only half a ton.

After coal and copper, petroleum is the most important mineral
product of Japan, but only a fourth of the demand is met within the
Empire. The output is not increasing, the annual amount averaging
only two million barrels. This yield is equivalent to only 70 per cent
of that of the United States for a single day. Lacking potential sources
in Japan proper, Korea and Formosa, Japan has made an agreement
with the Soviet government permitting her to exploit oil fields in
northern Sakhalin. The Russian government receives from 5 to 15
per cent of the oil and alternate fields are in the hands of Russian
interests. Within five years Japan has been able to meet about 20 per
cent of her requirements from these drillings. Many difficulties exist,
however; the ports of the island are blocked by ice for nine months;
the coasts are too shallow to accommodate small tankers; and the wells
do not gush but must be pumped. Since 1930, government aid has
been given Japanese companies in acquiring oil properties abroad. A
concession has recently been secured in Dutch Borneo.

Copper production is second in value to that of coal. For many
years Japan was second, though a poor second, to the United States
as a producer of copper. At the present, however, copper production
has greatly declined and Japan is importing twenty thousand tons
and exporting only three thousand tons a year. The possession of
copper, however, is of great value to Japan, especially in the electrical
equipment industry, which will increase in importance as the water
power resources are developed. It makes little difference whether
the domestic supply is adequate or not, for copper, small in bulk, can
be transported without burdensome charges. In fact, neither Germany
nor Great Britain produces any copper, and the former, especially, has
become a world leader in copper-consuming industries. Some gold
and silver are mined in Japan, though in insufficient amounts to be

of importance in the financial system. Small quantities of lead, zinc, and tin are extracted, but it is unlikely that the supply will ever overhaul the demand. Since these metals, like copper, are readily transported their scarcity does not hamper industrial growth.

Sulphur, which is abundant owing to the volcanic nature of the islands, is the most important non-metal, non-fuel resource. The fact that it is difficult and dangerous to transport sulphuric acid adds to the importance of this element. Sulphur is one of the basic industrial minerals, and because of the intensive type of agriculture prevailing in Japan it is important in the production of fertilizers. At one time Japan exported sulphur in considerable quantities, but recently, with the opening up of the beds of Texas and Louisiana, the United States has obtained a virtual monopoly of the export market. The Japanese, if they see fit, can secure American sulphur at a lower cost than domestic sulphur. With the exception of sulphur and coal derivatives Japan has few of the raw materials of the chemical industries. Even in the case of common salt, it is necessary to import large amounts to supplement the domestic supply, which is obtained by evaporating sea water.

Japan is reaching out to the mainland of Asia for coal and iron. Korea, as a colonial possession, Manchukuo, by virtue of leases and concessions, and the Yangtze Valley in China proper, by means of commercial and financial penetration, are all being tapped to supply Japan with the essentials of industry. In Korea, Japan possesses a territory which has large reserves of fair grade iron ore. These deposits, which are situated along the northwest coast in easy communication, send a third of their product to the iron and steel mills of Japan. The remainder is used in Korean mills which are controlled by Japanese. Though the production of pig iron in Korea has grown from forty thousand tons in 1918 to 130,000 tons in 1928, this increase has no great significance. The great handicap of the Korean iron and steel industry is the lack of coal. The output of coal there is about 400,000 tons, but to keep the mills running, it was necessary to import a million tons in 1927 from Japan, China, and Manchuria. The only anthracite deposits in the Japanese Empire are in Korea, and the greater part of the output is converted into a smokeless fuel for the use of the Japanese navy.

Failing to provide for her wants in Korea, Japan has turned her attention to Manchuria. As has been explained in the chapter on China,

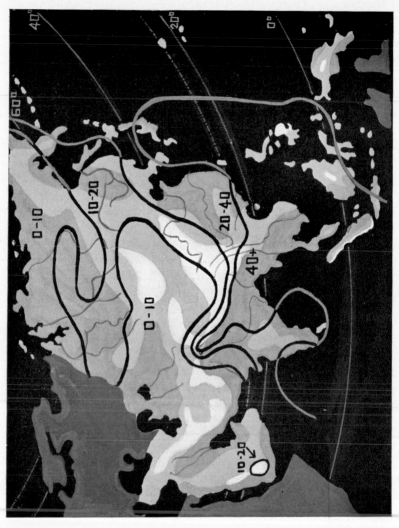

PLATE IX. ASIA—JULY RAINFALL

Manchuria is a rich agricultural province producing both food and industrial crops. Japan can use the food, cotton, and timber of Manchuria, but she has been far more interested in exploiting the coal and iron resources there. Japan controls over half the Manchurian coal lands, but the same condition exists with regard to their coal as to her own. The supply is small in proportion to Japanese needs and only a little of it can be converted into metallurgical coke. Manchurian coal, however, can be profitably utilized in developing the railways and in supporting a variety of manufactures along the South Manchurian line.

Manchuria has large iron ore deposits. Yet these deposits are too low in quality to warrant the shipping of any large amount of ore to Japan. An effort is being made to convert the ore into pig iron and export the product to Japan. This effort has not met with success, for the Manchurian plants are operating at a great financial loss. In 1929, 60 per cent of the pig iron consumed in Japan was imported from British India. Japan's pig iron imports from India are over 75 per cent larger than those from Manchuria, and in spite of the very long haul are cheaper by two or three dollars a ton at the port of unloading. Undoubtedly, there is another consideration and a weighty one; the Imperial relation to Manchuria. The Japanese lease on Liaotung, the commercial outlet of Manchuria, expires at the end of the century. The right of operation of the South Manchurian Railway expires at the same time. Recently, however, with the creation of the nominally-autonomous state of Manchukuo Japan obtained a virtual protectorate over Manchuria. In view of Chinese hostility, the inundation of Manchuria with Chinese peasants, and the feeling of several world powers, the security of the Japanese investment there is still precarious. Control of Manchukuo will help to balance the equation of food and population in Japan proper, where potential food resources are few, but it will do little to provide Japan with the mineral resources she lacks. It is evident that Japan no longer looks to Manchuria for the solution of her industrial problem; more and more she is examining the possibilities of China and more distant lands bordering on the Pacific.

78. Climate

Japan has been called the "Britain of the East," but this analogy is a poor one geographically as well as industrially. Though both are island kingdoms lying adjacent to great mainlands, the climatic influences are so dissimilar that the agricultural responses of the two people vary widely. The larger portion of the Japanese Empire lies in the latitudes 30° to 45° N. while the British Isles are situated in latitudes 50° to 60° N. Japan, therefore, does not lie wholly in the temperate zone. Secondly, the British Isles have a Maritime type of climate; in other words, their climate is governed solely by oceanic influences. Japan, however, in spite of its insular position, is affected somewhat by the climatic conditions that prevail on the adjoining continental land mass.

By virtue of its insular location Japan enjoys a higher winter temperature than the adjoining mainland coast. Vladivostok has a mean January temperature of 5°, Sapporo in Japan, 21°; Shanghai has a mean of 38°, Kagoshima in Japan, 45°.[1] The west coast of Honshu is warmer than the east coast in winter; as a result tea and other tropical plants flourish further north on the west coast. This is not what one would expect since the west coast of Japan is exposed to cold northwest winds from the continental interior and the east coast is sheltered from those winds. The explanation lies in the course of the ocean currents about Japan. The Kuro Siwo, the great warm current of the Pacific, flows northward along the east coast of China and divides just south of Japan, one branch flowing into the Sea of Japan, the other into the open Pacific. The cold current from the north, the Okhotsk Current, also divides to the north of Japan, sending one branch into the Japan Sea, and the other around the east coast. Since rotational deflection causes currents flowing from the north to keep westward of those flowing from the south, the west coast of Japan is washed by the warm Kuro Siwo while the cold Okhotsk Current hugs the coast of China. The northern current adheres closely to the east coast of the islands causing the winter's cold to be severe as far south as the 37th parallel of latitude. The prevailing northwest winds are considerably warmed upon approaching the west coast but are chilled as they blow over the high snowcapped range of central Japan.

The summer temperatures vary with latitude; in the south the August mean is 80°, in the north it is 65°. The northeast coast of Honshu and the east coasts further north are kept cool by the cold current. The annual range of temperature also varies with latitude but

[1] Examine carefully Plates I, VI, VII, VIII, IX.

again because of Japan's insular position the extremes are not so great as those of China. Hokkaido, the northern island, has four months with a mean temperature below 32°. In the interior the January mean is about 14°. The winter is long and severe, and the weather raw because of the moist air. Southern Japan enjoys very mild winters with a temperature far above the freezing point. Here flourish the palm tree, the orange tree, and the camphor tree. In February, the coast may be sprinkled with flowers, while inland the ice of the lakes is frozen so solidly that fairs are held upon it.

Japan has a modified monsoon type of climate. The northwest winds of winter, already mentioned, are abnormal in character because they are intensified as they blow from the high pressure pole of interior Siberia. Southeast winds are set up in summer in reaction to the low pressure center of the interior of the continent, but these winds are feeble and irregular in comparison with the monsoon of China.

The rainfall of Japan though monsoonal in character varies widely from this type. As in China, summer is the rainy season, but the winters are never dry. The cold, dry, wintry blasts of Asia pick up moisture crossing the Japan Sea and yield a heavy precipitation as they pass over the western slopes of the mountains. The east coast is relatively dry since the winds have lost their moisture in crossing the mountains. The precipitation falls largely in the form of snow. The villages on the western side of the islands are frequently snowbound and their inhabitants can do little work. At times the snowfall exceeds twenty feet.

The west coast of Japan receives more precipitation in winter than in summer. Kanazawa receives thirty-two inches in December, January, and February and only twenty-two inches in June, July, and August. Tokyo on the east coast, however, receives only seven inches during the three winter months. The summer rainfall is brought by the southeast monsoon and is heaviest on the windward coasts of the south and east. Curiously the Japanese monsoon has two maxima of rainfall, one in June and one in September. The causes of this irregularity have never been satisfactorily explained. The first spell is called the *Bai-u* meaning "plum rains," or *Tsuyu,* "period of long continued rains." For the inhabitants this is a period of dampness and unpleasantness. The walls and pavements are always damp and furniture and clothes moldy. Agriculturally, however, the *Bai-u* is very important. The abundant rainfall soaks the rice fields and makes it possible to transplant the seedlings under excellent conditions. This early rainfall is experienced in all Japan south of Hokkaido. It is also perceptible at Hongkong, in parts of the Yangtze basin, in Formosa, and in Korea. It lasts from the middle of June until the middle of July and is heavier than the late July and August rains. The September maximum is due largely to typhoons that pass along the Japanese coasts. They develop over the sea to the east of the Philippines, moving first northwest, then northeast, following the warm waters of the Kuro Siwo Current. Indeed this current is a favorite course of cyclonic depressions and explains the absence of a marked dry season in Japan.

The rainfall over the whole of Japan during the monsoon season is abundant and most heavy along the south and southeast coasts. It is the season of greatest rainfall for all Japan except the west coast of Honshu. The annual total exceeds eighty inches there and on the south coasts of Kyushu and Shokoku. The lowest rainfall is in the north of Hokkaido, where it is less than thirty inches. Around the Inland Sea the surrounding hills reduce the total to forty inches. In Honshu, the main island, the west coast has a heavy rainfall, but the center and the east coast are comparatively dry. This generalization is particularly true of the northern half of the island.

79. Natural Vegetation

The natural vegetation of Japan is forest, and since the topography is very rugged, much of the forest has never been cleared. Nearly half of Japan proper remains under forest. The types of forest vary with respect to latitude and altitude. Southern Japan, south of 39°, is subtropical and the prevailing species are broad-leafed evergreens such as the camphor and evergreen oak. Some deciduous varieties are present and several species of pines. The temperate forests on the slopes overlooking the Sea of Japan on the west and the Pacific on the east are commercially the most important. The temperate forest is a mixture of deciduous and coniferous stands. The "cold" temperate forests cover most of Hokkaido and Karafuto, and are found also in Honshu at altitudes of four to five thousand feet. In Japan proper there are a half million acres of forest land, owned in equal amounts by the state and private individuals.

The coniferous species, especially *sugi*, pine, and *hinoki*, are of value to the Japanese for fuel, in lieu of coal, and in the building and paper industries. Yet the demand is greater than the supply and in recent years Japan has been importing lumber from the United States. In the future, however, Japan will depend for its supply upon the mainland of Asia.

Four industries have arisen from derivatives of the natural vegetation. The bamboo is probably the most important Japanese tree. At present it is planted and cared for as a field crop. The Japanese can construct a whole dwelling from bamboo, the framework, floor, walls, and roof; in addition, it is used for the making of receptacles and utensils of all sorts. The young shoots serve as food. Because of the lack of other resources paper is made to serve many uses. Not only the trees but other forms of vegetation are employed in the manufacture of paper; a cheap paper is made from rice straw, a durable paper from seaweed, and a very strong paper from the bark of a bush called the paper plant (*udo*). Lacking leather, paper is used as a substitute; lacking cheap glass, it is used for window panes. Possibly the combination of bamboo and paper is the least dangerous type of dwelling in an earthquake zone. The lacquer tree is important since the transparent varnish used in lacquer wares is derived from the sap of this tree. Camphor, a resin distilled from the tree of that name which grows in most of Japan, still features prominently in the export trade. Unfortunately, the camphor resources of Japan proper are diminishing at a time when new uses have been found for camphor in the celluloid industry. In Formosa, where the camphor industry is a government monopoly, the careful husbanding of the trees has enabled Japan to control the greater part of the export trade. The French in Cochin-China and the Dutch East India planters are becoming interested in camphor planting. It is now possible to derive more camphor from the leaves and the twigs than from the trunk so that it is unnecessary to destroy the tree. The United States has borrowed the growing of camphor and bamboo from Japan, while the latter is building pulp factories on the American model. Camphor is now grown in Florida and bamboo in the South Atlantic and Gulf States. The Japanese pulp factory at Toamakwai in the forested north island is the largest of its kind in the Orient and supplies half the Japanese demand for pulp. It was equipped with electrical and paper machinery from the United States and was constructed under the direction of an American engineer.

80. Overpopulation and Food Resources

The absolute increase of population in Japan is about 900,000 a year, one that is rivaled only in Russia and the United States. In most countries during recent years the population has grown owing to a decreasing death rate rather than an increasing birth rate. In Japan, however, the increase (34.4 per thousand) is the result of the remarkable fertility of the people, for the death rate (19.9 per thousand) has not declined. This huge augmentation of population is not traditional in Japan. For example, during a whole century from 1740 to 1840, the population was practically stationary, in the neighborhood of 27,000,000. With the advent of Japan upon the world stage there has come the conviction that Japan's safety depends in a measure upon a great population. The large family has become a sacred institution, yet it is no part of the religious or the cultural heritage of the Japanese.

The Japanese approach their problems under no illusions for they are scientifically minded. In terms of rice, their staple food, they have ascertained that a normal annual increase of population, 900,000, necessitates an increase of rice lands to the extent of 133,000 acres a year. During the past twenty years the augmentation has averaged from 25,000 to 35,000 acres. Various solutions come to mind: more intensive agriculture through scientific cropping and mechanized agriculture, the adoption of a lower standard of living, the creation of wealth through industry, an extension of the empire, or, finally, the imposition of checks upon population growth.

The discrepancy between food and population has become manifest only during the past ten years. During the generation preceding 1925 Japan moved rapidly in the direction of an increased standard of living. Taking the years 1890 and 1925 as representative of the limits of a generation, we find that the consumption of the staple grain, rice, had increased by 18 per cent. The consumption of barley and naked barley diminished 26 and 29 per cent respectively, a reduction which meant that thousands were able to substitute a better article of diet for a poorer one. At the same time wheat flour, an import, hence a luxury, began to appear on the tables of the upper classes. The total consumption of these four cereals has increased 11 per cent during the thirty-five year period. Fish, after rice, is regarded as a staple article of food. The increase in fish consumption has been nearly 200 per cent. Meat consumption has been limited to the wealthier classes largely because the killing and eating of livestock was tabu before the opening up of Japan. Yet the per capita increase was from one to four pounds. The Japanese eats nearly four times as much fish as an American while the latter consumes about 150 pounds of meat per annum to the Japanese's four pounds. Sugar, like meat, is a luxury in Japan yet during the thirty-five year period there was an increase of 25 per cent in the consumption of sugar. It is quite clear that not only has Japan been able to meet the demands of a rapidly increasing population without sacrificing her standard of living but also that the standard of living has actually risen. At the present time Japan imports about 15 per cent of the food consumed within the country, and competent observers are of the opinion that she could, if necessary, meet the requirements of the nation. It is the rapid increase of population, an augmentation that cannot be easily checked, that has given rise to the present difficulty.

Japan has a smaller proportion of arable land than any other great nation. Because of the large size of the agricultural population, 5,600,000 farming households, the size of the average holding is only 2.7 acres. Over 90 per cent of the farmers have less than five acres and nearly a third of them engage in some subsidiary occupation. It has been carefully estimated that the arable land can be increased by a third, five million acres, through the reclamation and consolidation of small fields. Yet this effort, if successful, would add only an acre to each holding. The government, however, has no great faith in carrying out such an expensive program for it proposes to add only 75,000 acres a year through reclamation. If this annual increment were to be entirely devoted to the cultivation of food crops, it would be capable of supporting an additional farming population of 150,000. This is a relatively small proportion of the annual increase.

Were it not for the fact that the Japanese are such skillful farmers the solution of the problem might lie along the lines of a more intensive system of agriculture. But it is said that the Japanese can teach the Western farmer much concerning the maintenance of soil fertility. The Japanese farmer obtains a yield of 2,350 pounds of rice per acre; the American farmer obtains about 1,000 pounds. The Japanese farmer carries on rice cultivation without the aid of machinery or domestic animals; from planting to harvesting the work is done by hand. It is now realized that there is a limit to the amount the soil can be made to produce, and that the Japanese have approached that limit may be seen in the slower rate of increase per acre during the last few years.

From what has been said it appears that the mechanization of agriculture is out of the question. Small holdings and rugged terrain render the use of machinery in planting impossible. In fact the mechanization of agriculture in parts of the world such as the United States, Canada, and Russia is likely to upset the agricultural balance in Japan. To permit the dumping of cheap wheat into Japan would have the effect of disengaging the farming class from its occupation. Already the large landowners are complaining that they can obtain no return upon their investment and are asking aid from the government. On the other hand the tenant farmers argue that because of high rents there is not enough money left after the sale of the crop to pay for the labor. Agricultural protection meets with opposition by the manufacturers who assert that high food prices will provoke a rise of wages that will prevent them from competing in the markets of the world. A lower standard of living is obviously out of the question since at best a diet of rice is not very nourishing. The large amount of starch so dilutes the amount of protein consumed that excessively large quantities of rice must be eaten, thus placing a severe strain upon the digestive organs. Diseases of the digestive organs cause more deaths than any other ailment in Japan. It has been suggested that sweet potatoes be grown instead of rice since the food bulk would be slightly greater per acre. Then the land released from rice could be devoted to fresh fruits and vegetables. This solution is not promising since it is certain that the deprivation of rice would be regarded by the people as a lowering of the standard of living. It is apparent that the solution of the problem of overpopulation does not lie in the realm of agriculture.

81. Crops

Japanese agriculture, like Chinese, may be characterized as "garden farming" because of the small size of the holding, and a "hoe culture" because of the extreme simplicity of the methods. Like the Chinese, the Japanese make use of every resource that comes to hand to preserve the fertility of their fields. Farmyard manure, human excreta, fish guano, wood ash, and rice bran are widely used as manures. The Japanese, however, import large quantities of fertilizers—Chilean nitrates and chemical fertilizers, and phosphates from Christmas Island and Oceanica.

Rice and fish are the staples of food. More land is devoted to the cultivation of rice than to all the other cereals and vegetables taken together. In 1927, 318,000,000 bushels of rice were obtained from 7,300,000 acres of land. Since this amount was insufficient to provide for the wants of the people, over 21,000,000 bushels had to be imported. Rice cultivation is almost entirely in irrigated paddy fields, relatively little rice being raised in ordinary dry fields. Rivers and streams supply about 65 per cent of the water for irrigation, reservoirs about 20 per cent, and water carried by hand accounts for the rest. All the work is done by hand, for, as in China, human labor is cheaper than that of the domesticated animal. After the rice has ripened, the fields are drained, and the sheaves are elevated upon bamboo cribs to dry because the ground is moist. The rice, after drying, is threshed by hand. The common method is to draw the stalk through a narrow slit cut in a board. The husk about the kernel is not removed, however, until the time has come to cook the rice. As in all Eastern lands, the kernel is pounded out by using a mallet or a pestle. The Japanese eat "paddy," not polished rice as we do. The polishing destroys the vitamins and leaves only starch. Rice, in Japan, takes the place of potatoes and bread. Since it is impossible to manufacture a bread from rice because of the lack of glutinous content, the rice is simply boiled. Yet rice may be eaten in a variety of ways and can be seasoned according to taste. Dishes combining rice and fish, or more rarely, meat, are popular.

The secondary grain crops are principally rye, wheat, and barley. Unfortunately, the tendency is toward a greater cultivation of rice at the expense of other cereals. Barley is not so popular as rice and is cultivated largely because it will grow under conditions that will not support rice. The barley crop is only a fifth of that of the rice crop. The position of wheat is still more unfavorable: it is only one-fifteenth as large as the rice production. Within the limits of the whole Empire, only bleak Karafuto offers a possibility of extending wheat culture. There it may be possible to cultivate winter wheat. Buckwheat, millet, and maize complete the list of grains.

The soya bean is of increasing importance in Japan, as in China, because it can be utilized either for food or industrial purposes. As a food it is the Eastern substitute for meat, milk, and cheese and acts as a balance to rice in the diet. Other legumes, beans and peas, are widely cultivated for the same purpose but none has the variety of uses of the soya bean. In addition to its use as a vegetable, it yields an oil from which a substitute for butter or lard can be made, and by permitting the meal to ferment in water a substitute for milk is obtained. Even cheeses are made from this "milk." The oil cake made from the soya bean may be used in feeding livestock or as a fertilizer. Some tobacco is raised in Japan for domestic consumption.

Meat is not prominent in the Japanese diet since, in addition to the old tabu upon meat, pasture land is very scarce. In much of the land that might be allocated to pasture, the natural type of vegetation is bamboo which is inedible as far as livestock is concerned. Bamboo is very difficult to combat because of its rapid growth. In spite of the efforts of the government to promote the livestock industry Japan is far behind other nations; there are only 5 per cent as many cattle and horses as people; about 1 per cent as many hogs; and very few sheep and goats.

No account can be taken of the food supply without discussion of the part played by sea food. The continental shelf around Japan is one of the great fishing grounds of the world. Here are found a large variety of fish. Nearly two million people are engaged in fishing, including women and children, and about 400,000 small craft are employed. The value of the catch is greater than that of the British catch, and the by-products, guano and fish fertilizers, are important. Sea weed is marketable and is widely used as a relish for soup and rice or may be manufactured into a jelly. It is also utilized in making isinglass. But fish, above all, is essential as a part of the Japanese diet.

The outer dependencies, principally Formosa and Korea, supply in part the food deficiencies of Japan proper. Over 80 per cent of all Formosa's exports go to Japan, and over 90 per cent of Korea's. From Formosa come welcome supplies of rice and, in addition, sugar, which cannot be grown in Japan proper. From Korea come stores of rice and soya beans. Yet neither Formosa's nor Korea's contribution is sufficient to make Japan independent of foreign food supplies. At present about 15 per cent of her imports are in foods, and at the present rate of population growth, these imports are likely to increase.

The mulberry leaf is by a wide margin the principal industrial crop of Japan. Grain for milling and *saki,* a kind of beer made from rice, are of negligible importance in comparison with raw silk. Silk reeling takes place in every prefecture of Japan, even in Hokkaido, the northerly island. Geography plays a very important part in the extent and distribution of the raw silk production. Cocoons, however, are secondary in importance to food. As the pressure upon the food growing areas has increased, the mulberry has been forced to recede to places where rice cannot be grown. Hence the trees are found principally on lands that are too rugged, too dry, or too porous for rice. The seven mountainous prefectures in central Honshu have attained a preeminent place in the production of raw silk. Yet even here the mulberry is confined to the steep slopes and mountain valleys where the alluvium is too sandy and gravelly for rice growing. Frequently rice is forced to compete with dry crops such as barley, wheat, and less often grapes. The mulberry makes some demands of its own; it is unwise, especially, to plant it in soil that is too sterile, for there exists a definite relationship between soil fertility and the quality and yield of the leaves.

The mulberry, all in all, is very hardy and can withstand the rigorous winter of mountainous regions. In Hokkaido only the spring crop is important, but in central Honshu where the mild seasons are longer the combined summer and autumn crops greatly exceed the spring crop. On the whole the rainfall of Japan is suitable for the cultivation of the mulberry because of the summer maximum. Though the mulberry does not require so much precipitation as rice, yet fairly abundant moisture is necessary to a luxuriant growth of tender leaves.

The silk worm fortunately thrives in the type of climate that is most suitable for the production of its food. The worms are raised in the cottages of the farmers, and though it is possible to regulate to some extent the temperature and humidity, outside atmospheric conditions prevail, for the houses are flimsily built. Conditions are best for rearing worms, as for growing the mulberry, in the mountainous prefectures of central Honshu. In the north of Japan difficulties are encountered in raising the worms because of the cold temperatures. The coastal plains, curiously, are less suitable for the cultivation of the worm than the mountainous area because the dampness hinders the proper storage of the cocoons during the winter.

In addition to favorable environmental conditions the production of the raw silk requires cheap labor. Other regions such as South Africa, eastern Australia, southern Brazil, and the American Atlantic states are suitable for the cultivation of the mulberry and the worm, but raw silk production cannot be undertaken in competition with Japan because of the peculiar economic situation existing in the latter country. The rearing of cocoons is comparable to the home industries carried on in remote rural districts in western Europe. The only visible cost, in the mind of the Japanese farmer, is the expenditure for the egg sheets. The rent of the mulberry land is inconsiderable since rent of the holding is based upon the acreage of arable rice land. Any return over and above these items is reckoned as profit; the labor expended upon the cocoons is never taken into account. Where the land is less arable, the farmer must devote his time to subsidiary occupations, however small the income is.

Most of the labor of sericulture is performed by the women and children. In the reeling of silk, a mechanical process, other regions could compete successfully with Japan. The labor obstacle, however, is insuperable when it comes to the rearing of cocoons, for not only is cheap labor required but labor of the most skilled type. The rearing of cocoons demands painstaking care, day and night, over a long period of time. During incubation the eggs must be kept for several months at an average temperature of 64°. The worms, when finally hatched, have voracious appetites. Each pound of eggs requires about ten tons of leaves. After seven weeks of feeding the worm is fully grown and has become a caterpillar. Each caterpillar must be placed by hand on clean straw in a suitable position. Great delicacy of manipulation is necessary else the loss will be exceedingly great. The Japanese, trained from childhood, acquire a sense of manipulation that has baffled prospective rivals. As yet the West has discovered no labor-saving device in this sphere. "It is peculiar," writes Professor Orchard, "that this industry, turning out an article of luxury, should be a parasitic industry dependent upon unpaid or underpaid labor from the production of raw materials in Japan to the final weaving of cloth in American centers where the women and children of miners and steel workers are used in the mills."

82. Industry

The modernization of Japan which has been going on since 1854 is represented in the economic field by the change from agriculture to an economy that combines agriculture with diversified manufacturing. This rapid transformation well deserves the epithet "phenomenal." Recently, however, there are indications that the industrial growth of Japan is subject to rather strict limitations. In the field of raw materials, as we have seen, the iron ore reserves are inadequate to support an industrial plant of even moderate size, and there is practically no coking coal available in Japan. It is becoming clear also that neither Korea, Manchukuo, nor China can supply these deficiencies. A longer haul would only increase the costs of manufacturing, and dependence upon remote lands would serve to render Japan defenseless in time of war. Of all the countries of Asia, Japan is making the most determined effort to industrialize, yet Japan is poorest in basic resources of iron ore and coking coal.

Japan possesses one resource necessary to industrialization, water power. Her reserves are exceeded only by those of the United States, Russia, Norway, and Sweden. Her developed water power resources are surpassed only by those of the United States and Italy, the latter country having reached the limit of its development. Since, in Japan, all the power sites are the property of the government, regardless of ownership of the stream banks, development proceeds without waste and costly competition. On the basis of stream flow for the "lower" six months fourteen million horse power are available. Since 1891, when the first hydro-electric power plant was erected, nearly three million horse power have been developed. To-day 60 per cent of the electric power production is derived from water power. Most of the installations are not in the leading industrial area, Osaka, but in the mountainous area of eastern and central Honshu, tributary to Tokyo. The Osaka industrial area is older than the Tokyo area, and the dependence upon steam plants for power was established before the use of hydro-electric power on a large scale began. Osaka, situated on the Inland Sea, is nearer the coal fields of Kyushu than Tokyo. The abundance of hydro-electric power in addition to aiding industry has done much to raise the standard of living. Electric lighting has become available throughout Japan, even in the rural districts. Electric power is more and more employed in transportation, and eventually the whole railway system will be electrified.

It should be realized, however, that water power cannot overcome the deficiencies of Japanese industry. Because of the scarcity of coal this resource cannot be developed to its fullest capacity. Furthermore manufacturing must compete with other economic activities for the use of power. Transportation, lighting, and scientific agriculture are already making large demands upon a limited store of power. In addition to the ordinary uses of power about the farmyard, electric pumps for draining and irrigating and power for the reeling of silk are essential needs. Fortunately the demands of agriculture coincide with the period of maximum generation, during the rainy season, and provide a market for the seasonal surplus of power. It has been estimated that the power supply derived from coal and water power can be increased, at most, only 60 per cent. The power resources would then be small, not comparable to those of the great industrial states of the Western world. At present the water power development in Japan is similar in influence to the employment of coal in British industry many decades ago.

The transportation problem in Japan has been solved through the direction of the government. In 1907, after a preliminary period of sporadic building, the railroads were nationalized. Since that time the government has extended the trunk lines into untouched sections of the country, has built connecting links where necessary, and has unified the whole system. In 1927, railway construction was responsible for nearly 30 per cent of the outstanding national debt; an amount equal to that incurred for military purposes. Private ownership has not been abandoned; in fact since 1907 private lines have been increased by means of guarantees and subsidies from 450 miles to 3,500 miles. The activities of private companies, however, have been confined to the construction of local roads, strictly in accord with the plans of national development. To-day Japan has nearly twelve thousand miles of road; a mileage greater than any Asiatic state except India [1] and comparable to that of smaller European states such as Italy. The means of communication—telegraph and telephone —have been developed rapidly by means of government construction and operation.

The Japanese industries fall roughly into two classes, the textile manufactures, and all others. The textile industries in order of importance are silk reeling, cotton spinning, cotton weaving, silk weaving, woolen and linen manufactures, and the finishing of cloth. These industries employ half of all the workers in the factories and contribute half the value of all manufactures. They account, also, for 70 per cent of Japanese exports. Their relatively low standing in power consumed and in capital invested arises from the character of their processes: these industries require relatively small plants and light machinery consuming little power. The statistical summaries, however, present an imperfect picture of the volume of the textile

---

[1] India has 54,000 miles, mainly state owned.

industries because they take into account only the factory production. It should be realized that, with the exception of the spinning of yarn, the textile industries are carried on in farm houses and in small workshops as subsidiary occupations of the rural populace. This factor, for example, explains the apparent discrepancy between textile manufactures and textile exports.

The reeling of silk is the foremost of Japanese industries. It employs over 400,000 hands, a fifth of the factory workers; and accounts for 12 per cent, in value, of all manufactures. Its importance is due to the fact that it draws its raw materials entirely from within the country. Since the beginning of modern industry in Japan, silk reeling has furnished 40 per cent of the exports, fully twice that of its nearest rival, the cotton manufacturing industry. Silk reeling is distinguished in Japanese industry for another reason. It is located in the mountain core of Honshu, the cocoon-producing area. All the other industries are concentrated in the main industrial area extending along the south shore of the island; an area conspicuous for its dense population, its excellent communications, its excellent harbors, and its accessibility to basic raw materials such as iron and coal. The silk industry, however, possesses none of these advantages. Central Honshu is far from the sea and difficult of access by land. Many of the filiatures are located in steep-sided valleys, tapped by railroads built at great cost. One important filiature near Nogoya is still using horse and cart to carry its output four miles to the nearest railroad. Until recently it was impossible to provide a safe means for transporting the cocoons, which, though light, are perishable. Though this difficulty has been overcome, the availability of water power has been a deciding factor in favor of maintaining the filiatures in the districts where the cocoons are produced.

With the possible exception of China, where accurate statistics are lacking, Japan produces more raw silk that any other nation. Her export, however, is three times as great as that of China and five times as large as that of Italy, her chief Western rival. Japan has secured this position by developing steam filiatures, and through the persistent efforts of the government to improve the quality of the raw silk. Though silk reeling is a comparatively simple mechanical process requiring little power and no complicated machinery, China lacks the necessary direction to assimilate the cost-reducing aids of modern industry.

The weaving of silk tissues does not rank high among Japanese manufactures. Even among the textiles it is exceeded by cotton spinning and cotton weaving, in addition to silk reeling. Ninety per cent of Japanese silk exports are raw silk. For two reasons it is probable that Japanese silks will never dominate the world markets. In the first place silk fineries are a luxury; consequently both quality and design are subject to the fancies of style. The Japanese, alien in culture, have no comprehension of the Western fickleness in fashions, and imitative as they are, Western styles are prone to change too quickly for them to keep pace. The second obstacle is equally formidable. The countries possessing silk manufactures—France, Germany, Switzerland, and the United States—are able to protect their producers by means of prohibitive tariffs. The United States, for example, though making no raw silk, has built up a silk manufacturing industry employing 130,000 workers and producing goods valued at three-fourths of a billion dollars annually. It has the advantage of tapping the richest market in the world and enjoys a monopoly of that market by virtue of its high tariff.

Cotton spinning and weaving rank second and third respectively both in number of workers employed and in the value of the product. Cotton spinning is entirely a factory industry and, since it is entirely divorced from agriculture, it is a measure of the industrialization of Japan. From a single small mill in 1863 the spinning industry has grown to a huge plant of two hundred factories and over 200,000 workers. Yet in comparison with the Western states the Japanese advance has not been phenomenal. Her spindles are not equal in number to those of the industrial leaders, Great Britain, United States and Germany, nor even to those of France, Russia, and India. Bristol County, Massachusetts, has more than six million spindles thus rivaling Japan's 6,500,000. Two American states, North and South Carolina, entering the spinning industry in 1880, have each increased in the number of spindles as rapidly as Japan. India, with nine million spindles has advanced as rapidly as Japan though her yarn output is less because the Indian mills do not operate at night.

Cotton weaving has not reached the same degree of industrialization as cotton spinning. Over a fourth of the looms are operated by hand, and the small scale of the industry is revealed by the fact that the average number of looms per establishment is only five. If domestic workers are added to factory workers, the total number of weavers would greatly exceed the number of spinners. The spinning mill operatives are full time workers while many of the weavers engage in other occupations. Cotton weaving is important in Japanese industry because of the value of its export. Japan exports more cloth than any country except Great Britain. Most of the cloth, however, is of a coarse variety suitable only for the Asiatic market.

In summing up we have seen that Japan has made tremendous strides toward industrialization in the field of textiles. Silk reeling and cotton spinning have been mechanized, and cotton weaving though far from being a factory industry has made its mark in the export trade. The Japanese silk cloth industry cannot overcome the peculiar obstacles of competition imposed by the Western world and is as yet unimportant. Where the article of consumption is fairly standardized, such as in the silk hose industry, the Japanese have been able to make some progress.

The other major industries of Japan are shipbuilding, brewing, and the weaving of mixed silk cloth. The brewing industry includes not only the alcoholic drinks, beer and *sake,* but also the brewing of protein food products, *shoyu* and *miso,* made from the soya bean. The latter activity is essential in a country where the consumption of meat is strictly limited. The shipbuilding industry does not stand on its own legs. It has been earmarked as an essential national industry because of its importance in defense and trade, and as such, receives large subsidies from the state. The other industries worthy of note are the manufacture of electrical machinery, printing and bookbinding, the weaving of woolen cloth, and the manufacture of paper and pulp. This list of industries does not include the manufacture of matches, pottery, bamboo mats, and lacquer ware. Some of these are well known in the world trade and others because they are peculiarly Japanese activities. Most of them, it will be observed, are household industries.

One weakness may be noticed before taking leave of the subject of Japanese industry: the subordinate position of the metal industries. Among the industrial leaders of the world primary metallurgy is regarded not only as an essential but as the basic industry. Heavy industries provide the sinews for the other industries. Without the capacity to produce iron and steel in large quantities no nation has ever become a manufacturing state of great note. Over half the workers of Japan engaged in the primary refining of metals are employed by the Imperial Steel Works which produces four-fifths of the pig iron of Japan. The smaller plants are having a difficult time in spite of liberal subsidies. In addition to erecting the Imperial plant the government has had to expend $70,000,000 to keep it going. An additional $25,000,000 has been spent in subsidizing the Hanyehp'ing Iron and Coal Company whence comes most of the ore for the Imperial Steel Works. The deposits of this company are situated along the Yangtze in China, and in view of the political condition of China, it is doubtful whether the government loans can ever be liquidated. At present the pig iron output of Japan is exceeded by that of Belgium, and even Luxembourg, while the production of coal is less than half that of France.

83. Foreign Trade

Japan exports mainly two classes of goods, manufactured wares and raw silk. Each constitutes about 40 per cent of the total. As raw silk is the product of a simple mechanical process, it cannot be considered as other than raw material. Yet in export value it equals all other manufactured articles, i. e. cotton cloth, iron and steel products, novelties, pottery, and clothing. Since 1900 Japan has exhibited progress in manufacturing but she is by no means a successful industrial state. During the present century exports have exceeded imports during only six years, four of which coincided with the World War when industry was temporarily dislocated in the West.

Progress in industrialization will depend largely upon Japan's ability to expand her foreign trade. A peculiar situation exists in that Japanese industry is dependent upon foreign sources for its raw materials, with the exception of silk, and upon foreign markets for the disposal of its products. Thus the cotton spinning industry obtains all its raw cotton abroad, the woolen industry three-fourths of its raw material, the iron and steel industry over 90 per cent of its iron ore and nearly half its pig iron. The engineering and chemical industries are in a like state of dependence. Even food and fertilizers must be imported. Japan, poor in raw materials, has little besides an abundance of cheap labor upon which to erect an industrial structure.

The difficulty of obtaining a favorable trade balance increases with the rapid growth of the population. At the present time Japan is straining every effort to export her wares. Ninety per cent of her raw silk is sent abroad and a fourth of the silk tissues; nearly two-thirds of her cotton manufactures are exported and a third of the pottery ware and tea. Yet, since the World War, imports have exceeded exports annually by large amounts. "This unfavorable trade balance is part of a vicious circle of economic endeavor wherein the poverty of resources necessitates the import of raw materials; the excess of imports stimulates industry to develop an export trade to balance the account; and this development of industry for supplying export products increases the import demand still further."

The reduction of imports is impossible. About 70 per cent is in necessary raw materials or materials for further manufacture. Half the remainder is in manufactured goods, half in food products. Although there is some export of food, food importation is nearly three times as great as export. Food production is lagging as population steadily increases. The pressure upon the land for food will not permit the undertaking of cotton-growing. This situation is paralleled in Korea, which was once regarded as a potential cotton grower. Absolute exploitation of Manchukuo will not solve the cotton problem, for it has been estimated that a fully matured cotton growing program in Manchukuo will reduce cotton imports from India and the United States by only 20 per cent. The sheep growing industry is in the same plight. Sheep growing is not an industry suited to a densely populated country. Furthermore the mountain pastures of Japan cannot be utilized because the native growth of bamboo, which produces inflammation of the stomach, is fatal to sheep. Machine tools, iron and steel, and pig iron constitute 10 per cent of Japan's total imports and in view of past performances it seems likely that these importations cannot be diminished. Drugs and chemicals make up an additional 11 per cent of Japanese imports. The principal members of this class are rubber, which cannot be produced in Japan, and fertilizers like sulphate of ammonia and nitrate of soda, which will be needed more and more as the soil is exhausted. The same comment applies to petroleum and timber, which constitute 7 per cent of all imports. Japan is already purchasing 75 per cent of her petroleum abroad. Yet the imports of Japan must first satisfy the wants of her own population and secondly provide the materials out of which her export commodities are manufactured.

Japan cannot reduce her imports, hence the only way out is to enlarge her industrial plant so as to increase her export trade. Only an expansion of the cotton textile trade will provide a solution. Raw silk brings great wealth to its producers and to Japan as a nation, but this huge export is in a sense the dissipation of a resource that might have been the basis of a gigantic silk tissue industry. Even the position of the Japanese raw silk market is not impregnable: the increasing development of the artificial silk industry is one threat, and the growth of raw silk production in China, a second. About 95 per cent of Japan's raw silk is absorbed in the United States, where artificial silk is making the most rapid strides. In the field of cotton textiles the market is more diversified; 46 per cent going to China and 34 per cent to other Oriental markets. Here the Japanese enjoy certain tangible advantages; the distance is less, and the understanding of the peculiar wants of the Asian consumer quite clear. During the World War Japan was enabled to supply a great part of Asia, the outstanding potential cotton market of the world, with her textiles; and once established, she has been able to retain a large part of the advantage. Japan has prospects of competing successfully in Africa and has certainly marts in the Dutch East Indies, Malaya, and the Philippines.

On the other hand there are influences that operate against any large extension of the textile industry. Although the cotton goods trade with India has advanced rapidly since the World War, the British will not permit too great inroads upon a lucrative market over which they exercise political control. Great Britain still retains over 80 per cent of the import trade of India. In addition, the Hindu textiles continue to develop. At the present moment India possesses more spindles than Japan. With cheaper labor and a vast home market to exploit, the Indian mill owners are in an enviable position. The Chinese also are nurturing a budding textile industry; and although their spindle capacity is little more than 50 per cent of the Japanese, their textile output has increased 250 per cent since the World War. A third of the spindles and looms are owned by the Japanese who appreciate the advantages of nearness to the market and the supply of raw material. The textile industry of Japan has been and will be peculiarly sensitive to the political relationship between Japan and China. The Chinese, lacking military strength, have been able to cope effectively with their oppressors by means of the economic boycott. Seven times since the beginning of the century this weapon has been employed to hold the Japanese at bay. A cessation of orders from China is immediately felt throughout the whole of the delicately ordered economic structure of Japan, whose textile exports are the veritable balance wheel.

Besides the raw silk and textiles, which account for 70 per cent of the export trade, the only industries capable of expansion are pottery and glassware. The chief market for these products is in the United States, and if the Japanese are successful in meeting the demands of fashion or in creating a demand for the Japanese motif, growth seems certain. The demand for aquatic products is limited to China while the demand for tea has fallen off sharply in Great Britain and Russia. Most of the tea cargoes go to the United States. The match trade has declined because of the superior product issued under the auspices of Swedish interests. The refining of raw sugar is a relatively new industry in Japan and with the newly found patronage of China it is likely to flourish within limited bounds. Among the minor exports is a group of articles, peculiarly Japanese, for which there has always existed a small though steady demand. The most popular articles of this trade are straw braids, matting, lamps, lacquer ware, umbrellas, tooth brushes, and iron ware. These articles are subsidiary to agriculture and their production will undoubtedly be speeded up with the introduction of small motors in the cottages of the farmers.

CHAPTER X

RUSSIA: AN EXPERIMENT IN GEOGRAPHICAL ADAPTATION

84. Introduction

Geographically Russia is dominated by the Eurasian land mass with its marked fluctuations in temperature and rainfall. Only the meager Baltic lands may be said to "face west" climatically. For the rest, with small exception, the winter is the season of diminishing rainfall and sharply declining temperatures. Practically all the Soviet territory lies within the zone of the Westerly winds which carry moisture from the Atlantic. True, the cyclones penetrate far into Siberia, but their frequency decreases in proportion to their remoteness from the sea. In consequence the rainfall decreases gradually from west to east, imposing limitations upon agriculture and population.

The topographical features of Soviet Russia have little effect upon its climatic régime. The Great Lowland Plain of Eurasia extends from the Atlantic to the Pacific with monotonous uniformity. No gigantic ranges such as the American Sierras impede the progress of the cyclone-bearing Westerlies. The Urals are in no sense a climatic barrier for their average elevation is but two thousand feet. In central Asia the Soviet boundaries skirt the high plateaus and mountains. That part of Russia is comparatively dry, not because it lies in a rain shadow but because of its vast distance from the Atlantic.

The Great Plain of Russia is divisible into three large concentric belts: forest, steppe, and desert. The location of these belts and the interplay of the human environments which they have induced is the key to the history of Russia. Nearly two-thirds of the Soviet territory lies in the great northern forest. This belt extends north of a line running approximately through Kiev, Kazan, Tomsk, and Irkutsk. Most of the forest is coniferous, *taiga*, but along its southwestern borders in Europe, where moisture is more plentiful and the growing season longer, deciduous varieties are common. The steppe occupies a broad belt south of the forest; in European Russia most of the land not under forest is steppe; in Western Siberia, however, the southern continental desert of Turkestan limits its range; and in Eastern Siberia it is bound narrowly between the *taiga* and the high plateaus of central Asia. The northern half of the steppe, the central grassland region, has always been a more favorable environment for man than the southern half, the dry grassland region, for its rainfall is greater and its black soil, *chernozem,* is much richer. The desert belt includes most of Turkestan. It extends also about the northern edge of the Caspian, and extreme dryness is characteristic also of the lower Ural and Volga basin lands.

The inhabitants of this vast interior were originally nomads wandering about the steppe with their flocks. In the course of time, agriculture developed along the edge of the forest, and slowly villages and towns arose in the areas adjacent to such clearings. First Novgorod, then Moscow,[1] further west, attained political hegemony. Agriculture gave a solidarity and centralization, which nomadism, in spite of its spectacular though short-lived conquests, could not provide. Eventually stabilized government brought the inhabitants of the steppe under control, and the best soil areas were turned to agriculture.

The forest yielded more slowly to economic development than the steppe. Only in recent centuries and at the price of stupendous efforts has Russia been able to advance through the forest zone to the Baltic. Petrograd, now Leningrad, symbolizes Russia's triumph. Yet, because the steppe and its rivers, the arteries of contact and commerce, pointed toward the south, the religious and other attributes of Russian civilization remained Eastern, rather than Western, in form and substance. Not until late in the nineteenth century did Russia make a sustained effort to adopt the industrial devices and the political outlook of a modern European state.

To-day Russia functions through Moscow, and Leningrad has had to forego its privilege as capital of the Russian state and assume the humbler rôle of Russia's western port. Moscow is the true geographical capital of Russia by virtue of its location between the forest and the steppe. Furthermore, it is the centrum where all that is indigenous in Russian culture has been molded. The transformation now taking place in Russian life and economy must first receive the sanction of Moscow, for Moscow is Russia.

[1] Moskva.

Under the Soviet government a supreme effort is being made to adapt the resources of Russia to the fundamental needs of the people. Consciously or unconsciously all modern states attempt to do the same thing. In the United States, for example, there is a fruit belt, a corn belt, and a wheat belt. In other words, up to a certain point, the agricultural adaptation to environment naturally coincides with a proper development of the resources of a state. Yet even in the United States, there seems to be much maladjustment. Where land is suited to several crops, the farmer will plant what appears to be the most likely money crop. The alternative crop, calling for a heavier capital investment, is frequently neglected with the consequence that overproduction of the staple results in great loss to the whole community. Similarly the mineral and power resources of a nation may be heedlessly exploited. Yet what is wasted to-day under a system of unrestricted competition may be of untold value a few generations hence.

Russia is in a position to guard against such maladjustments because the institution of private property has been abolished. The government can dictate the manner in which the resources shall be developed. The programs that have been laid down for the development of agricultural and mineral resources seem wise. The country has been divided into agricultural zones, and it is intended that each section shall raise the crop or variety of live stock best suited to the climate and soil of that area. The Ukraine, formerly the granary of Russia, will soon raise no wheat because flax, the sunflower seed, and other industrial crops can be grown there to the better advantage of the whole country. No longer will the valuable irrigated lands of Turkestan be utilized for grain production but they will be devoted entirely to cotton planting. In the same manner will the mineral and power resources be developed. Coal, for example, will be burned at the mines because it is more economical to transmit power than to transport coal. No one will question the wisdom of such a rational system of national economy.

The Russians, through a curious turn of affairs, are in an enviable position. The Revolution and subsequent events have enabled the Soviet government to wipe the slate clean. They can build from the bottom, and if they build wisely, they will attain in the sphere of geographical adaptation an adjustment unparalleled in human annals. None can predict the success of the plans that have been drawn up.

Miracles are rare in the affairs of men, and a succession of miracles is needed for the Russians to attain their ends. Not only is the country laboring under the handicaps of poverty and ignorance, but its affairs are in the hands of a bureaucracy which is revealing all the frailties and few of the virtues necessary for such an experiment.

From the point of view of adaptation to geographical environment, then, an interesting experiment is going on in Russia. The paper program is excellent and several factors favor its ultimate success. As part of the general socialistic plan of reconstruction it has a spiritual bias, for Bolshevism has an appeal to the younger Communists approximating religious fanaticism. But even more significant is the necessity for success. The Soviet government must above all prove itself able to feed, clothe, and provide the necessities of life for 160,000,000 people. If it fails in this respect, not only will Bolshevism fail, but Russia will be plunged into chaos. Under such circumstances, Stalin and the other leaders are exerting themselves feverishly to make the economic program a success. To understand more fully the economic problem and the environmental adaptation which it entails, it is necessary to view at close range the geography of Russia.

85. Climate

In spite of the fact that Russia embraces about one-seventh of the land area of the globe the climatic controls are few and readily comprehended. First, all the country but a very small part lies north of parallel 40°, thus establishing for Russia the marked seasons, winter and summer, common to the temperate zone.[1] Secondly, as has been hinted, the size of the land mass, rather than such features as shape and altitude, are responsible for the accentuation of the temperatures and the diminution of the rainfall. Any discussion, therefore, of the climatic conditions prevailing in Russia must center about a precise measuring of the effects of the land mass.

During the winter, distance from the sea rather than latitude regulates the temperature régime in Russia. At Verkhoyansk in the northeast of Siberia, three thousand miles from the Atlantic, the mean January temperature is −59°, the most extreme temperature found anywhere, not excluding the poles. The Pacific exerts no

[1] Examine carefully Plates I, VI-IX, XVIII-XXI.

moderating influence because the winds are off-shore winds. The Westerly Winds, however, because of the unobstructed nature of the topography, moderate the continental temperatures of Russia for hundreds of miles inland. Nevertheless, practically the whole of Russia has a mean January temperature below freezing. Only southern Crimea and the southeastern shores of the Caspian have a mean January temperature above the freezing point. In Georgia and Transcaucasia where much of the land is mountainous the temperature is below 32°. The northeast shores of the Caspian (47° N.) have a colder winter temperature than Leningrad (60° N.). All of Siberia has a January temperature below 0° except the south Pacific coastal strip, but even at Vladivostok the January mean is only 5°. Northeastern European Russia and the whole of Siberia have experienced temperatures of −40°, and all central Siberia below −60°. Verkhoyansk has the dubious honor of having had the lowest temperature ever recorded, −90°.

The Siberian winter is not unbearably cold in spite of the low temperatures. The air is dry, invigorating, and frequently calm. The inhabitants are able to protect themselves adequately by wearing heavy furs. Central Europe, with damp winds and temperatures which oscillate about the freezing point, has a winter that is much more cruel and exacting. Russians dread only the great snow storms. Wild winds such as the *buran* from the interior, or the *purga* from the tundra, sweep these storms through the steppes of Siberia and South Russia. The thick snow is picked up and whirled about and the cold is extremely bitter. The penalty of losing one's way is likely to be death.

The Russian winter is very long; in central Asia freezing weather lasts for seven months or longer, from September until April. The ground is covered with snow, the rivers and lakes are frozen over, and the only means of travel is by sledge. The rivers of northern Russia are frozen over for at least six months; those of central Russia, including the middle and upper Volga, for five months; and even in the west the Dniester and the middle Vistula are icebound for three months. A greater handicap for Russia is the freezing of her ports. For many centuries much of Russia's energy in foreign affairs has been directed toward gaining an outlet to open water. Even the Black Sea ports are frozen over part of the year, during January and February. The Sea of Azov is frozen over entirely during mid-winter. In the west, the Gulf of Finland, the outlet of Leningrad, is closed from early November until the beginning of April, over four months. On the Arctic coast between Varanger Fjord and the White Sea lies the Murman coast. Here, because of the moderating influence of the Atlantic Drift, there is no fixed ice. Only during the coldest winters is this coast frozen up for more than a few weeks. The Soviet government is preparing to take advantage of these conditions by developing Murmansk 69° N), at the head of the sheltered Kola Bay into a great port. It is advertised as the most northerly port of the world. During the World War, Alexandrovsk in the same vicinity was utilized because of the impossibility of shipping from Archangel,[1] which is frozen up half the year. Odessa on the Black Sea and Vladivostok on the Pacific, though they freeze up at intervals during the winter, are kept open by means of ice breakers.

The amount and distribution of the rainfall are of greatest importance to Russia since it is primarily an agricultural country. Because of the flat relief the amount of precipitation is very uniform. Most of Russia has less than twenty inches of rainfall. In the west the line of twenty-inch rainfall extends as far inland as Moscow, but in the east it is closely restricted to the Pacific coast. In fact, only the Pacific provinces of Sikhotalin and Kamchatka experience an annual rainfall exceeding twenty inches. The Pacific coast is damp and cool in summer, but in the winter it is less disagreeable than the interior where strong northwest winds prevail. The Amur Valley receives a heavy precipitation during the summer and much of the basin is water-logged; in the winter there is little rain because the low pressure indraught has ceased. Before examining in detail the rainfall of the great central belt, attention should be called to the mountain types of climate existing in the Caucasus. Georgia has very cold winters, notwithstanding its latitude, and hot and rainy summers. The eastern Black Sea coast, with an annual precipitation exceeding sixty inches, is the rainiest part of all Russia. The low pressure system that forms over the water causes south and southeast winds to precipitate moisture upon the windward slopes. Russia also has a Mediterranean belt which includes the southern part of Crimea

[1] Arkhangelsk.

and some of the eastern Black Sea coast. The Crimea is a true Mediterranean type, with mild, rainy winters, hot sunny summers and subtropical vegetation and crops.

Reverting to what has been termed the great central belt, which includes that portion of Russia extending from the Polish border

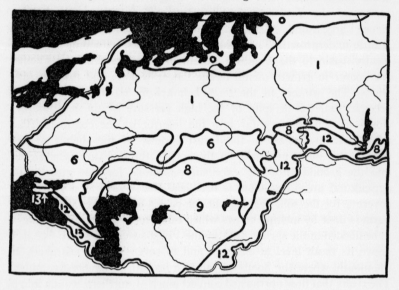

FIG. 12—NATURAL AGRICULTURAL REGIONS OF SOVIET RUSSIA
(*After C. F. Marbut*)

0—The Tundra Region   8—Dry Grassland Region
1—Northern Forest Region   9—Desert Plains Region
6—Central Grassland Region   12—Mountainous Region
              13—South Caucasus Region

to the Amur basin, two facts stand out: first, that the total amount of rainfall is scanty, and secondly, that most of the precipitation occurs during the summer. The tundra borders the Arctic, extending inland for several hundred miles. Here, though the winters are not as extreme as in the interior, the ground is frozen most of the year, for the summers are quite cold. When the surface does thaw for a month or so the ground becomes water-logged and is useless. Between the tundra and the steppe lies the great coniferous forest belt. West of the Urals the rainfall may average as much as twenty inches, east of the Urals from sixteen to ten inches, and in the cold pole belt of Eastern Siberia from twelve to eight inches. The forests diminish with the rainfall, from west to east. The Ob basin is marshy; the firs are interspersed with thick undergrowth and, along the streams, with fringes of willow, alder and poplar. The forests of the Yenisei basin, a relatively dry region, are of great value. Large stands of fir, pine, and spruce predominate, and there is little undergrowth. The East Siberian forests, extending from the Yenisei basin to the Stanovoi Mountains, bordering on the Pacific, are poorer in growth owing to the longer winters and the cold dry winds. The winters in the *taiga* belt are by no means lacking in precipitation, for in spite of the high pressure of the interior, cyclones make their way far into the interior of the continent. The snow remains longest in the forest because of the shelter of the trees. As it melts gradually in the spring, the moisture is absorbed into the ground affording excellent conditions for tree growth. In agricultural areas the snow is beneficial, for it acts as a protective covering for the soil, keeping out the cold. On the other hand, much harm is done by melting snows which cause many of the river valleys to be flooded in the spring. In May the Volga swells to twenty-five feet above its mean level at Samara, and to seven feet at Astrakan, at the mouth, where the floods spread to a breadth of twenty-five miles. The rivers that flow northward convert much of northern Russia into a vast marshland. The snow melts in the south before it does in the north; thus the run-off is over the banks rather than along the channel of the stream.

South of the *taiga* lies the steppe belt. Between the two, lies the narrow wooded-steppe belt where firs have given way to birches, aspens, and willows. The forests occur, however, principally along the stream banks and are interspersed with broad expanses of grassland. The wooded steppe is part of the fertile black soil region. The steppe extends as far west as the Dniester and as far east as Lake Balkhash. Feather grass, *stipa,* is the characteristic plant growth. Trees are rare, flowers are everywhere, and dwarfed, thorny bushes such as broom, hawthorne, and tamarisk, are common. In Eastern Siberia south of Lake Baikal, the steppe reappears sporadically, but this region is as yet relatively uninhabited.

The climate of the steppe duplicates the seasonal extremes of temperature and the scanty rainfall of the forest belt. Relatively little snow settles upon the steppe, however, because it is treeless and windy. As the ground temperature is very low in winter, insufficient moisture is absorbed during the spring to support tree growth. Grasses alone flourish. In the winter the wild animals take refuge in the forest area, because it is there that they find shelter and food. Steppe rainfall amounts to from ten to twenty inches a year, but in Russia the steppe rainfall rarely attains the maximum. Along the coast of the Black Sea from the mouth of the Dniester to the Crimea, for example, the rainfall averages but twelve inches. During the winter precipitation in the steppe is almost impossible because the outblowing winds from the interior high pressure ridge tend to keep out cyclones. During the summer the rainfall comes earlier than in the *taiga,* in May and June rather than in July and August, because the ground heats more rapidly than the air above. These conditions are favorable to convectional overturnings which produce thunderstorms. Unfortunately, these heavy rains are of little benefit to the steppe. Only a small portion of the moisture percolates into the soil; most of it runs off rapidly and is wasted. In parts the surface is so caked with hard mud that it is almost impossible to break it up even with a horse and plow.

On both sides of the Volga, north of the Caspian, and in Turkestan, are huge deserts where the rainfall is less than ten inches a year. During the winter the temperature, except along the southern border, is below the freezing point, while during the summer it is very hot, over 85° in July. The air is very dry and the skies are cloudless. Rainfall is scant in these areas because of their remoteness from the Atlantic. In the far south, the desert's edge falls under the influence of the Northeast Trades, which are drying winds blowing from land to sea. The desert lands of Turkestan, however, are not without human inhabitants. Nomads raise large herds of cattle on the highlands, and large areas are irrigated by water from the streams that flow from the mountains.

86. Topography and Transportation

The population of Soviet Russia is 160,000,000. About 10 per cent lives in Asia and is concentrated in those districts where agriculture flourishes. In fact all the towns of fifty thousand or over excepting

Tashkent and Samarkand in southern Turkestan lie in the steppe. Despite the greater density of population in European Russia, its inhabitants, too, are widely distributed, and the only part of the country with a density exceeding sixty per square mile is the Ukraine. The major task of Soviet Russia is to provide food and clothing for a population which is not only large but which is increasing as rapidly as any in the world. In a scheme which is essentially industrial, transportation will play a large rôle. Facilities for getting grain to the cities and clothing and other manufactured necessities to the country must be provided. Furthermore, adequate transportation is necessary to bring relief to those districts where famine is likely to occur. Finally, since the erection of an industrial régime depends upon securing credits from abroad, and since such credits can be secured only by the sale of easily accessible raw materials such as timber and oil, means must be found for moving goods to ports like Odessa, Leningrad, and Archangel.

It is difficult to realize that in a country as monotonously flat as Russia, there do exist almost insuperable obstacles to transportation. There are a million miles of roadway in Russia, but only forty thousand miles are surfaced, and there are only fifty thousand miles of railroads. This lack of transportation facilities is ascribed to backwardness, ignorance, lack of progress, and inability to obtain capital. The inland waterways, of which Russia has fifty thousand miles, are used in preference to the wagon roads because they afford, for part of the year at least, a superior means of transporting goods. The roads, however, are unimproved mainly because of the heavy outlay of capital necessary for their construction. Road-building in Russia is exceedingly expensive because of obstacles imposed by nature. In the first place, especially in the north, there are large marshy areas. In the south materials for construction, such as stone and wood, are lacking. Everywhere the network of streams and the danger of flood add to the cost. The proportion of bridges per hundred miles in Russia is enormous. For like reasons, the cost of railway building is even greater. Even the inland waterways system is unsatisfactory, for not only are the streams frozen in winter and flooded during the spring, but their direction is poor. The most navigable rivers flow into the Arctic. The rivers flowing into the Black Sea are shallow. The Volga system with seven thousand miles of navigable waterways flows into the Caspian, an inland sea. To transport goods into the Black Sea it is necessary to transfer them to rail at Stalingrad and reload them on barges on the shallow Don. Two changes of bulk before the port of distribution is reached make the cost of transportation very high.

War and revolution resulted in chaos and the movement of goods as well as their production came to a standstill. In 1921 the destruction of tracks, the deterioration of rolling stock, and the lack of fuel caused railway traffic to fall to 20 per cent of the pre-war level. Not until 1927 was the 1913 volume equaled. This restoration to normalcy was accomplished not so much by increasing the capital investment in the railroads as by adopting measures calculated to utilize the old plant to better advantage. Lower-powered locomotives were replaced by higher-powered locomotives since the latter will draw a greater load. Cars of larger capacity were substituted for smaller ones. Repair work upon the rolling stock was more quickly and efficiently attended to. Finally the junctions were unified under a single management, and a method was adopted of interchanging cars and locomotives from one road to another in accordance with the traffic demands. During harvest season, for example, a greater proportion of freight cars is allotted to the agricultural districts.

As the industrial and agricultural map of Russia is changed, the routes of transport will also change. The general scheme of building under the Five Year Plan (1928-33) of reconstruction called for a system of trunk lines, to be electrified wherever possible because of the saving in fuel and locomotives. Motor truck feeders were to tap outlying districts. Over half of the new construction was earmarked for agricultural purposes, and less than half for industrial purposes. New railways are planned to tap those regions in Asia where vast new resources have been found—in Kazakstan [1] in the Urals, and in Siberia. The Turkestan-Siberian railroad was completed in the spring of 1930. It links up three of the largest regions of the Republic: Western Siberia, Kazakstan, and Central Asia. The principal purpose in constructing the road was to aid in the development of the cotton growing region of Central Asia, soon to be the principal source of cotton for the textile manufactures. In turn, Central Asia will be able to obtain grain and lumber from Western Siberia. Finally this road will assist in developing the rich mineral resources of Kazakstan. Many lines of similar economic

[1] Turkestan.

importance are planned. The task of improving nearly a million miles of dirt roads so as to fit them for motor transport has made little progress because of the necessity of devoting available capital to more essential needs. Yet in a country whose land surface is more than double that of the United States, every possible system of transport must be fully developed. Airways are used in Russia for the ordinary purposes: mail, freight, passenger and military service. More important, however, are the newer purposes to which airplanes have been put. They accompany exploring expeditions and are employed as scouts searching out hidden resources. Aerial photography has assisted in locating routes for the new roads and in making maps of forest and agricultural reserves. Planes are also used in the hunting and fishing expeditions, huge businesses in Russia; in guiding Arctic trading expeditions; and finally in agriculture, particularly in spraying operations.

Because of the demands of the transport system in the relocation of agricultural, mineral, and industrial areas under the Soviet government it has been necessary to turn to the improvement of the inland waterways. Russia has the largest system of potential navigable inland waterways in the world. To-day only a fourth is utilized for transportation. Development will proceed in the direction of increasing the mileage and of providing suitable ships for river traffic. The plans, like all the Soviet plans, are ambitious, but the lack of capital will postpone action for many years. Three of the projects, however, are of great geographical interest. It is planned to dig a wide canal from the Volga to the Don, and this improvement is calculated to raise the volume of freight carried on the Volga-Don to six million tons. With the completion of the largest hydro-electric power plant in the world in 1932 at Dnepropetrovsk on the Dnieper, that river will be dammed, deepening the channel and backing up its waters with the result that it will be navigable far up to the sources. A system of locks at Dnepropetrovsk will make it possible to navigate the district of the rapids. A more spectacular project calls for the linking of the Volga system with the Arctic. The Pechora River flows into the Arctic and the Kama into the Volga. Both rise in the same vast swamp. It is planned to convert the swamp into a lake by imprisoning the waters of the melting winter snows. Lumber will then flow north to the Arctic from the forest; ships will be able to tap inaccessible calcium deposits on the upper Kama; and a power plant will arise at the headwaters of the latter stream. This is environmental adaptation with a vengeance, yet this is but one of a score of projects which to us seem singularly fantastic.

87. Resources and Industry

The Soviet state has taken over control of the major economic functions of production and distribution. It has become a huge corporation engaged in every industry. It has commandeered not only the workers but also all the resources of the country. The creation of wealth is to depend upon the mechanization of all industry: mining, agriculture, manufacturing, and transport. The natural resources of the country will be utilized to their fullest extent to build up an industrial plant large enough to satisfy the needs of all Russia. The minerals such as coal, coke, and peat will furnish fuel; the streams will provide power; oil will furnish fuel and lubrication for machinery; and the metal resources such as iron, copper, and aluminum will be employed in constructing the machines. To the machines will be brought the products of the soil to be transformed into consumers' goods: food and clothing. Less and less will the human being be called upon to labor, for the machine under man's supervision will perform the work of a thousand men. More and more will men emancipate themselves from their environment by compelling the elements of the environment—soil, fuel, power, metal and mineral resources—to toil for them and leave them free for the enjoyment of life. This, of course, is an ideal common to men of all nations; but in Russia alone has the state itself essayed the task of achieving the millennium.

Our task is to examine her geographical resources to see whether Russia possesses the basic materials out of which an industrial society can be fashioned, and to what extent the readjustments in Russia are in harmony with the physical environment. We shall make a rough classification of the resources of Russia, industrial and agricultural, and discuss each in turn.

To erect an industrial machine of such huge dimensions as Russia contemplates the prime need is the building of producers' machinery. Unless the heavy industries flourish, there will be forthcoming no machinery for the manufacture of consumers' goods. Of what use are cotton, flax, hides, and grain without the means of converting such raw materials into clothing, shoes, and flour? In consequence a large proportion of available capital has been assigned to the development of the heavy industries. At present there is a dearth of such necessities as clothing and shoes because of this policy. The Russian people are called upon to make harsh sacrifices, for the time at least, until the foundations of a machine economy are firmly laid.

In order to develop the heavy industries, "machines for making machines," three essentials are necessary: capital, technical skill, and mineral resources. Of these Russia at present possesses only the last. In order to obtain capital the Soviet government has pursued a policy of selling vast quantities of surplus raw materials. If the export list of Soviet Russia be examined it will be found that materials such as petroleum, coal, timber, manganese, iron ore, wheat, barley, and rye head the list. In return Russia purchases steel, iron and steel manufactures, machinery of all kinds, fertilizers, and sugar. The *Enonomic Handbook of the Soviet Union,* issued annually, contains a complete record of such transactions. An illustration of the nature of the present day trade is a contract by the British Electrical Federation agreeing to purchase from the Soviet agency twenty million gallons of gasoline. Soviet trade with the United States has risen to tremendous proportions. In 1919 Russia was seventeenth on our list of customers. In 1930 she had risen to eighth place, being the only country in the world increasing its imports from the United States during that year. American exports consisted largely of machinery and equipment. In 1929 Russia was the third largest buyer of American industrial equipment, being exceeded only by Canada and Great Britain. Five years before she was fourteenth on the list. In 1930 Russia became the leading market for American agricultural machinery and supplies. Tractors and combines made up the largest part of such shipments.

In purchasing machinery abroad, Russia obtains aid in overcoming her second great shortcoming—lack of technical skill. Many contracting firms send out engineers to Russia to assist in setting up the equipment and to teach the Soviet engineers how to operate the machinery. Furthermore, since these purchases represent the latest product of the manufacturing genius of the industrial world, Russia, in time, will be in a position to duplicate such machinery. Russia also expends part of her export credits in employing foreign experts to work in her factories. In 1930 there were in force more than a hundred contracts with foreign corporations calling for the services of engineers. Four-fifths of these contracts were with American and German firms.

Russia is admirably equipped with the metal, mineral, and timber resources necessary for the development of the heavy industries. Her supplies of coal, peat, coke, and oil are practically unlimited; and almost every year new reserves are discovered. She possesses roughly 20 per cent of the potential water power resources of the world; more than any country with the possible exception of the United States. In timber resources she ranks first, with approximately 30 per cent of the world's reserves. The northern part of the Russian dominion is a vast mass of coniferous forest, with pines, firs, and spruces predominating. In the Caucasus there is a second vast forest belt containing over a hundred deciduous varieties. A fifth consists of oak, another fifth of birch—both commercially valuable. Russia has supplies of iron ore and manganese, necessary in the manufacture of steel, that are more than ample for her needs. There are large deposits of copper, potassium, platinum, and gold. To complete the list would entail a very long enumeration.

Under the auspices of the Academy of Science four hundred expeditions have been sent out by the Soviet government in search of new resources. The results have been spectacular, revealing the fact that the Romanoffs were practically ignorant of the resources of the territory over which they had ruled for so many centuries. To illustrate at random: in the tundra region of Karelia were found mountains of nephelite and apatite; the former useful in the manufacture of glass, the latter in the manufacture of phosphate fertilizer. The desert of Kara Kum, in southern Turkestan, is composed of sand and sulphur. The latter can be used in the manufacture of paper and rubber, and in spraying grain and cotton. In the lakes of Siberia were found huge deposits of soda, and in far off Yakutsk large quantities of rock salt. The whole region from the middle Volga to the Urals, it has been ascertained, is one vast deposit of petroleum. In the region of the lower Volga iron ore deposits have been discovered, and shortly a factory capable of producing 650,000 tons of pig iron a year will be completed. The coal reserves of the Kuznetsk basin in Siberia were formerly reckoned at 250 billion tons; now they are estimated to contain nearly double that amount. There is no end to the story.

In 1931 Russia mined 65,000,000 tons of coal, only an eighth of that mined in the United States, yet enough to give Russia fourth place among the coal-producing nations. Soviet Russia is now producing annually twice the output of pre-war Russia. Asia possesses about 85 per cent of the coal reserves of the Soviet domain, yet because of the lack of transportation facilities and of capital to develop these deposits, production there represents only 15 per cent of the total. The coal reserves of the Kuznetsk basin of Siberia are estimated at 400 billion tons, roughly three-fourths of the reserves of the Soviet Republic. It is planned to open up eighty new mines there within a few years. At present there are only seventeen mines being worked in that section. The government has concentrated upon the Don basin mines, which are yielding about 75 per cent of the Soviet output. There vast strides have been made, not only because of the opening up of new mines but because of the mechanization of the mining industry. The employment of cutting machines in particular has enabled the Russian output to advance by leaps and bounds during the last ten years, and huge coal exports are in part responsible for the present progress of Russian industrial development.

Coke and peat have received considerable attention during the past ten years. Formerly the Russian iron industry was located at Moscow and Leningrad because the vast forests of the surrounding districts were converted into charcoal, then necessary in the smelting of iron. At the present time the conversion of coal into coke is much better economy because the by-products of coke manufacture are as valuable as the coke and the forests are not wasted unnecessarily. It has been calculated that Russia will eventually produce six million tons of coke a year. To-day, however, only a small fraction of this amount is manufactured. Kerch is the leading producer now, but shortly the new factories at Dnepropetrovsk and Voroshilovsk will produce a half million tons a year. The plant at Magnitogorsk in the Urals which is being constructed under the supervision of American engineers will, when completed, be the largest coke producer in the world.

Russia possesses three-fourths of the peat reserves of the world. Peat is important in modern industry for two reasons: first, because it can be used as raw material in manufacturing many goods— gas, coke, paper, for example; and secondly, because it provides a cheap fuel for power plants. A number of the most important regional power plants are to be located near the vast peat bogs of northern and central Russia, and Siberia. The output of peat is about eight million tons, already five times that of pre-war Russia.

The amazing oil reserves of Soviet Russia have been mentioned. They are estimated at 40 billion barrels, with possibilities of much more, but at present, practically all the oil is pumped from the two fields of Baku and Grozny. Under Soviet supervision not only has the pre-war output more than doubled, but the technique of extraction has been modernized. Deep pumping has succeeded bailing; rotary and turbine drilling have replaced the costly percussion system; and electrical power has been substituted for steam. Of this transformation Gorky, the novelist, writes: "Over an infinite expanse of oil fields crouch iron pumps with clanking chains; the great watch towers of the past are disappearing; everywhere swing the clumsy pilgrims. Almost noiselessly they pump the oil from the depths of the earth. In a little wooden shed on a flat surface spins a central generator. Like a spider it stretches out its long iron legs in all directions. Nowhere can one see workers smeared with black oil. Nowhere can one hear the shouting or howling of superiors. Only the clinking and clanging of iron upon iron as the pilgrims bow to the earth."

Instead of being content to ship merely crude oil and kerosene, the only pre-war products of the wells, the Soviet government has undertaken to refine the oil into various grades as is done in the United States. Profiting by American experience, too, refineries have been erected at the ports of export. Oil is pumped from Grozny to Tuapse, a distance of 390 miles, and from Baku to Batum, a distance of 535 miles. For domestic uses oil will be pumped from Emba to Samara in eastern European Russia, and eventually Moscow's needs will be supplied by a pipe line running from the Caspian.

Russian iron ore reserves are estimated at three billion tons and her potential resources at many billions more. The production of pig iron is a barometer of the industrial trend in any manufacturing country. If pig iron production be taken as the gauge of the progress of Russia under the Five Year Plan, the revised program has been about 60 per cent successful. The output of coal and oil are poor guides because both are easily extracted from the earth. Metallurgical processes, however, are required to convert ore into pig iron.

The program called for the production of 8,300,000 tons during 1931 but only 4,900,000 were produced. The 1932–1933 program was variously planned at ten, fifteen and even seventeen million tons, but has been finally graded downward to nine million tons. The Russians have a childlike faith in statistics and their efforts to attain certain totals has led them into devious channels.

At present the output of pig iron barely exceeds the pre-war production, which was 4,200,000 tons. The old Krivoy Rog works in the Ukraine still account for 60 per cent of the iron ore of Russia, but shortly new deposits will be worked. Magnetnaya Mountain in the Urals contains immense quantities of high grade ore. To utilize this ore two great steel plants are being erected under the supervision of American engineers, one at Magnitogorsk near the mines, and the other at Kuznetsk, the seat of the great coal beds of Western Siberia. In a few years there will be five steel plants, each capable of producing over a million tons a year. The capacity of Magnitogorsk is estimated at four million tons. Russia has immense supplies of manganese ore. The Chiaturi deposits in the Georgian Republic, the most important, are reserved entirely for export. At present the United States takes nearly 40 per cent of the Soviet manganese export. Russia is also provided with other metals necessary in industry but as yet has been unable to meet the demand of the electrical and chemical industries for copper, zinc, lead, nickel, and aluminum. Large quantities of all five must be imported at the present time. Soviet purchases of non-ferrous metals from the United States, for example, amount to $3,000,000 per annum.

Russia has an abundance of raw stuffs and unskilled labor. Her deficiencies in capital and technical information are supplied by selling off surplus materials to foreign countries. She is engaged in developing her heavy industries, at the same time trying to bridge the time gap by producing just enough consumers' goods to feed and clothe her vast population. By the end of 1932 her industrial production was estimated at several times that of pre-war Russia. One reason why her industrial program proceeds so slowly is that her exports cannot keep pace with the demands for such imports as machines, rails, and structural steel. In 1931 the balance against her exceeded $125,000,000. Yet Russia plunges ahead and makes purchases wherever credit is available, for she is convinced that her heavy industries will soon reach a state of development sufficient to enable her to construct the machinery necessary for supplying her population with ample manufactured goods. Largely upon the outcome of this venture rests the success of the Russian experiment.

This discussion would not be complete without a brief description of the program for the heavy industries in Russia. In large the plan is to erect huge machine plants near the sources of power and of coal and iron. This step has necessitated the erection of new mills and the enlargement of all the old ones which it is feasible to retain. It is planned to consolidate the heavier industries in a few giant plants. Already the existing nine hundred works have been reduced to forty-seven. By concentrating industries in a few places economy will be served; the cost of maintenance will be reduced, needless duplication of endeavor wiped out, and the lighter industries producing the machinery most useful to the district in which the plant is located will be able to tap the same power plant. Thus, at Dnepropetrovsk, the giant hydro-electric station on the Dnieper, will arise an industrial combine about which will center the production of steel, aluminum goods, chemical products, fertilizers, and ferro-manganese products. Furthermore, this station will provide heat and light for the industrial city, and power to prevent the Don basin mines from flooding during the spring months. Needless to say, the industrial map of Russia will be entirely changed. Large cities will arise where formerly there were barren wastes. At Kramatos in the Ukraine, for example, will soon appear a plant employing sixty thousand workers. Rostov on the Don is earmarked as the greatest agricultural machine factory in Europe, and at Tashkent in the extreme south of Turkestan will be erected an industrial plant producing not only textile machinery but also machinery necessary for incubators, brooders, and milkers. Tashkent will be the seat of a vast textile industry, for into its mills will pour all the cotton of Turkestan. Here also will be located the dairy and poultry industries of that region. Thus Rostov and Tashkent will become large metropoli.

The heavy industries of Russia are engaged in manufacturing industrial equipment such as Diesel engines, steam boilers, lathes for metal work, machinery for working up textiles and for textile factories. Machines never before built in Russia are being constructed; coal cutting machinery, high power boilers, refrigerating apparatus, chemical apparatus, and high power locomotives. The heavy industries are far from serving the needs of the new industry. In 1931 they supplied only 70 per cent of the locomotives, 70 per cent of the oil drilling equipment, 65 per cent of the coal mining machinery, and 40 per cent of the chemical apparatus demanded. The heavy industries have hardly begun to supply the needs of mechanized agriculture. Tractors and automobiles are in greatest demand, and though a dozen huge factories are being constructed, only two of them, one at Moscow and one at Leningrad, are in operation. The demand for automobiles will for many years exceed the output. The need for building materials like glass, bricks, and cement is also very pressing; likewise, it is still necessary to import prepared fertilizers in spite of the huge deposits of raw materials which exist in Russia. To build from the bottom is Russia's opportunity, but to attain any degree of success will entail endless sacrifice. Hence it has become essential to transform Communism into a religion in the service of which one must be prepared to sacrifice all.

Many of the huge industrial combines will be located near the sources of electrical power. We have already mentioned Dnepropetrovsk and Rostov, which are power stations. Cheap power greatly lessens the overhead in all manufacturing. Russia is planning to erect seventy-six great power stations to serve the new industrial development. These will be located at the sources of cheap fuel. Coal will not be burned because it is too valuable. Instead peat, lignite, anthracite dust, crude oil, and water power will be utilized to generate power. The Dnieper power plant when completed will be the largest power plant station in the world. It will furnish 750,000 horse power. Many American advisers are engaged in its construction, including the General Electric Company. The power system of Soviet Russia, at completion, will furnish for industry over ten million horse power.

88. Soviet Agriculture

The most noteworthy soil belt of Russia, the black earth belt, extends roughly from Kiev in Europe east through northern Kazakstan reappearing here and there along the border of Siberia. It is a narrow belt, corresponding roughly to the lands lying between the 50th and 55th parallels of latitude. The soil is a deep loess and derives its color from the rich proportion of humus which it contains. No other soil in Russia approaches it in fertility; in fact, the other soils of Russia are either very mediocre or poor.

In the tundra region the surface soil is saturated with moisture and rests upon subsoil that is permanently frozen. In the northwest, in European Russia, the soil is clayey, and the terrain is very swampy. Little agriculture is supported there. The largest soil belt of Russia is the so-called *podzol* [1] belt, a wide zone lying between the tundra and the black earth belts. It extends from central European Russia to the eastern reaches of Siberia, a zone almost identical with the coniferous forest. This soil is ash colored, sandy in character, and poor in fertility. South of the black earth belt lie three narrow zones of soils that are rather poor for agriculture. On the dry steppe is a chestnut colored soil, south of it a red soil consisting of sandy, saline ingredients, and in the extreme south near the Kazak-Persian border, a grey soil characteristic of a region of great aridity. The last three soil zones run from west to east, describing arcs about the Black and Caspian seas.

Climate has a greater influence than soil upon agriculture in Russia. Even the black earth belt is subject to the vagaries of the rainfall, for here as in other parts of Russia the precipitation is likely to be insufficient from place to place and from year to year. A rainfall of from ten to twenty inches a year is the minimum for agriculture even under the best soil conditions. Failure of the rainfall to materialize was responsible for thirty-five "poor" years during the period 1800–1850. The Soviet government has classified the years 1917 to 1927 as two famine years, five poor years, and three good years. A "poor" year in Russia would be reckoned as a famine year in the United States, as production is off from 20 to 30 per cent.

The pre-war portrait of agricultural prosperity was painted in too vivid colors. Each year ten million tons of grain were exported from the Ukraine. The failure of Soviet Russia to feed its population constitutes in our minds a major indictment against the whole system. Now, however, we are beginning to realize that the Russian grain export was a "fictitious" export. A vast peasant population was being exploited by a landlord class, with the connivance of the government. There was a great display of prosperity at the front door, while at the back large numbers of people were hovering on the verge of starvation.

With the liquidation of the landlord class following the revolution of 1917 peasant holdings increased from fifteen million to twenty-five

---

[1] *Podzol* means "ash colored underneath."

million in number and the size of the average holding doubled. Yet
there appeared no such surplus of food as had apparently existed before. The peasants began to consume a larger proportion of the wheat
and rye, meat and eggs, and dairy produce. The meat consumption
of the average household doubled. Ninety per cent of the grain
produce was eaten up by the peasants. Some of the more tangible results of an adequate food supply were a decline of infant mortality,
a decline in the death rate, and an increase of population from
130,000,000 to 160,000,000. To-day, unless the harvest is a good
one, there is not enough food to go round.

The Soviet government held itself responsible for providing sufficient food for the country. This meant not only relieving famine
wherever it appeared but also providing food for an urban population
of 20 per cent. The peasants were extremely reluctant to share their
produce with the urban districts, for they felt that the prices offered for their produce did not reward them adequately for their
labor. They preferred to raise only so much as they were able to
consume. Among the more energetic there arose a system of farming on a large scale and employing labor. These farmers began to
sell goods to a needy government. But the principle of private wealth
was obnoxious to the Soviet ideal of communism, so in 1929 steps
were taken to liquidate the *kulaks*. For the most part their property
was ruthlessly confiscated.

A way had to be found to communize agriculture. This proved
to be a difficult proposition among a people to whom ownership of
land meant everything. From the examination and discussion of every
phase of the problem rose a policy that has wrought tremendous
changes in Russian agriculture. From a purely geographical point
of view, it represents a more scientific adjustment to the physical
environment than the old estates system of agriculture.

The cardinal points of present-day agriculture in Russia are first,
mechanization, and secondly, scientific adaptation. The average-sized
peasant holding in Russia before the inauguration of the Five Year
Plan in 1928 was from twenty to forty acres. Obviously it would not
pay to introduce upon such a small farm tractors, combines, steam
plows, or other agricultural machinery. A tractor is used to the
fullest advantage upon a farm exceeding two thousand acres in
size. There is no country where even one per cent of the farms are
of such magnitude. In fact, in Germany, farms of two hundred acres

and over do not equal one per cent of the farms. In order to solve her food problem Russia decided upon a policy of mechanized agriculture. This meant, first of all, that the farms must be combined into larger units. Thus collectivism was introduced. The peasants were "persuaded" to pool not only their lands but also their live stock and other appurtenances and to rent or purchase from the government the machines for planting and harvesting. They accepted socialized agriculture very reluctantly partly because they hated giving up the land, partly because of the experience of the *kulaks* whose possessions were confiscated, and partly because of the coercive attitude of the government. The argument that they would share in the harvest in proportion to the capital goods and land that they contributed and in accordance with the amount of labor that they expended did not greatly attract them.

The movement was slow in getting started. Suddenly, probably because of the successful experience of a few, the tide turned. In addition, collectivism offered attractive inducements such as exemption from arrears of taxes, exemption from taxes for several years, and promises of profit sharing. Under the collectivist system, wages are drawn against the approaching harvest. There are five grades of labor rating. The lowest (100) for carting manure and similar unskilled jobs, the next in rank (125) for planting potatoes and other simple tasks, the next (150) for plowing with horses. Threshers and skilled laborers such as carpenters are rated higher (175), and at the top (200) are the tractor drivers, the bookkeepers, and the agronomists. In 1928 the average size of a collectivist farm was one hundred acres; to-day it is ten times as large, and in the grain growing districts, three thousand acres. The profits to the individual from mechanized agriculture far exceed those of the individual farmer working with horse and plow. Within three years 40 per cent of the peasantry have joined collectivist farms, and at the present rate all will have accepted socialized agriculture within another three years. Only 10 per cent of the arable land of Russia is farmed with the aid of machinery, but the difficulty now lies in turning out the machinery rather than in persuading the peasants to pool their lands.

Another type of farm has developed in Soviet Russia—the state farm. Several years ago the government decided to experiment with uninhabited lands in the vast steppe belt of southeast European Russia in order to learn whether industrial crops could be cultivated there with the aid of machinery. At the time only limited stocks of flax, cotton, and sunflower seed were reaching the industrial districts. Before this project could be developed, however, the country was confronted with a grain shortage. Many peasants had refused to raise grain for the urban markets. In desperation grain was planted in the lands set off for state farms. The experiment was entirely satisfactory, with the result that the Grain Trust was assigned thirty million acres of untilled land. In 1930, three million acres were planted and the next year twelve million acres. The state grain farm has come to stay, for here has been attained the largest yield at the lowest costs. The "Giant" is the largest state farm. It is situated along the Don River and comprises 600,000 acres on which are planted 170,000 acres in winter wheat, 250,000 acres in spring wheat, 25,000 acres in barley, and 10,000 acres in corn. The staff consists of 90 per cent engineers and only 10 per cent agronomists. Only 1,500 men are required to run this huge grain factory. They are assisted, however, by two hundred tractors, three hundred combines, and other machines. Only at harvest is supplementary labor required. In 1929 it cost about fifty-one cents to raise a bushel of wheat; in 1931 the cost fell to thirty-eight cents. The number of bushels per acre increased proportionately.

To-day about 100,000,000 acres have been allocated to state farming. The various farms are specialized and are grouped according to their activity into vast trusts. There is a Grain Trust, a Sugar Trust, a Cotton Trust, a Sheep Breeding Trust, a Pig Breeding Trust, a Cattle Breeding Trust, and several others. The Grain Trust and the Sheep and Cattle Breeding Trusts have been assigned the largest acreages. The average size of a state farm is now 170,000 acres and this average will be increased to 250,000 acres. The grain farms eventually will average from 500,000 to 750,000 acres each, and there will be five of them. The yield per acre on state farms is about 20 per cent higher than upon the collectivist farms.

The stock breeding farms and the industrial crop farms have not made so much progress as the grain farms because of the shortage of grain. At present, attention is being concentrated upon hog raising because of the existing meat shortage. The Hog Breeding Trust was formed in May, 1930, with a capital investment of three hundred farms and 177,000 pigs. Since pigs breed more rapidly than any meat-bearing stock, it was anticipated that in 1933 seven million pigs would be ready for the slaughter house. In 1931, 400,000 hogs were brought to market by the trust, and the yield from the collectivist piggeries had greatly increased.

All over Russia are being established machine tractor stations whose function it is to provide mechanical power and technical equipment to collectivist farms within a radius of about fifteen miles. At present there are well over two thousand such stations. The government favors those regions capable of growing industrial crops such as the sugar beet and cotton because of the shortage that exists in these commodities. At present, raw cotton and raw wool are being imported to satisfy the demands of the textile plants.

89. Crop Adaptation

Mechanized agriculture is singularly adapted to Russian land because of the flat topography of the country. Tractors and combines are able to work in large numbers in military formation for mile after mile. Only in the western parts of the United States and Canada is there to be found a parallel. Furthermore, mechanized agriculture has created an agricultural domain in regions never before given over to agriculture. The state Grain Trust, for example, operates in vast regions uninhabited save for a handful of wandering nomads. The thirty million acres which it is exploiting are located in such areas in the northern Caucasus, southern Ukraine, the middle and lower Volga, and southwest Siberia. In these steppe and arid lands, the rainfall is never more than fifteen inches a year; in the northern Caucasus and southern Ukraine it rarely exceeds ten inches. These districts formerly supported no population because the hard, parched soil could not be plowed and because the rainfall was too unreliable to tempt the farmer to risk its failure. In the less favored regions of the Ukraine, the *sukovey,* a hot dry wind, is strong enough to blow off the top soil.

The Soviet government combats this unfavorable environment by using machinery in plowing, sowing and reaping. The hard surface of the soil is plowed up by tractors; the lack of rain is met in using drought-proof seed; and the wind is thwarted by speed in plowing and sowing. It is fully realized that in years of drought there will be crop failure. In fact, the Soviet government is prepared to accept crop failure in any district once in five or six years. It is not likely, however, that the rainfall will fail throughout an area extending from the western end of the Black Sea to eastern Siberia. But should failure occur on any of the state farms, none of the population will be threatened by famine for mechanized agriculture is nomadic. The workers move about in camps. The loss is merely a business loss in labor, seed, and overhead, written off in the general accounting of the state farms.

Each district under the state planning system will raise the crop best suited to its climate and soil. This dictum applies to collectivist as well as to state farms. In the black earth belt, practically no wheat will be raised for these lands are too valuable for wheat growing. They will be devoted to the raising of industrial crops such as flax, sunflower seed, and the sugar beet. Nor will grain be raised on the irrigated lands of Turkestan for here is to be the cotton emporium of Russia. Wheat will be planted only on lands unsuited to industrial crops.

That the mechanization of agriculture should influence the agricultural zonation of Russia to a certain point is clear, but the Soviet program entails much more than this; it is an endeavor to uproot completely the century-old distribution of crops and to re-shape the agricultural geography of the country. An excerpt from the report of the Commissar of Agriculture will serve to emphasize this point: "At present the Ukraine, the Kuban and the Northern Caucasus constitute the main granary of Russia. But it is contended that it is wasteful to grow wheat in such areas which could more profitably be utilized to raise more valuable crops such as soya beans and sunflowers. Wheat, on the other hand, it is claimed, can be grown on areas which are too dry to produce the more intensive crops. Hence the decision to cultivate regions in the trans-Volga region, in Kazakstan and in southeastern Siberia. The total acreage of these areas is, in round figures, 400 million hectares, of which less than 35 millions are actually under cultivation. It is now proposed to increase the area under cultivation in the next three years by at least another 20 million hectares. . . ." At the present a great effort is being made not only to release Turkestan from grain growing, but to increase to the fullest extent the amount of irrigated land. Thus when the heavy industries are capable of producing a large number of textile machines, an adequate supply of cotton will be ready. Concurrently, wheat is gradually being pushed up to the very edges of the wheat growing belt.

This program of the future is a spectacular illustration of agricultural adaptation and planning. It was formulated by The Institute . . . of the Commissariat of Agriculture, a division of the Lenin Academy of Agricultural Sciences, and has been accepted by the Soviet government. Russia from the Baltic to the Bering has been divided into five large zones in accordance with the type of agriculture best adapted to the climate and soil of each. Industrial crops and intensive stock breeding are to be located in southeastern Ukraine and the Central Black Soil region. Special districts in the northern Caucasus and in the Far East have been assigned to the production of soya beans, sunflower seeds, cotton, and tobacco, and to stock breeding. The vegetable crop zone, in combination with dairying, will be located in the suburbs of the large cities, especially Leningrad, Moscow, and the newer industrial metropoli. A beginning has been made in encouraging the collectivists in these areas to specialize.

The subtropical crop zone will be located in Transcaucasia and along the southern coast of the Crimea. This zone is to be a Russian California, producing cotton, tea, grapes, plums, apples, melons and oranges. "Is it not a disgrace," writes the Commissar of Agriculture, "that grain is grown here?" The dry steppe districts of the lower Volga and Kazakstan, and the mountainous areas of southern Siberia have been earmarked as pasture. Here will center the activities of the cattle and sheep growing trusts. The forest zone, occupying a half of the area of the country and extending from Archangel to the Pacific, will provide reserves of arable land. This belt has been placed under the jurisdiction of the Supreme Economic Council. Its first task will be to enlarge the territory suitable for cultivation in northwest European Russia where the forests are the cause of the extreme marshy condition of the soil. This then is the Soviet plan of crop adaptation and should it succeed it will represent, to say the least, an outstanding achievement in the sphere of scientific agriculture.

CHAPTER XI

THE MEDITERRANEAN ENVIRONMENT

90. Location and Topography

The Mediterranean or Subtropical type of environment occurs in California, in Middle Chile, in the southwestern tips of South Africa and Australia as well as along the margins of the Mediterranean Sea. With the exception of the Mediterranean basin, however, all Subtropical lands are narrowly limited in extent. In the New World, both in California and in Chile, the Mediterranean region is sandwiched between the ocean and mountains that will not permit the passage of moisture. In the northern hemisphere of the Old World, however, the cyclones that move down to latitudes 31° to 39° during the winter season encounter not an insuperable range but a trough or basin which allows them to travel unimpeded from Gibraltar to Beirut, a distance of two thousand miles. Indeed some traverse the whole Near East occasioning winter rains as far as the trans-Indus province of Punjab.

From west to east the Mediterranean environment decreases in intensity and extent. In the western basin, divided from the eastern by the toe of Italy and Sicily, where the oceanic influence is great, the Mediterranean environment transcends its usual bounds, reaching as far south as the Canary Isles and as far north as the Maritime Alps, beyond the French Riviera. The olive, a representative plant species, is found through the southern two-thirds of the Spanish peninsula. The eastern basin, on the other hand, lies in more southerly latitudes and is remote from the source of cyclonic storms. These factors impose a limiting influence, restricting the true Mediterranean environment to the coasts. The mountains and the deserts rather than the cyclones dominate. The Anatolian coast, however, which fronts the Westerlies, receives the full cyclonic influence; and here the Mediterranean régime is extensive. In fact, far interior to the eastern coast, traces of the Mediterranean influence are revealed in the predominance of winter rainfall.

A second limiting influence is imposed by the southern desert and the northern forest. In the west their influences are modified by the frequency of the winter cyclones, but in the eastern basin they advance at the expense of the sea. Thus east of Tunis on the African coast, Mediterranean conditions seem to exist at the pleasure of the Sahara. Only in western Libya and on the Cyrenaica plateau in eastern Libya, do they establish themselves with a degree of certainty. The desert rules the southern shore for long stretches along the Gulf of Sidra and along the whole Egyptian coast. In southeast Europe, again, a hostile environment intrudes close to the sea. The mountain forest and the cold dry winter of the Humid Continental Interior are met throughout the Balkan core and along the north coast of the Ægean.

Conditions of local relief impose a third restricting influence upon the limits of the Old World Mediterranean. The leeward sides of mountainous regions experience such a sharp diminution of winter rainfall that typical Mediterranean conditions obtain only on the coasts. Thus parts of eastern Spain, eastern Italy, the eastern Balkans, and the eastern parts of larger islands such as Corsica and Sardinia, do not possess the characteristics of a typical Mediterranean environment. In summary, then, Subtropical areas attain their greatest degree of intensity in northern Morocco and Algeria, in western, southern, and northeastern (sub-Pyrenees) Spain, in western Italy, and along the Syrian and Anatolian coasts. The French Riviera (40°N.) is typically Mediterranean, thanks to the Maritime Alps which block the cold winds of the north. Protecting ranges likewise shelter the Italian Lake section and the Dalmatian Riviera.

91. Climate

The main features of the Mediterranean climate, here as elsewhere, are winter rainfall, summer drought, and small temperature range. This type is essentially a transition between the Trade Wind Desert type and the Continental type of climate.[1] During the summers, when it is under the influence of the Subtropical Belt of High Pressure and the Northeast Trades, the Mediterranean basin may

[1] Examine carefully Plates I, II–V, XVIII–XXI.

be said to belong to the Sahara. The *meltem* winds, which blow across the sea, are part of the trade wind system. In the eastern Mediterranean they frequently attain the force of a gale during the day. Since the skies are always clear and the sunshine bright, only marine influences prohibit the parched atmospheric conditions that prevail in the desert. Temperatures are high, especially in the east and south, and increase rapidly as the interior is approached. Streams dry up, vegetation and herbs wither, and only the vineyards and the irrigated patches retain their greenness. The heat is intense but not sultry for humidity is low, evaporation rapid, and the air is always in motion. Only in the valleys and basins of the interior is it really oppressive. The nights are likely to be cool because of the rapid evaporation.

During the winter there is moderate rainfall, most pronounced on windward shores. These coasts are exposed to moist rain-bearing Westerlies which, when they encounter highlands, yield considerable rainfall. The eastern shore of the Adriatic receives the heaviest annual rainfall in all Europe—as much as 183 inches has been recorded—while the opposite shore receives only twenty inches. Similar differences in temperature occur. Leghorn [1] on the west Italian coast has a mean January temperature of 45°, while Ancona on the eastern coast has a temperature of only 42°. Thus the factor of relief intrudes everywhere in a consideration of the climate of the Mediterranean basin. The east coasts of Greece experience only half as much rainfall as the west coasts, while the eastern parts of Spain are much drier than Portugal.

The Mediterranean suffers an intrusion of northerly and southerly conditions from winds that originate in alien territory. In the winter the high pressure system of interior Europe leaks through troughs that lead to the sea. Of these winter winds the *mistral,* which blows down the Rhone depression, is the most forceful. Descending winds warm by compression, but the *mistral* is so cold before it starts that it sustains freezing temperatures until it reaches the sea. So strong is it that the trees are inclined toward the southeast. The cottages of the poor have windows and doors only on their southeast sides. The *bora* is experienced from Trieste to Albania, and northerly winds likewise reach the shores of the Ægean Sea. From the Sahara, the Subtropical High Pressure center during the winter, blows the

[1] Livorno.

sirocco. Passing into the Mediterranean low pressure basin, it brings hot, enervating spells to northern shores. The name *sirocco* is also applied to hot dry winds that occasionally blow in from the Sahara during the summer, often covering the roofs of houses in towns of the northern Mediterranean with a fine red sandy powder carried from the desert. The former, however, is the true *sirocco* since it is more widespread and more generally recognized.

The winter rainfall of the Mediterranean is distinguished from that of western Europe (Maritime) not because it is greater in amount but because it all falls in a comparatively few days. Thus, while St. Malo (Brittany) and Nice have the same amount of rainfall, that of the former is distributed over 189 days while that of the latter falls in sixty-seven days. This is due partly, of course, to the relative absence of rainfall throughout the summer half year, but in the winter, the rain falls during a relatively few days and in a few hours during those days. This "deluge" type of precipitation is likely to cause flood damage especially where the run-off is from mountains. White limestone rock, a common feature of Mediterranean slopes, reveals that the soil cover was washed down before vegetation had a chance to germinate. The Mediterranean, with its warm sunny climate, is popular as a winter resort. The hours of sunshine are commonly double those of Great Britain during the year. The relative humidity is low during the winter season, especially along the northern Mediterranean where drying air descending from the mountains is a common feature. Genoa [1] has a relative humidity of only 62 per cent, Rome [2] of 65 per cent, and Naples [3] of 69 per cent.

As might be expected from the influence of latitude and sea, the seasonal range of temperature is much less than either that of interior Europe or of the Sahara. Autumn is everywhere warmer than spring, a true maritime feature. The average yearly range of temperature rarely exceeds 30°; most common is the January mean of 50° and the July mean of 80°. So moderating is the maritime influence that the French riviera has a January mean only five degrees lower than the Algerian coast, five hundred miles further south. Frost does occur on all European Mediterranean coasts except in the southern islands, but snow is rare except in northern regions. In leeward

[1] Genova.
[2] Roma.
[3] Napoli.

parts of the north, in the mountains, snow remains on the ground for long periods. For man the Mediterranean is a hospitable climate, but because the rainy season does not correspond with the growing season, he must make special adjustments to safeguard his food supply.

92. Natural Vegetation

The plant life of the Mediterranean differs widely from that of surrounding vegetation belts. Yet the Subtropical belt about the Mediterranean Sea, because of its extensiveness, permitted an expansion of settlement that was impossible in any other Subtropical belt. In a true Mediterranean climate, the climatic rhythm is so highly specialized that both plant and human life must subject themselves to a very strict regimen in order to survive. Civilization here was of necessity dependent upon a very fine adjustment to the physical surroundings. Greece and Rome could never have risen to such cultural heights were not the Subtropical environment extensive enough to permit an expansion of peoples. Greece fortunately found in the west a Magna Græcia; and Rome discovered pillars of strength to the south and west. Indeed these communities revealed a reluctance to penetrate where the environment changed. Thus Greece clung closely to the shores of the Black Sea, and Rome faltered when the Danube was reached. Rome moved northward only in the west, where her standards were carried as far as Scotland. There is a reason for this. In northwest Europe the winters are mild and the general aspect is green. In large parts of England and along the coasts of western Europe snow is not frequent. There, too, are found plant species similar to those of the Mediterranean—evergreen arbutus, noble laurel, myrtle, rosemary, and Mediterranean heath. Eastward, in central Europe, the scene is unfamiliar; from the snow blanket in the highlands protrude conifers; and, in the moist lowlands, deciduous varieties like the beech and oak appear. Here the farmer, unlike his Mediterranean neighbor, is inactive during the winter.

The summers, too, show a marked contrast. Then the Mediterranean lands are parched and baked. Between the dry and dusty leaves of evergreens is seen only dry and impotent land. The flowers, poppies, irises, and gladioli, have disappeared. The desert appears to be advancing. In central Europe, in contrast, the rains coincide with the warmth of spring and summer, and the dryness of fall promotes a harvest, neither green nor brown, but golden. Further east, as the rainfall diminishes and the growing season grows shorter and shorter, the land becomes finally useless to man.

The climatic contrast between the western and eastern basins of the Mediterranean is reflected in the plant cover. The latter is the area of fewer cyclonic visitations and its more southerly latitude brings it closer to the desert. Much of the African coast, as we have seen, is beyond the Mediterranean pale. Indeed, special conditions are necessary to induce a Mediterranean environment. On the plateaus of Cyrenaica and about the town of Tripoli, for example, the rainfall is to be attributed to altitude (*circa* 1,500 feet). About the Gulf of Sidra, at a lower latitude and altitude (*circa* 500 feet), the rainfall is negligible. The favored coasts of Libya receive only sixteen inches rainfall in contrast with the Algerian coast, several hundred miles north, which receives thirty inches. In the eastern basin, as a result, true Mediterranean vegetation has an impoverished appearance and flourishes only locally. On every side are the desert alfa grasses, which extend westward among the Atlas Mountains and well up into Spain. On the whole it is the western, not the eastern, portion of the African coast where the true Mediterranean forms are found. The early Mediterranean civilizations founded along the eastern coasts were only transient impermanent settlements on lands that were at best marginal and precarious to the accustomed mode of living. Until the coming of the Arabs, who worked along different lines (combining pasture with crop irrigation) only Carthage, which was situated in a most favorable environment, was successfully developed.

Shrubs and trees are the prevailing forms of Mediterranean vegetation. They are evergreens, leaf growth in the winter being necessary to the building up of plant food for the summer. The summer is a period of dryness; consequently the plants take measures to protect themselves against drought. The leaves of some are leathery or waxen; the leaves of others are small and hairy. Others dispense with leaves and substitute thorns and prickles. Resins and aromatic substances are characteristic. A considerable variety of plant life is encountered because of the ruggedness of most of the lands. The high forest of upper altitudes contains pines and oaks, mostly evergreen. These forests have always been a boon to man. To-day the cork oak is used in conjunction with the wine industry, and tanning materials are obtained from the Valonia oak in the eastern

Mediterranean. Acorns furnish food for pigs, and in parts of Turkey and North Africa, for man too. Because the forests do not penetrate into the lowlands, some believe that these lands were deforested by man. The bare hillslopes of Dalmatia are supposed to be the result of the Venetian need of timber in times past. Others ascribe the dearth of forest to goats, prevalent everywhere, who have an undue fondness for the seedlings and young trees. Yet because of the very nature of the climate, it is doubtful whether trees could sustain themselves except on the most favored sites. Tall trees are more exposed to drying winds than bushes, and need a larger supply of moisture than is attainable in the lowland.

The *maquis* is more characteristic and widespread than the high forest. This form of plant cover is a tangled mass of scrub forest— an impenetrable mixture of shrub, undergrowth, vine, and small trees. It is found in large areas in Spain, Italy, Greece, and elsewhere. Many of the bushes contain beautiful blooms. In Algeria, the *oleander* is called the "fever plant" by the French colonists; however, the malaria does not come from the flowers, but from the mosquitoes that infest the stream banks where the flowers grow.

A third type of vegetation is associated with the thin soil cover, so frequent throughout the Mediterranean region. In this region of rugged relief and sudden rains, soil has little chance to accumulate. In addition, the bright sunshine and summer drought dry out the thin soil so quickly that few plants have time to develop a root system extensive enough to enable them to sustain growth. Under such circumstances the plant cover is scattered and its members are of an intensive drought-resisting variety. *Garigue* is the commonly accepted name for these "half-shrubs" which are neither herb nor shrubs but something in between. Lavender, thyme, sage, juniper, and various brooms and gorses are representative of this low, scrambling vegetation of aromatic foliage and bright short-lived flowers. The *asphodel* characterizes another whole class possessed of fleshy roots and tubers tucked deep into the rocks. In this class is listed the dwarf palm which alone, of the palms of north Africa, is not an importation. It is rare in Europe but is evidence that a land bridge once existed. In Atlas lands, the hair that covers the young leaves is used to-day as a stuffing material. The *cactus* (prickly pear) and the *agave* (aloe) are Spanish importations from America. They are true desert plants but have taken hold in the rock exposed surfaces of the Mediterranean. *Garigue* lands are of little agricultural importance, but the goat ekes out enough food for a living, and the flowering plants are favored by bees, important in an environment where for long honey was the only form of sweetening.

Two plant groups occur in regions where climatic modification exists. First, there are mountain forests comprised of broad-leaved trees such as the beech and sweet chestnut. Here the land is high enough and sufficiently exposed to the wind to get rain in summer. These timber lands are of historical importance. Secondly, areas are found where herbs and grasses flourish during the winter in lieu of the typical woody plants. The wide plains at the mouth of the Rhone are useful for pasture, but winter cold prevents other growth, while in the Campagna, where the volcanic rock is too impermeable for the winter rains to sink in, grass also grows. Both regions dry out thoroughly during the summer, hence the livestock must migrate during this season. In contrast, there exist grass pastures high up on slopes that are snow-covered during much of the winter. This type of vegetation is common in northwest Spain, in north Italy, and in the heart of the Balkans. It is more commonly associated with the summer rains of the central European climatic type. Thus the Humid Continental Interior environment hems in the Mediterranean environment. In the highlands of central Spain, central Asia Minor, and the Atlas lands, a scanty steppe type of vegetation prevails.

93. The Agricultural Response

The nature of the soil imposes a further limitation upon the utilization of land by man in Mediterranean areas. Transported soils, generally high in fertility, are almost lacking. There are practically no glaciated or æolian soils as in central Europe. The alluvial soil belts are restricted in dimension because the rivers are uniformly small save in northern Italy, which lies outside the general area. The residual soils, too, over large areas are poor because they are so slowly renewed. Chemical action is necessarily at a minimum where the warm season corresponds with drought. Mechanical weathering is largely dependent upon marked temperature changes, especially the action of frost; but Mediterranean temperatures are noted for their seasonal uniformity. Soil building, then, is inactive, while soil destruction proceeds at a rapid rate because of the action of cloudbursts upon the slopes. Only recently has attention been given to replenishing the soil by artificial fertilizer. In the more primitive areas, soil alleviation is as yet unknown. Irrigation is practised, but is limited in extent since most of the streams dry up during the summer.

Under such circumstances it is not to be wondered at that good land is at a premium. Indeed, for agriculture, only those coastal regions protected by ranges are really ideal. Land is reckoned by the square yard rather than by the acre. Mediterranean man is said to live in oases surrounded by deserts of stone. On the other hand, close cultivation with large yields enables him to support dense settlements and affords him a well-developed social life with much leisure. The house is only a place to sleep in, for the bright sunshine attracts him outdoors either to work in the fields or to take part in community enterprise. Isolated houses are few, and community spirit is strong; the old abhorrence of being "cityless"—a calamity in the mind of the ancient Greek—is still present.

European geographers have adopted a classification of agricultural areas for the Mediterranean that corresponds rather closely to the nature of the plant cover. There is a humid (or sub-humid) belt that comprises coastal and interior divisions, and a semi-arid belt. The humid belt in general is characterized by wheat and barley crops, with rye on infertile lands. Wheat and barley are the staple cereals; and barley is also used for animal food, replacing the oats of the north. Forage and root crops, upon which rest the great dairying industry of western Europe, are conspicuously absent here, as are potatoes and corn. Grapes are grown everywhere, and olives, fruits, and nuts have a wide range. Figs, dates, cotton, and less frequently, sugar cane and bananas, are common, but most are importations grown only under special conditions.

In the coastal humid belt dwell approximately two-thirds of all the inhabitants. These favored districts are small in area, but densely populated. Grapes and citrus fruits are combined with wheat and beans in a system of productive agriculture. The grape is indigenous, unlike the citrus fruits which were spread by the Arabs who were masters in irrigation. The growing of citrus fruits to-day is a lucrative industry, largely because of the heavy demands of the nearby markets of western Europe. Sooner or later, with the improvement of methods of shipping, the competition of better suited lands will limit citrus-fruit growing to those Mediterranean areas that employ a skilled system of irrigation.

The grape, like the olive, is said to be an artificial extension of the *maquis*. The vine is planted at suitable intervals to insure freedom from competition for water, and is severely pruned so that the strength will go into the fruit rather than the leaves. Wine is prominent in the Mediterranean diet for it supplies the means of quenching the thirst when pure drinking water is not available. At the time of the year when the thirst is greatest the streams are practically dried up. The grapes, however, are swelling with juice; thus man utilizes the waters of the subsoil, otherwise inaccessible, in the form of wine. A kind of yeast in the waxy bloom causes spontaneous fermentation when the grapes are crushed, yielding light wines when treated properly. Wine fits in admirably with the other constituents of the diet; bread, beans, salad, and oil. Long before the grapes are harvested, the Mediterranean farmer has gathered his crops of wheat and pulses. These are winter crops, planted in the late fall and harvested in the spring. Wheat has always been a problem to dense Mediterranean populations for the wheat growing areas are severely restricted. In consequence beans of various sorts have always been raised. In Italy to-day, where the density of population per square mile exceeds three hundred, wheat, together with meat, is the principal agricultural import. In Greece, too, these products are the leading food importations. Just as the grape is a modified *maquis,* so wheat is said to be a modified *garigue* variety. In the interior humid belt fruits give way to pasture, but wheat and pulses remain the dominant agricultural crops. These interior lands are generally rugged.

The olive is widely distributed throughout the humid area, where the dependable rainfall exceeds 20 inches a year. The olive, like the grape, matures slowly and thrives on relatively little water. As it is slightly more sensitive to frost than the vine, its distribution is not so wide. Since the olive like the grape is harvested late in the year (in some places the olive is harvested during the winter), the farmer is kept busy all year round for he cultivates cereals and pulses during both the winter and spring. The cereals and pulses may be planted in the olive groves, for they depend upon the moisture in the top soil, while the perennials obtain their moisture from the subsoil.

At this point it is necessary to emphasize the differences between

Mediterranean agriculture and that prevailing in western and central Europe. The former is intensive and in consequence has been labeled a "hoe" rather than a plow type of agriculture. Lands are few and vast level spaces for grain-growing operations are lacking. Secondly, the most important Mediterranean crops, the vine and the olive, depend upon the waters stored in the subsoil for their summer sustenance. In Germany the viniculturist fears root rot from excessive summer rains and saturated soils. The Dalmatian peasant, on the other hand, must drain the surface waters into the deeper subsoil. Thus, the German plants his vines upon a hill, *Weinberg,* while the Dalmatian plants his in small artificial depressions, whose blankets are used as bean hills.

The semi-arid belt is found in the driest parts of the Mediterranean and is particularly prominent in the southeastern portions of peninsulas and islands and in typical parts of north Africa, western Asia, and southern Russia. It is designated as "the semi-arid barley, wheat, olive and pasture region." In the Balkans such lands are limited to the coasts and those parts of the interior where the combination of sufficient rainfall and rich volcanic soils earmarked them from earliest times as wheat-producing districts. In Italy the semi-arid belt is drier, and pasture predominates, while in Spain not only is this belt dry, but it is more extensive than elsewhere. In Spain, especially, is irrigation significant though it is practised in many semi-arid regions. Rich crops are produced in small, irrigated valleys, while the surrounding lands are generally barren and uncultivated. Many of the irrigation canals and aqueducts in use to-day were built by the Moors. The citrus fruit-bearing districts of Valencia and Murcia are irrigated lands, and such tracts are known significantly as *huertas* or gardens. Many of the Spanish lands can support only cattle grasses such as *esparto.* As these grasses dry up during the summer drought, *transhumance*—the shifting of livestock to the north in summer and south in winter—is characteristic of stock raising not only in Spain, but in southern France, northern Italy, and elsewhere.

Mediterranean man's great achievement is that he has, wherever possible, replaced the natural vegetation by a series of crops which make use of every drop of water, every square foot of soil, and yield him a complete diet. Wine, the olive (which yields a necessary digestible fat in an environment where little meat fat is to be had), and wheat are the mainstays of subsistence. The pulses, beans, and peas are important as proteid because of the scarcity of meat. Flavoring substances such as garlic and onions are used to correct the taste-lessness of vegetable foods. In addition there are a variety of common edible fruits and nuts that have not been mentioned, particularly the fig, the apricot, the pomegranate, and the almond. Figs and apricots are of special importance because they can be dried and used during the winter. In north Italy, Spain, and southern France, rice is grown; in Algeria the banana appears as a supplementary food; and in the drier parts of north Africa, the date intrudes from the desert. Fish, from the nearby waters, are important.

94. Occupations

The occupations of Mediterranean peoples necessarily center about agricultural production. But there are relatively few cash crops. Insufficiency of suitable land interdicts any considerable export of wheat or other cereals. The chief exports are wine and olives. Until the rivalry of California became a factor, these lands had no competitor in the field of preserved olives and olive oils. Wines, however, encounter great competition in western Europe and are becoming less valuable as an export. The raisins of Spain and the currants of Greece and Asia Minor enjoyed a monopoly position until the products of other Subtropical environments—California and Australia—appeared. The dried figs of Asia Minor, notwithstanding the competition of California, are still popular. The oranges of Spain, Portugal, the Atlas lands, and Palestine, and the lemons of Sicily are of importance principally because they are the nearest source of supply for western Europe. The competition at present is very severe since the citrus fruits grown upon irrigated lands in California, Subtropical Australia, South Africa, and in southerly areas of ample summer rainfall such as Florida, are sent to Europe in increasing quantities.

Pasturing, particularly of goats, pigs, and sheep, occupies many, but the products are consumed locally and do not feature in trade. The same may be said of the donkeys and horses that are in evidence everywhere. Where goats are plentiful, tanning is important, and the trees and shrubs that yield dyeing fluids contribute materially to the leather industry. In Sicily the *sumach* shrub is important for this purpose, and Asia Minor exports acorns, valuable for *tannin*. Scented substances, oils, resins and gums, derived from various plants, enter commerce in small amounts.

Lumbering is not a major industry in the Mediterranean environment, for saw-mill woods in large quantities are absent. The chief interest in connection with the forest industry arises from the oaks of Spain and Portugal that supply most of the world's cork. Much is utilized locally in connection with the wine industry, but there is a considerable export. The outer bark of the oak is cut from the trunk of the tree every ten years. An acre of seventy trees will yield a ton of cork, which brings a high price. Some of these oaks are more than 150 years old. In the cork-producing vicinities of Portugal the trees alone are sold, the land being thrown in for good measure. This industry is complementary to livestock raising, for the goats thin out the underbrush, while the pigs feed upon the acorns that fall from the trees. The mulberry tree, whose foliage provides food for the silkworm, is a Chinese importation. Yet neither the mulberry nor the worm is ideally suited to the typical Mediterranean environment. The tree, while it requires mild, uniform temperatures, also needs moisture during the summer. It is a deciduous species, and the more summer moisture it receives, the richer the foliage. North Italy is unique in providing a long warm season, summer rains, and cheap labor. True Mediterranean regions producing raw silk, however, generally employ irrigation. The rainfall of north Italy is not a Mediterranean type but resembles that of the Humid Continental Interior. The mulberry does not thrive as well in southern France because of the danger of frost in extra-Mediterranean areas; but the French are the largest silk manufacturers in Europe, purchasing most of the Italian raw silk. The intrusion of the Humid Continental Interior with summer rainfall in north Italy, Spain, and elsewhere in Mediterranean Europe affects the agriculture there. Not only the mulberry is grown but also corn, the sugar beet, and hemp, all of which require summer rain.

There is little manufacturing in Mediterranean countries because of the dearth of iron ore, coking coal, and other essential materials. The Spanish peninsula, however, has always been rich in metals and minerals, and to-day the 200,000 miners provide a considerable export in coal, copper, lead, and iron ore. Both Spain and Portugal have cotton textile industries that supply local needs. The cotton is for the most part imported, but in Spain, at least, Merino wool and raw silk sustain small industrial enterprises. Italy has built up a large textile industry by developing almost to capacity the water power resources of the country. More than four million Italians are employed in manufacturing. Cheap labor and cheap hydro-electric power are Italy's chief industrial advantages, but against these must be balanced the importations of coal, iron and steel, cotton, and wool. Close government oversight of industrial development is responsible for a doubling of the export trade since 1914, but even at present the trade balance is unfavorable for the exports per capita are valued at $19, the imports per capita at $27. With Italy the end has been reached in Mediterranean manufactures. From Greece, around the sea to Morocco, society is founded solidly upon an agricultural base supplemented by domestic, mainly household, industries.

95. The Mediterranean Mode of Life

Anatolia, comprising most of the territory of post-war Turkey, affords excellent materials for a study of the Mediterranean environment at close range. Whereas the Mediterranean lands of Europe are in close proximity to continental influences and the Mediterranean lands of Africa are infringed upon by desert influences, Anatolia reveals simply the transition from humid coasts to semi-arid interior. It might be called the most typical of all Mediterranean environments because here are found all the conditions and ways of life that one is led to expect from a general description of the Mediterranean milieu.

The population, which is largely rural, decreases in density as the drier interior is approached. Thus the population of the largest coastal city, Smyrna,[1] is 150,000, but that of the largest interior town is little more than half that size. Modern Turkey has located its capital at Angora[2] far inland upon the Anatolian plateau. She has withdrawn from the maelstrom of European influences hoping to husband all that is best in the prevailing mode of life. Angora is far enough away to escape foreign influences which at closer range are all but irresistible, yet not so isolated as to be entirely out of contact with the more beneficent forces of world civilization.

[1] Izmir.
[2] Ankara.

In Anatolia are found three environmental subdivisions, humid lowlands and slopes, a plateau interior, and three widely separated forest belts. The first is characterized by typical Mediterranean agriculture, the second by pastoral nomadism, and the last by forest exploitation. The humid lowlands extend from the western coasts to a distance of roughly two hundred miles into the interior, while the semi-arid belt occupies the remainder of Anatolia. The forest belts are marginal. Two are narrow coastal strips, one located on the Black Sea coast, the other along the southern coast. The remaining forest belt is located in the heart of northern Anatolia, in the province of Brusa. Because of the very ruggedness of this region it is little known even to-day, though its western border approaches the Mediterranean coast.

Anatolia as a whole exhibits characteristic Mediterranean features. The rainy season and the cool season coincide, thus the moisture comes when vegetation is dormant. The hot season and the dry season coincide, resulting in a type of climate that prohibits the growth of vegetation but is admirable for ripening drought-resistant grains. Spring and fall, when the sun is fairly hot and rainfall fairly abundant, are the periods of greatest agricultural activity. The lands are everywhere rather rugged, restricting the cultivable land area even in the humid west. High relief then, is a factor in confining agriculture to the stream bottoms and their immediate slopes. In the west is encountered less residual soil deposit than is normally found in the humid Mediterranean environment. The action of violent rainstorms upon higher lands makes for erosion, deforestation, and extensive wastage of soil, while the correspondence of the dry and hot seasons retards rock disintegration and renders soil renewal very slow. For these reasons, then, there is more dependence upon alluvial soil, a transported type, than upon the residual soil cover.

In the humid area the grains are the most important crops. Probably four-fifths of the cultivated lands are devoted to them. Wheat and barley, eminently suited to the régime of winter rainfall, are of necessity the staples. These are sown in the fall and germinate during the season of autumnal rains. Low temperatures retard growth during the winter but with the rising temperatures of spring the seedlings grow rapidly. The moisture of the subsoil, supplemented by ever-diminishing rains in the spring, supplies the necessary moisture. Harvesting takes place from May until August, depending upon the locality. Agricultural methods are quite primitive: the seed is broadcast by hand, and the threshing is done upon hard-packed earthen floors. Rice, too, is cultivated, but as climatic conditions are hardly suitable for this crop, it is grown only under extraordinary conditions. When the means of irrigation is extended, rice will be more widely grown, for it is highly valued as a foodstuff. At present its cultivation is limited to low marshy lands where stagnant waters are available. The conditions of rice culture were so unfavorable to man in some districts that the government was forced to forbid its cultivation in order to curtail the ravages of malaria.

Tobacco is the money crop of this belt, although the tobaccos of Macedonia and Samsun are more highly regarded than Smyrna tobacco. Peculiar conditions of soil and climate give Turkish tobacco an aroma that is much desired in the cigarette industry Indeed it is said that without the addition of some Turkish tobacco a good cigarette cannot be manufactured. American corporations import large quantities of Turkish tobaccos, and although some have gone to the extent of importing quantities of soil from Anatolia in an endeavor to attain this aroma, all attempts have failed. The tobacco land must be fertilized; the seed is sown in March, transplanted in June, and harvested in September.

Spring rains and hot summers have made possible the cultivation of cotton in limited areas in western Anatolia and in the Cilician coastal plain. During the summer drought heavy dews are relied upon to furnish moisture. The crop is sown in March and harvested in October. Under a system of irrigation the rich cotton soils that exist in certain sections would undoubtedly make a profitable crop, but at present the methods of culture are very crude. The farmers often plant sesame seeds, which draw nutrient materials from the soil, and melons, which use up much moisture, along with cotton. Cloudbursts, hailstorms, and locust plagues render cultivation still more precarious. Cotton culture, however, persists because of the need of coarse cotton clothing of special design.

Tree crops and fruit crops have a great importance in western Anatolia. Among the densely populated sections the olive is necessary as a substitute for butter and animal fats. The tree grows in districts where the winter rainfall exceeds ten inches, a condition met throughout the humid belt. Too much moisture is unfavorable for the olive because the fruit diminishes in succulence, and spring frost will ruin the crop. In consequence this tree is planted at intermediate levels where the moisture of the subsoil will drain away and in places protected from cold northern winds. The olive crop is harvested leisurely in November and December. In this region olive production ranges from 150,000 to 450,000 tons annually. Grapes are produced in even more prodigious quantities, a harvest of 800,000 tons not being considered unusual. Like the olive, the grape is esteemed as a food necessity and is consumed locally. From Smyrna, however, there is a considerable export of the famous Sultana raisin. Not so much wine is made here as in other Mediterranean regions since Moslems are forbidden alcohol. The fruit is eaten fresh or in the dried form. In Turkey, and in Syria as well, large quantities of *raki* are made from grapes. This is not a wine, but a distilled liquor, about the strength of vodka. The Turk prepares a special liquid, *pekmez,* as a way of preserving the juice of the grape. Grape juice is boiled and beaten, converting it from a thin fluid to a thick, partially crystallized substance not unlike honey. The beating must be done by the open hand, and unless the beating is continuous, all will be spoiled. Sometimes the beating lasts all day and all night, and women and girls as well as men participate. Another method, more commonly employed, is to "tread out" the grapes by bare feet in a stone vat from which the juice runs into jars. The making of *pekmez* is a commonplace in all the villages of this region after the grape harvest. The distribution of the fig corresponds to that of the olive, and the dry fig industry is most flourishing in the vicinity of shipping towns. The Smyrna dried fig is given preference in the export trade because of its peculiar flavor, which is attributed to the large number of ripe seeds the fig contains. In addition, the crop seems to be dependent upon a fertilizing insect and can be grown only where the winters are sufficiently mild to enable this insect to survive. The fig has the quality of withstanding high temperatures and the characteristic summer drought of Mediterranean regions.

Stock raising has more than average importance as an occupation in western Anatolia because of the small extent of cultivable lands. The industry here, however, differs from that of the semi-arid interior in two important respects; it is not nomadic, and it deals with different types of animals. Cattle and water buffalo, for example, require more abundant pasturage than can be found in the plateau. The stock raising might be called semi-nomadic, however, because of the alternation of plain and mountain as pasture. During the damp, cool winter the herdsmen pitch their tents upon the lowland plains, but when the summer drought begins to turn the plain brown, they retreat with their herds to the nearby hills and mountains. Thus here, as elsewhere in the Mediterranean zone, transhumance is a feature of the stock-raising industry. Pasture lands are most plentiful in the lowlands where the river bottoms are shifting and on the slopes where the forest has been cut over.

Relatively few are engaged in industries other than agriculture. Small amounts of coal, lignite, silver, lead, and zinc are mined, but more interest is attached to chromite, emery, and meerschaum. Western Anatolia ranks with Greece and Russia as a chromite producer, and each of these regions has, at one time or another, ranked second to New Caledonia as the chief producer in the world. Turkish emery is highly valued as a finishing polisher for plate glass and optical glass, for its quality is better than any other emery mined. The meerschaum of Eskishekir monopolizes the world market. The industry is a government monopoly, but the individual seekers obtain permits to gather the nodules from the pits. Practically the whole product is shipped to Vienna for working. Forest industries are likewise of minor importance. Pines, oaks, larches, chestnuts, and beeches, the most common varieties in western Anatolia, are employed in construction, in furniture making, and for firewood after conversion into charcoal. The acorn cups of the valonia oak are gathered and shipped, being valuable for their tannin extract. Wherever accessible these stands have been cut over long ago, but, because of the topographical difficulties encountered in getting at the wood, large districts still abound in timber. There is really no lumbering industry for saw-mills are as yet very rare. The Turkish government is attempting to foster reforestation.

Manufacturing is based largely upon the resources of the humid region and its hinterland. The government aids the feeble cotton-textile industry by tariff and subsidy, and recently it has permitted Ford to establish an automobile assembly plant. Western Anatolia, however, is known principally for two exports—carpets and raw silk. The silk industry has not prospered because of disease among the worms. Smyrna is the center of the carpet and rug industry, and over fifty thousand people are engaged in it. Most of the rugs are knitted by women and girls, but foreigners, chiefly British, have set up carpet-weaving mills. Sheep are driven in from the hinterland and clipped before being slaughtered for meat. This wool, together with that provided by the vicinity, enables the dealers to supply the weavers with sufficient yarn. Minor manufacturers are cotton goods, soaps made from olive oils, pottery, and tiles.

The semi-arid region of pastoral nomadism embraces far more territory than any of the other regions of Anatolia. Compared with western Anatolia its population is sparse and its products are much less valuable. Climatically, because of diminishing rainfall as the central interior is approached, the type changes gradually from a Mediterranean to a Trade Wind Desert variety. The annual rainfall average for the whole zone is less than fourteen inches a year. The dry summer is interrupted only by occasional convectional showers induced by the proximity of waters that surround the peninsula on three sides. Only on the mountain slopes is there any rainfall, because inblowing winds tend to increase their moisture-holding capacity as they blow over heated land surfaces. In the winter the wind movements are reversed and only occasionally do rain-bearing Westerlies reach the interior. Semi-arid Anatolia lacks extensive areas of good soil. In many places there is no soil at all, the land surface being covered with stones and the rocks washed clean by heavy showers. The rapid evaporation is responsible for the formation of an infertile alkali crust in many places. Tuz Lake, in the drier southeast, is a shallow expanse of four hundred square miles. It has a salt content of 32 per cent, and because of the summer evaporation the people are able to gather large quantities of salt on the exposed shores.

In such an environment tillage is difficult. There is, however, some agriculture, especially in regions where the mountain rains can be utilized and along streams that flow toward the interior depression. But stock raising constitutes the usual means of making a living. Transhumance and nomadism are prevalent. Although this is a plateau region, much of the surface is rugged. In consequence, the stock are pastured upon higher slopes during the summer and driven down to lower levels (usually of high altitude) during the winter season. The plant cover, however, is very scanty; therefore it is necessary to move the flocks constantly over wide areas in order to provide them with sufficient nutriment in the form of grasses.

Sheep are the most important live stock because the grass is not rich enough to support cattle, and hog products are tabu for those of the Moslem faith. Sheep furnish milk, meat, and wool. There is a large demand for sheep in Constantinople [1] and Smyrna, and large flocks move from all directions upon these markets. Sheep are driven frequently clear across Anatolia from Kurdistan, sometimes occupying a whole year in transit. This practice could only exist in a land where the settled agricultural interest is very small. Most of the wool is utilized in making homespuns, but some reaches the rug weavers' establishments. The milk of the ewes, as well as that of cattle, buffalo, and goats, is converted into a substance of the solidity of junket, called *yoghurt*. It is a food of nomadic origin which is now used in the villages as well as in the pasture lands. "Drink the raw milk of the country and you die with an approach to certainty; but experience shows you may eat yoghurt anywhere and fear no ill." Yoghurt is made by heating the milk to blood temperature, then allowing it to cool to a point at which the addition of a small spoonful of old yoghurt may be introduced. This causes the whole to congeal.

Goats, which are almost as numerous as sheep, are useful, too, for their milk, their hair, and their meat. The mohair of some districts is very valuable, particularly that produced in the region northwest of Angora which has a long white fleecy quality. Each year more than three million pounds of it are baled and shipped abroad. The goats are found in very sparsely vegetated regions and can eke out a living where sheep and cattle cannot. In large parts of the plateau they have changed the aspect of the vegetation, for by their constant nibbling of the young shoots they are able to keep such familiar species as the oak and the beech to the height of bushes. The water buffalo is raised where the land is low and swampy, generally in places where it is too unhealthy to raise other animals. They are shipped all over Anatolia and used as draft animals. The camels and horses are raised in the drier districts where the railway has not penetrated as yet.

Agriculture in the semi-arid region is limited to localities where more than normal moisture can be depended upon. Mountain streams, favorable to a homely type of irrigation, are scattered about in sequestered places. Grain can be grown in many places without irrigation but all other crops require watering. The olive and the fig

[1] Istanbul.

cannot withstand the low winter temperature, while the apple, pear, and other frost-resistant fruits cannot obtain sufficient moisture. The Angora district, however, is famous for its pears, and the Kastamonu district for its apples. The grape is ubiquitous. Opium is the only cash crop of value. It is suited to the dry climate, and its small bulk enables it to bear the cost of transport to the markets. Like many other crops in regions of winter rainfall, it is planted before the autumn frosts and harvested in July. Anatolian opium is held to be superior to the India and China varieties, and much of it is sold in the West where it is used for medicinal purposes. In the semi-arid region there is very little mining or lumbering because of the lack of development. The charcoal burner is the sole inhabitant of the mountain forest.

In the forest regions proper, along the northern and southern coasts, and in the province of Brusa, the same geographical relation prevails. Yet these regions include excellent stands of wood and constitute for Turkey a considerable forest reserve. The Black Sea coast rises precipitously to a height of four thousand feet; consequently the sea winds in attaining the crest are forced high up and yield heavy rainfall. In this district, given the sobriquet "Sea of Trees," species such as the oak, beech, fir, chestnut, elm, and black pine grow in profusion. There are at least fifty-two varieties of oak, more than any other region in the world can boast. A little of the timber has from time immemorable been used in ship building but these forests *in extenso* are not only unexploited but they are unknown. This district, however, exports large quantities of hazel nuts. The forests of the Brusa area, as has been mentioned, have not been exploited for timber because of the ruggedness of the land. The southern forest is the most important economically, largely because of the dependence of the inhabitants of the densely settled plain of Adana upon them for wood. Here, as on the northern shores, the forests provided the raw materials of an ancient ship-building industry. Cattle and other stock graze upon the coastwise slopes; parched inhabitants seek shelter during the summer from the hot sun; and charcoal burners, as elsewhere, infest its deepnesses, but otherwise the southern forest has hardly been disturbed. In times to come Anatolia will undoubtedly furnish timber to forest-poor neighbors such as Egypt.

CHAPTER XII

SOUTH AMERICA: THE GEOGRAPHY OF A CONTINENT

96. Topographical Features

Notwithstanding the fact that the population of South America has doubled in the last fifty years and during the same period a foreign investment approximating ten billion dollars has been made, that continent is no more an El Dorado than it was three centuries ago. The density of population is less than ten per square mile, and at the present writing four-fifths of the post-war American investment of a billion dollars is in default of interest. Theodore Roosevelt's prophecy that the twentieth century would be the century of South America has not yet materialized, and although the building of the Panama Canal constitutes a splendid achievement, it has removed only one of a large number of obstacles placed by nature in the path of progress.

Roughly two-thirds of South America is situated in tropical latitudes, and that portion of the continent is practically uninhabitable except in the relatively small highland areas. The temperate belt south of the Tropic of Cancer constitutes but a small proportion of the whole continent. South America tapers rapidly so that the west and east coasts meet at Cape Horn, about 55° S. Furthermore, the temperate belt lies far from the main highways of ocean commerce. The coast line of South America is very regular; there are few gulfs and bays and in consequence few good harbors. Along the eastern seaboard, with the exception of Rio de Janeiro, an excellent harbor, the coasts are emergent and the waters shallow. Buenos Aires maintains its oceanic communication only by constantly dredging a narrow channel at an enormous expense. On the north coast, the estuaries are blocked by sand bars. At Puerto Colombia, on the coast of Colombia, only six vessels can dock along the pier which extends fully a mile into the water. Willemstad, the port of the island of Curaçao, controls much of the trade of Venezuela because of its location near the entrance of the shallow Lake Maracaibo. The west coast lacks a single good harbor; even Valparaiso, which affords dockage to large vessels, is an open harbor. Everywhere freight must be transferred to lighters and the change of bulk adds enormously to shipping costs.

The principal physiographical features of South America are distinctly unfavorable in comparison with those of other continents. On the west, the Andes Mountains form the longest continuous range in the world. Their height is so great that commercial intercourse between west and east is practically prohibited. The great interior plains of the continent lie for the most part within the unhealthy tropics. Here the river facilities are excellent, in contrast to those of the more settled south. The Eastern Highlands rising rather abruptly from the sea not only limit the coastal plain but are, in addition, a barrier to the interior. On the other hand, their high slopes gives rise to types of economic activity that would otherwise be non-existent in tropical latitudes. Though containing a relatively small desert area South America has a larger proportion of uninhabited land than any other continent.

The Andes dominate South America. Over four thousand miles in length and for the greater part over ten thousand feet in height, they furnish a uniform environment for the inhabitants of that part of the continent. Here, as in East Africa, altitude rather than latitude, has the more profound influence. The more significant effects are as follows: first, the Andes insure a temperate climate in tropical latitudes; secondly, their snowcapped peaks provide waters for irrigation; thirdly, they furnish the adjacent valleys with fine soil. In giving rise to rain shadows they have a dominant influence upon the climate of adjoining areas.

The Andes enter South America at two points along the Caribbean, near the Orinoco Delta and near Lake Maracaibo, and the two branches meet in central Colombia. To Venezuela and Colombia, situated in equatorial latitudes, the mountains are of great benefit, for the coastal lands are hot, sultry, and swampy. Here they are not such an insuperable hindrance to communication as elsewhere; in Colombia, the movement of commerce follows the direction of the mountains, while in Venezuela the ranges are parallel to the coasts.

Between southern Colombia and northern Argentina three parallel chains are discernible: the Cordillera Occidental on the west, the Cordillera Central in the middle, and the Cordillera Oriental in the east. At various places they lose their identity, joining in huge rugged knots in southern Colombia, in southern Ecuador, in central Peru, and about Lake Titicaca. The Cordillera Occidental rises abruptly from the coast and attains great heights. Though they harbor rich mineral resources, they constitute the greatest barrier to transportation in South America. These generalizations are true of the Central Cordillera also. Between the two lies the *altiplano,* a great plateau of gentle relief and interior drainage. In the south the altiplano encloses extensive salt plains, but around Lake Titicaca, whose altitude is 12,500 feet, the soils are relatively fertile. Minor plateaus in Peru and Ecuador known as High Pampas support the principal agricultural activities in those countries. The Cordillera Oriental, though high (the Cordillera Real of Bolivia averages twenty thousand feet for a hundred miles) is less precipitous, and its eastern slopes leading to the interior plains contain much rich, though isolated, agricultural land. South of Bolivia, the Andes present a single compact system. About 36° S. the appearance of the mountains changes, for the Westerlies bring moisture from the Pacific, and the western slopes are transformed from arid brown to verdant green. In the far south there is much glaciation, and icebergs are common along the coasts. Here several structural breaks permit communication between Chile and Argentina.

The western coast of South America has an inhospitable aspect. The coastal plain on the whole is narrow except at the mouth of the Guayas River, a broad, swampy estuary. In Peru and northern Chile, the coastlands are arid and mountain-bound. In Chile, the coastal range is very formidable, rising to eight thousand feet. Between the coastal range and the Andes, however, lies the fertile Central Valley of Chile, the counterpart of the Mediterranean valley of California.

Colombia possesses two lowland areas, the Magdalena-Cauca plain, built up by sediment, and the Maracaibo basin, a shallow bay-lake surrounded by swampy lands. With the exception of the Eastern Highlands and the Patagonian Tablelands the remainder of South America, more than half the continent, consists of the Central Interior Plains. They extend from the Caribbean to the Rio Negro in Argentina. The northern portions, the llanos consisting of the Amazon basin and the Paraguay-Paraná Plains, have been built up by alluvial sediment from the Andes, while the southern portion, the pampas, consists of a deep accumulation of æolian sediment blown from the mountains. All the plainlands have an elevation of less than one thousand feet.

The llanos lie between the Andes and the Guiana Highlands. They drain into the Orinoco River but because of the gentle gradient much of the country is flooded during the rainy season. On a larger scale, the same is true of the enormous Amazon basin. At a distance of two thousand miles from the sea, the elevation is but 250 feet; consequently the Amazon and many of its branches are unable to carry off the heavy rains. The Paraguay-Paraná Plains, draining into the Rio de la Plata, are even more unfavorably situated. The run-off is poorer, and in the *chaco* west of the Paraguay River are some of the greatest swamplands of the world. The pampas evidence the same lack of drainage, indeed only three small streams cross them in an extent of seven hundred miles, yet other factors render them one of the finest agricultural areas of the world.

The Eastern Highlands consist of the Guiana and Brazilian Highlands. These highlands are interrupted only by the Amazon basin. The Guiana Highlands have built up the largest coastal plain in South America but much of it takes the form of a low tidal flat. They are sparsely settled because access to them has been denied on account of the uninviting character of the piedmont. The Brazilian Highlands, large in extent and varied in relief, are densely populated. The land consists of a succession of ranges and plateaus. The drainage, however, is north, west, and south, rather than east, for the coastal mountains attain a height of nine thousand feet and act as a fluvial barrier. The São Francisco River, the principal plateau stream, flows northward behind the coastal ranges, while the southern portion of the highlands is drained by the Paraná system.

The Patagonian Tableland is a curious geological structure extending through southern Argentina. Rising to a height of five thousand feet, it is flanked on the west by an arid depression parallel to the Andes and on the east by a ribbonlike coastal plain. The northern portion—a windy, uninhabited, arid land—is composed of large areas of sandstone cut by streams vainly trying to reach the sea. In the south, however, the altitude diminishes, the rains are heavier, and the land is more hospitable.

97. Climatic Features

South America is unique among the great continents in that it exhibits little seasonal variation in temperature.[1] This is primarily because so much of it lies within tropical latitudes. In the second place, the land lying in the temperate zone is narrow in breadth thus permitting the moderating influences of the oceans to be fully effective. Although the great interior plains have an annual temperature exceeding 70°, they are less hot than tropical Africa because of their greater cloudiness and rainfall. Moreover, because of the proximity of the cool Peru Current, the trade wind desert on the west coast is not subject to the daily and seasonal variations that occur in the Sahara. Indeed, this current establishes almost uniform temperature conditions along the coastal border from 30° S. to the equator, a distance of two thousand miles. Thus the annual temperature at Callao (12° S.) is 67°, while 350 miles further south it is only 65°. In temperate latitudes the seasonal range of temperature rarely exceeds 30°, a remarkably small range in comparison with that of the continental interiors of the northern hemisphere.[2]

As in East Africa and other tropical highlands, temperatures vary precisely in accordance with altitude. The following zones are well marked in the Andean region: *tierra caliente* (below three thousand feet), *tierra templada* (three to six thousand feet), *tierra fria* (six to ten thousand feet), and the *paramos* (ten to thirteen thousand feet). The *caliente* has a temperature range from 83° to 75° and supports a luxuriant tropical vegetation. The *templada* has a range from 75° to 65° and is suitable for maize and coffee. The *tierra fria* with a range of 65° to 54° is a region capable of growing wheat and temperate fruits. The *paramos* are too cold for trees or cultivation of any sort. Above the thirteen-thousand foot level there is perpetual snow. Quito and Bogotá are about nine thousand feet above sea level; the former has an annual temperature of 65°, the latter, 58°. The uniformity of temperature is remarkable; Quito has a seasonal variation of 1° and Bogotá of 2°.

Pressure and wind belts in South America vary little from those encountered in the same latitudes elsewhere, though the mountain

---

[1] Examine carefully Plates X, XI, XII, XIII.

[2] The isotherm 32° in China extends to within 35° of the equator, but in South America it never reaches Cape Horn, 56° from the equator.

barriers have a marked influence upon the amount and seasonal distribution of the rainfall. The Equatorial Low Pressure Belt is very extensive because the land mass is greatest in equatorial latitudes. In January the doldrums hold sway throughout Brazil which embraces almost half the continent. Tropical South America is strongly influenced by the trade wind systems. In January the Northeast Trades penetrate as far as the Amazon, but in July they are weak and interrupted owing to the northward extension of the doldrums. The humid Southeast Trades are most effective in July when they blow far north to the equator and far inland to the Andes. On the west coast the Southeast Trades are very dry and are forced to blow north parallel to the Andes. The Subtropical Belt of High Pressure exerts its usual drying influence along the western coast from latitudes 25° to 35°. But in the interior, in the plainlands drained by the Paraná and the Uruguay, the high pressure system is effective only during the winter months. This condition is abnormal and is probably due to the dominant influence of the doldrums of Amazonia. In consequence the interior at about 30° S., instead of being dry like southern Arizona, receives a considerable rainfall during the summer season. South of 40° the continent is under the influence of cyclone-bearing Westerlies all year round. The lee side of the Andes is a rain shadow, as would be expected, and in consequence most of Patagonia is a desert. At the tip of the continent where the mountain barrier disappears the lands are well watered. During the winter season the Westerlies shift northward as far as 31° S. along the west coast, but during the summer half year this Mediterranean region is under the control of the Subtropical Belt of High Pressure.

98. Climate Types and Natural Vegetation

With the exception of the Rio São Francisco lands in northeast Brazil, the whole of South America lying east of a diagonal line from Guayaquil (3° S.) on the Pacific to Florianopolis (28° S.) on the Atlantic receives an annual rainfall exceeding sixty inches. Nowhere in the world is there such a vast region of heavy rainfall. In this belt, comprising two-thirds of the continent, are found three tropical types of climate: Equatorial, Subequatorial, and Trade Wind with Ample Rain.

The Equatorial type, covering roughly the extent of the Amazon basin, exhibits the characteristic rainfall of 10° N. to 10° S., a double maximum corresponding with the equinoxes. Where the trades penetrate; in upper Amazonia, along the Guiana coast, and the west coast of Colombia, the precipitation is enormous. Manáos, in central Brazil, has an annual rainfall of seventy-two inches, while Iquitos, situated in the eastern slopes of the Peruvian Andes, receives 103 inches. Nothing, however, compares with the deluge in towns facing the trades along the west coast of Colombia. Buena Vista, for example, has an annual rainfall of 340 inches and Andogoya, 275 inches. In the Equatorial zone there is little seasonal range of temperature. In the Amazon basin, the difference between the warmest and the coolest months is about 4°; in western Colombia, it is only 1°. The daily range is greater than the seasonal range since, as in other Equatorial regions, afternoon showers produce falling temperatures. Winter is said to come each day at night.

The combination of heat and heavy rainfall produces in Equatorial regions the rain forest type of natural vegetation. The Amazonian forest extends almost uninterruptedly to the slopes of the Andes, a distance of 2,500 miles. Over large areas, where the double maximum prevails, giant evergreens form a huge canopy, causing plant life to take refuge in the foliage. Even flowers bloom in the trees. Elsewhere are thickets of mangrove, palm, bamboo, and masses of lianas and creepers, presenting a jungle-like appearance. The towering evergreens, the overhanging clouds, the dampness, the stifling heat, and the sogginess of much of the surface have won for Amazonia the sobriquet, "green hell." The rain forest appears also in Guiana and along the northern Pacific and Caribbean coasts. It extends into the interior where there exist depressions such as the Atrato and the Magdalena valleys and the Maracaibo basin.

The rain forest is a wretched environment for human beings. Even the aborigines have shunned these regions because of the difficulty of sustaining life. The forest Indians are classified by anthropologists as internally marginal because their environment rendered them incapable of adopting the higher cultures of their neighbors, the Inca and the Chibcha. The white man, too, has avoided the rain forest. His interest centers solely in the exploitation of forest products such as hardwoods, rubber, and cacao.

The Subequatorial type, as in Africa, appears both north and south of the Equatorial region. It is most pronounced in the southern hemisphere and is clearly marked as far south as Asunción (25° S.). Most of this region receives more than fifty inches of rainfall and all of it over thirty inches. The winter dry spell, even in the south, is much shorter than in the Sudan, for the trades that reach the chaco are humid. Conditions of temperature and rainfall are typical at Cuyaba (15° 30' S.), in the campos of south central Brazil. During nine months the temperature is about 80°, but in July it falls to 75°. The seasonal character of the rainfall is more pronounced; in January, Cuyaba receives twenty-eight inches, in July, two inches. In the northern hemisphere the Subequatorial type is less extensive in area. The Northeast Trades, however, blow uninterruptedly into the Orinoco basin with the result that a definite dry season is discernible to within 4° of the equator in southern Venezuela. A typical llano village, Calabozo, receives 99 per cent of its rainfall during the summer half year. When the trades are most pronounced, from December to February, Calabozo receives one-tenth of an inch of rainfall. In consequence the llanos, though their annual rainfall varies from thirty to fifty inches, suffer severe droughts.

As in Africa and elsewhere, the natural vegetation of the Subequatorial belt varies greatly with latitude. Where the wet season is of long duration, near the equatorial margin, tropical jungle is the prevailing type. Where the dry season is pronounced, tropical grass flourishes. The most important savanna lands in South America are the llanos, the campos, and the chaco. The llanos are situated in Colombia and Venezuela, between the Orinoco and the Andes. Only the tough bunch grass, green in the wet season and brown in the dry reason, is able to survive the blistering effects of the Northeast Trades that blow equatorward from November to March. The campos and the chaco are situated in the southern hemisphere, hence their period of drought extends from May until September. The campos of Brazil extend almost to the equator owing to the influence of altitude which varies from 1,600 to 2,500 feet. The chaco, to the contrary, is low land in southern Bolivia and western Paraguay. The llanos and the campos are inaccessible because of their interior location, while the chaco repels human habitation because during the rainy season it is transformed into a huge undrained swampland.

The Highlands of Brazil combine two types of climate which merge imperceptibly in the transition from tropical to temperate region. In the north, the prevailing type is Trade with Ample Rain; in the south, Continental with Marine Influence with a monsoonal in-draught such as exists along the warm southern coasts of the United States. Only on the windward slopes where the Southeast Trades are in evidence all the year round is the rainfall heavy, from forty to eighty inches. The humidity and the temperature are high with little seasonal range. Steady winds and higher altitudes, however, do much to alleviate conditions. The Brazilian Highlands, somewhat more ex-tensive than the trade wind belt, have a superb climate. Rainfall varies from thirty to fifty inches and is well distributed throughout the year. Some districts like that about São Paulo have relatively dry months but fortunately these do not correspond with the growing season. The temperature is equable; the summer temperature at São Paulo, for example, averages 70°, less than that of Rosaria, five hundred miles further south. The winters are mild, though care must be exercised in the location of plantations for frost is ruinous to coffee, which is the main crop in this section.

Jungle is the prevailing type of natural vegetation in the lowlands and on the lower slopes. The northern portion of the Eastern High-lands exhibits a combination of rain forest and jungle. The sombre greenness of Amazonia is present, yet plant life is more luxuriant and diversified. Proximity to the sea has assisted in the exploitation of timber, and remarkable soil fertility has led to an agricultural penetration far into the *mata* or forest zone. Further south in Brazil, the mixed type of forest is more prominent than the hardwoods. Much of this land, however, has been cleared, enabling the planters to profit from the rich *terra rosa* forest soils. This region is also transi-tional between wet coasts and lee interior; the coastal lands are char-acterized by evergreens, palms, and dense growths of bamboo and ferns, while in the lee interior appear cacti and other xerophytic [1] forms. In the southern portion of the plateau, comprised in southern Brazil and eastern Paraguay, grows the Paraná pine, of unique im-portance in a continent that is otherwise almost lacking in workable soft woods. This part of the plateau, however, has a climate more akin to the Continental with Marine Influence type than the Trade with Ample Rain type.

In the western part of the continent from the Gulf of Guayaquil (3° S.) to the southern margin of the Atacama Desert (*circa* 30° S.) is situated the most extensive of South American deserts. The

---

[1] A type of plant life able to endure scarcity of moisture.

Peruvian-Chilean trade wind desert includes not only the narrow coasts but also a large part of the Andean plateau. Many villages in this desert go for years without experiencing a real rainfall. Iquique, a coastal town in northern Chile, averages but a single rain during the year, and the annual total is $\frac{1}{500}$ of an inch. The temperature of the coastal border is much lower than that which usually prevails in trade wind deserts owing to the proximity of the cool Peru Current. Lima has a mean temperature 10° lower than Bahia [1] on the east coast. The Peru Current is also a factor in the extreme aridity of the region since winds which blow from it to the warmer land experience a sharp decline in relative humidity. Through the "winter" season the coasts are cloudy but precipitation does not follow. The Southeast Trades attracted by the hot lands blow inland, but as they cannot surmount the Andes, they are deflected to the north. For this reason the desert lands extend to within a few degrees of the equator. Needless to say, natural vegetation is limited almost entirely to cacti.

Only generalizations can be made concerning climatic conditions in the mountains where altitude is the predominating factor. The Andes extend through the whole of tropical South America. In general, the rainfall is heaviest in the north where the Northeast Trades penetrate and precipitate their moisture. Along the eastern slopes, however, the double maximum is discernible owing to proximity to Amazonia, and the Southeast Trades are a cause of heavy rainfall. Bogotá and Quito, in the mountains, receive over forty inches of rainfall annually, but southward and westward the totals decline; La Paz obtains only twenty-one inches; Cochabamba, eighteen; La Quiaca, thirteen. On the western slopes from 3° S. to 30° S. and in the southern interior the aridity is pronounced. Fortunately in the west and south the rainy season corresponds with the growing season, thus constituting the only aid the highland farmer receives from nature. The natural vegetation varies in accordance with conditions of temperature and precipitation. The *paramos* are too cold to support more than a meager covering of grasses, but at more temperate levels grass is rather plentiful and crops like potatoes, barley, and *quinoa* are able to endure the temperature if they are favored with some rain and sunshine.

In the west the transition from temperate to tropical climate types takes place in central Chile. The region from 31° to 39° S. lies in

[1] São Salvador.

the Subtropical Belt of High Pressure and in that of the Southeast Trade Winds during the summer half year. During the winter, however, the Westerly Winds move northward bringing cyclonic rains to central Chile. Thus there is a dearth of rain in the summer and moderate rainfall in the winter making it a true Mediterranean type.

The total amount of rainfall in the Subtropical belt depends to an extent upon latitude. Coquimbo, at the northern extremity of this region, obtains only five inches, while Valparaiso also on the coast but 4° further south, receives twenty-two inches of rainfall. Distance from the sea also influences the annual total; thus Santiago, at the head of the Central Valley, has only fifteen inches of precipitation. In any case, however, more than three-fourths of the rainfall is received during the winter months, from May to September. Temperatures also reveal the influence of latitude and distance from the sea. Valparaiso, on the coast, has a seasonal variation from 66° in January to 55° in July, a small range. In the Central Valley, however, the temperatures show greater extremes, from 68° to 46°. Daily ranges here vary from 96° to 25°, while on the coast the maximum rarely exceeds 85° and the minimum, 38°.

Plant life is of the dry forest variety because of the lack of rain during the growing season. The characteristic growth resembles the *chaparral* of the California Subtropical area or the *maquis* of the European Mediterranean. The transition from temperate to tropical conditions is reflected in the nature of the vegetation; in the south there are more trees and many laurels and acacias, while in the north the trees give way to cacti, low bushes, and grasses. The mountain slopes are heavily wooded, and stands of pine above five thousand feet and a mixed deciduous and evergreen growth below that level reveal the dominating influence of altitude. The tropical forest, however, intrudes as far south as Santiago. The fertile detritus, washed from the mountain slopes, and the unusual facilities for regulating the run-off combine to render the Central Valley of Chile one of the most prosperous agricultural regions in South America.

South of 40° in the western part of the continent lies one of the rainiest regions in the world. It is the most pronounced of all the maritime belts as the Westerlies are forced to yield their moisture as they ascend the steep slopes. The yearly amount of precipitation at high altitudes has never been recorded, but Valdivia and Evanjelistas, coastal towns, receive 110 and 117 inches of rainfall respec-

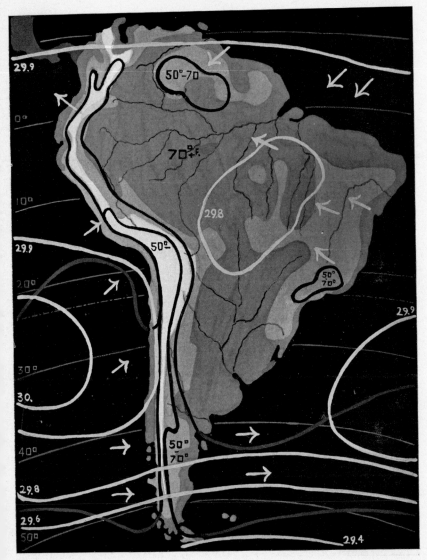

PLATE X. SOUTH AMERICA—JANUARY ISOTHERMS, ISOBARS, AND PREVAIL-
ING WINDS

(*After Goode*)

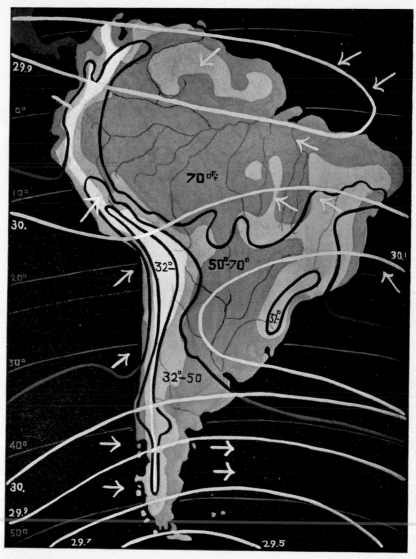

PLATE XI. SOUTH AMERICA—JULY ISOTHERMS, ISOBARS, AND PREVAILING
WINDS

(*After Goode*)

tively. Heavy rains fall every month, but in general the winter months obtain more than the summer months because of the predominance of cyclones during that reason. On the mountains there are tremendous snow falls, and owing to the cool summers the snow line descends to an altitude of 2,600 feet. Glaciers reach the sea as far south as latitude 46° S.

Wind velocities are high, especially at the southern extremity of the continent. The average is about thirty-five miles an hour, but speed of 151 miles has been recorded. In the Strait of Magellan, violent squalls known as "williwaws" are set up, to the terror even of modern navigators. Surface winds are deflected by the Andes; in consequence the wind direction may be anything except east. At higher altitudes, however, the planetary Westerlies prevail, and after crossing the Andes, they blow over Patagonia as dry winds. Temperatures are quite uniform owing to the influence of the sea; the winters are mild and the summers, cool.

The natural vegetation of the Maritime belt is the temperate rain forest, which extends through southern Chile for a distance of 1,000 miles. Only in the extreme south does the dense forest yield to stunted vegetation and barren lands, induced by cold and ice. Much of the forest consists of excellent stands comprising both deciduous and coniferous varieties. As yet these southern forests have been little worked, but because of their accessibility they constitute one of the most valuable timber reserves of the world.

East of the Andes the transition from type to type is similar to that experienced in the United States. Patagonia lies in the rain shadow of the Andes and receives little rainfall. As far north as the Rio Negro, it has less than ten inches annually and may be classified as a Continental Desert type. Even the coastlands receive little rainfall because of the influence of the cold Falkland Current. Between this belt and the Humid Continental Interior type to the northeast lies a narrow Steppe zone which receives from ten to twenty inches annually. The interior of northern Argentina is Humid Continental Interior, exhibiting the usual characteristics of that type: seasonal extremes of temperature; moderate rainfall, twenty to thirty-five inches, with a summer maximum. In general, the rainfall is greater in the eastern portion of this belt. The summers are hot; the winters are cold with frequent frosts.

Continental with Marine Influence is the climate type of the Rio

de la Plata estuary and the surrounding coasts. As would be anticipated, the temperatures do not have the extreme range of the interior,
and the rainfall is better distributed throughout the year. Buenos
Aires has an annual rainfall of thirty-six inches, with a maximum
in late summer and early fall.

Natural vegetation in the Cisandean region varies with the amount
and distribution of the rainfall. In Patagonia the appearance of the
country is semi-arid and desert. Plant life consists largely of drought-
resistant bushes and cacti. Only sheep, of the domestic animals, thrive
here; but the grazier must drive his sheep from plateau to mountain
to take advantage of seasonal pasturing. The rain shadow of the
Andes continues northward to the limits of the temperate belt; consequently through all of western Argentina there runs a conspicuous
desert border. Scattered about, however, are fertile oases which
derive their water supply from the mountains.

East of the arid lands, roughly from the Colorado to the Salado
(40° S. to 28° S.) lie the pampas. This is the grassland par excellence of South America and lies wholly within the bounds of Argentina. Over this huge flat expanse hardly a tree is found except along
the stream's edge. Rainfall varies from twenty to forty inches, thus
accounting for the richer and larger variety of grasses as one moves
eastward. Pasture gives way to agriculture in the rainier areas.

99. Geographical Environment and the Distribution of Population

South America is the home of 75,000,000 people, a small number
in proportion to the size of the continent. The density is ten per
square mile, less than that of any continent except Australia. More
than half the continent has an average density of less than one inhabitant per square mile. Until quite recently the white man's relation to South America was that of the exploiter who was seeking, in
the first place, precious metals, and in the second, forest products.
The present-day population influx, however, is in response to less
opportune attractions. The migrants come as home seekers who wish
to obtain and cultivate lands. In choosing their destinations, they are
likely to be guided by environmental factors such as climate and soil,
avoiding especially the arid wastes and the tropical lowlands.

Areas of comparative density are few in number and are rigidly circumscribed by geographical limitations. The great hubs of population about Rio de Janeiro, Buenos Aires, and Santiago are close to the sea. In tropical latitudes the people seek only the highlands, and those combining accessibility to the sea and fertility of soil are few in number. The interrange valleys of Colombia and the Brazilian Highlands are the most noteworthy, and though in countries like Ecuador, Peru, and Bolivia the population has taken refuge in the Andean Plateau, the density is relatively sparse because of the inaccessibility of the interior. The coasts of northeast Brazil and the Guianas are exceptional because their populations have lived there since the unhappy days when slaves were forced to labor on the tropical plantations.

In temperate regions, accessibility and fertility of soil are the principal criteria of density. Two concentrations are notable: in the east the estuary of the Rio de la Plata, and in the west the Central Valley of Chile together with its outlet Valparaiso. The pampas and the cattle lands of Uruguay, despite their economic importance, are not densely populated.

The remainder of the continent is practically uninhabited. Only the river banks, the mineral camps and their coastal outlets, and the oases in the rain shadow of Argentina, break the monotony of nature's reign. In fact, in glancing at a density map of South America, one is impressed far more by the uninhabited expanses than by the nuclei of densely populated areas. The great interior lowlands of Brazil and the Patagonian tablelands are almost devoid of inhabitants.

Only four of the republics contain a European population exceeding ten per cent. Argentina has 88 per cent; Uruguay, 86; while the other two, Brazil and Chile, have only 35 and 30 per cent respectively. In the other states the Indian and the mestizo elements predominate but do not rule. Bolivia, Peru, Ecuador, Colombia, Venezuela, and Paraguay comprise Indian-mestizo elements exceeding 85 per cent. Four of the republics reveal a marked Negroid element consisting of pure Negro, mulatto, and *zambo* (Negroid-Indian). Brazil with 20 per cent, Colombia with 35 per cent, Ecuador with 5 per cent, and Venezuela with 9 per cent account for most of the Negroid stock of South America. Peru with 50 per cent Indian stock, 35 per cent mestizo, 1 per cent Negroid, and 3 per cent Asiatic presents the most varied racial composition in South America. In addition to the imported oriental laborers, the Japanese and Chinese in Brazil and Peru and the Hindus and Javanese in the Guianas, there are large numbers of European immigrants. The Italians are most numerous in Argentina and east central Brazil, the Germans in southern Brazil and Chile, while Englishmen, as commercial factors and entrepreneurs are everywhere.

To ameliorate conditions among the lower classes so as to fit them to take an active part in the development of the body politic is a major problem in all the states except Argentina and Uruguay. The Indian in South America has withstood contact with the white man better than he has in North America. Because of the fewness of the whites, he has not been exterminated to make room for them; rather he has become the bond servant of the exploiting race. Where a high native culture existed, as in Peru and Bolivia, his fate has been pathetic. Here the Incas had developed an intricate system of irrigation works and had advanced independently to a civilization comparable to that of the Bronze Age of the Old World. Yet a few Spaniards armed with guns utterly destroyed this high culture and broke the spirit of the natives. The Inca and Aymara adopted a philosophy of passive submission toward the ruthless domination of their exploiters and to-day constitute a hard-working laboring population living at the margin of subsistence. They contribute little to the development of the states they live in, for they are illiterate and are victims of drink and drug. The descendants of the Chibcha of Colombia and Venezuela, too, have fallen from the high status of their ancestors. Only the ease of obtaining a living and the more sympathetic attitude of their rulers save them from the harsh suffering of the natives of Peru and Bolivia. In the great interior of the continental lowlands live many independent tribes in a state of savagery. The Indians of Brazil, few in number and widely scattered, offered no great impediment to national development. In temperate lands the natives, though possessing a lower type of culture, were fierce warriors. In Argentina and Uruguay they resisted their invaders until they were exterminated. And in Chile, the Araucanians fought the Spaniards and Chileans tooth and nail, with their backs to the deep forest. Failing to conquer them, the Chileans early established a *modus vivendi* and to-day these Indians are being slowly assimilated. The Patagonian tribes, fishers and huntsmen of the far south, are gradually disappearing. No one contests their occupation of these bleak southern wastes; yet, always a marginal people and culturally at the nadir among American tribes, they are perishing of sheer stagnation.

The mestizo class is comprised of the descendants of white and Indian crosses. In many states their status is low, but where the opportunity has been afforded, they have risen in the economic scale. This class is small in Argentina and Uruguay, while in Brazil it is large. In the latter country both the mestizo and the *zambo* have risen to a higher status than elsewhere because their labor is essential in the agricultural districts. South America is handicapped as a whole by her system of landholding which penalizes the lower classes. The best lands in every country were seized by small groups of white men whose descendants hold tenaciously to their privilege. Even in the temperate countries where the mestizo is a small class, this situation obtains and is a deterrent to immigration. In Chile the best lands are in control of 7 per cent of the population. Except in Brazil where it is possible to obtain small holdings, the lands are divided into great estates under the supervision of the aristocracy.

The combination of physical barriers and social handicaps has thus far conspired to limit progress to a minimum in South America. The small white class dominates the economic and political system. Its refusal to tax the exports of the great estates and its reluctance to tax its lands have led directly to national improverishment among the poorer states and to European exploitation in the progressive states. All the states have borrowed heavily to keep afloat, and the position of financial dependence into which they have fallen has rendered them impotent to develop their own resources. The railways, the mines, the port services, water, light, and sewage are in the hands of foreign entrepreneurs. The bulk of the population is illiterate and in many countries is deteriorating. These unsatisfactory conditions are reflected in the restlessness of political life, for revolution succeeds revolution even in the more prosperous states. Yet South America contains vast reserves, perhaps more than any other continent, of fertile lands, forests, minerals, and commodities more and more in demand in the world market. But until this is appreciated by the people of these states and their guardians, South America is doomed to exploitation.

100. Geographical Environment and Transportation

Climate and physiography have determined more than other factors the distribution of the population of South America. These factors constitute also the most formidable barriers to the exchange of goods both from interior to coast and from region to region. There are few articles of commerce valuable enough to induce the construction of railways in the Andean Highlands or in the tropical lowlands. The cost of maintenance would necessitate prohibitive rates. In consequence little progress in transportation has been made in lands situated in the Andes or in the tropical lowlands.

In Venezuela, Colombia, Ecuador, Peru, and Bolivia transportation is most primitive; yet, curiously, because of the physical handicaps the prevailing systems are able to compete wherever railway construction has been attempted. In the Andean countries, domestic animals are used as carriers except where human carriage is more profitable. In Peru and Bolivia, the llama, first domesticated by the Inca, is the common carrier. This sure-footed beast is best adapted to the high altitude and rare air of the mountains and plateaus. Northward the llama is replaced by the ox and the mule. In the tropical lowlands, the traffic follows the stream; where river transport does not materialize, man supplies the power. Here the domesticated animal cannot live.

South America is poorly provided with river facilities despite the fact that the Amazon has 25,000 miles of navigable waterways. It is true, of course, that large river steamers are able to reach Iquitos, two thousand miles from the coast, and that seaworthy vessels serve Manáos, a thousand miles from the river's mouth, yet this vast tropical hinterland furnishes little that is of service to man. Traffic obstacles such as floods and inundations and rapids and falls are encountered everywhere except on the Amazon. Where river traffic is of some importance, these hazards add enormously to the bills of lading. The Magdalena, the artery of movement in Colombia, affords a pertinent illustration of the shortcomings of river transportation in South America. Goods destined for Bogotá must be loaded six times and unloaded five times in the course of transit from Puerto Colombia, a distance of eight hundred miles. Only products small in bulk and high in value can stand such charges. Venezuela has many streams but even the most serviceable have serious drawbacks. The Catatumbo has a small hinterland and drains into Lake Maracaibo which is shallow; while the Orinoco, which affords the only means of reaching the llanos, drains a region of small economic importance. The west coast rivers are small, precipitous streams whose navigability, at most, is limited to a few miles. Only the streams emptying into the Gulf of Guayaquil have a mentionable significance since they permit access to the cacao lands of Ecuador. The river systems that converge at the Rio de la Plata—the Uruguay and the Paraguay-Paraná—in spite of the sand bars, shifting channels, floating islands, and other impediments are of great value in transportation. Sea-going ships can reach Rosario, even Santa Fé, thus permitting an egress for the cattle, grain, and other products of the hinterland. Boats of seven- to nine-foot draft may penetrate the Paraguay-Paraná under favorable auspices for a distance of two thousand miles.

Railways serve only those regions that are economically prosperous and are generally concerned with the task of getting raw materials to the coast. Innumerable short spurs lead directly to the mining camp or the tropical plantation. Only in the three most prosperous regions are there railway systems. They are nets, rather than systems, and indicate merely that the hinterland is more extensive than one tapped by a spur. In fact, excepting the Chilean system, there is hardly a mile of track that has not been constructed in response to purely commercial possibilities. The government-constructed Longitudinal System of Chile, extending 1,600 miles from north to south, has a striking resemblance to the Cape to Cairo Railway in eastern Africa. In both cases the spurs connecting the roads to the coast are of greater importance than the trunk.

The other nets, that of the Argentina pampa and that of the Brazilian highlands, are rigidly circumscribed by the economic status of their hinterlands. They are purely business enterprises: in fact the roads of Argentina and Uruguay and the best road in Brazil are British-controlled, concerned with the carriage of goods to harbors. They are in the wake rather than in the van of settlement. Although the Brazilian system comprises twenty thousand miles, the only first class roads are those carrying coffee from the plantations to the ports of Rio de Janeiro and Santos. The others are poorly built, poorly equipped, and yield an annual deficit. Some of the Brazilian railways are operated by corporations, some by the states, and the remainder by the Federal authority. This heterogeneity of ownership is reflected in the multiplicity of the gauges employed. Such confusion, of course, precludes the growth of a national rail system.

The Argentine network contains over 25,000 miles of road and is superior to any other in South America. The task of construction as well as the low cost of maintenance is as much a result of the level terrain as of the enterprise of the people: no mountains had to be transversed, no timber had to be cleared, and few streams had to be bridged. Here more clearly than elsewhere one realizes the utter simplicity of purpose of the South American railway. The productive pampas contain a thickly meshed net of roads; but beyond their borders are only spurs, each concerned in tapping a single resource.

Only two connections by rail join the Atlantic and Pacific · the Chile-Argentine Transandine Railway, a road that crosses the mountains at an altitude of ten thousand feet and which cost $300,000 a mile to build; and the circuitous route connecting Argentina and Bolivia. These roads cost so much to operate that they are kept open only with the assistance of the government. The most spectacular feats in railway engineering have been performed in attempting to reach lucrative mineral deposits. The Central Railway of Peru attains a height of 15,680 feet within 106 miles of the coast, after passing through sixty-five tunnels, over sixty-seven bridges, and after using sixteen switchbacks. A half dozen other roads are comparable in achievement to the Central Railway. Their average altitude is twelve thousand feet, while in comparison the Union Pacific reaches a height of only eight thousand feet and the Great Northern crosses the Continental Divide at five thousand feet. The American roads are part of the rail system of the country and serve rich hinterlands at either terminus, but the South American roads depend entirely upon the prosperity of the mining camps.

The extent to which the west coast countries are handicapped by the Andean barrier may be illustrated by the difficulty of a journey from Lima to Iquitos, the rubber-collecting center. From Lima to Oroya, travel is by rail and the main range of the Andes is crossed at a height of 15,665 feet; another day is consumed in crossing the eastern range by automobile; then follows an eight-day journey by pack-mule along narrow trails and a seven days' trip by canoe and river steamer. The whole journey of 1,200 miles cannot be accomplished in less than three weeks. The need of making a dozen changes of bulk *en route* renders profitable exchange of goods impossible, yet this route is old and well-traveled. East to west traffic by rail in South America cannot thrive because the cost of transportation is likely to exceed the value of the articles of commerce.

101. Geographical Environment and Regional Economy

The relation between physical environment and regional development is very striking in South America. Whatever economic activity flourishes beyond the quest for primary necessities is in direct response to the demands of the world market. Any economic depression in the industrial regions of the world is acutely felt in South America because there is little wealth to be created in intra-continental trade or in supplying goods for purely local markets. Indeed in some countries national prosperity depends solely upon the exploitation of a single commodity for the world market. South America sends no finished products to industrial lands; the traffic is limited to rawstuffs and materials which at most have undergone the simple processes necessary to preserve the commodity or to reduce its bulk. The smelting of ore, the preparation of hides, and the freezing of meats are the most important functions of this character.

In general three great economic areas stand out in South America: the mineral camps, the cattle warrens, and the tropical forests and plantations. In the nuclear areas only has there been a heightening of the primary economic functions. In the largest mining camps, smelting works have risen; in the pampas, cattle have given way to wheat; and in favored tropical spots the plantation system has appeared. The nuclear areas are few indeed, for South America must face the stern competition of other lands at every point in her economic development. São Paulo, for example, has learned to her sorrow that she cannot regulate the coffee markets of the world.

102. The Mineral Camps

The extraction of metals and minerals and the utilization of organic and inorganic deposits have played a large part in the history of Peru, Bolivia, and Chile. The Spanish, early in the seventeenth century, were attracted to these lands in their quest of precious metals—gold and silver. With a fine disregard for the destiny of the natives, the great

Inca Empire which extended from Quito to Santiago was summarily shattered. Spain destroyed not only an empire but, far worse, a culture second only to that of Ancient Maya in the New World. Five hundred years of progressive development, to speak of material achievement alone, had given rise to an economic system capable of caring for the welfare of twelve million subjects. The present states of Peru, Bolivia, and Chile have yet to reach the state of self-sufficiency attained by the Inca organization of nearly a thousand years ago. By means of scientific agriculture involving irrigation works, terracing, and the use of guano and nitrates for replenishing the lands, of roads for fostering the exchange of products, and of state granaries for safeguarding the population against drought and winter, the Incas succeeded in emancipating themselves from their harsh highland environment and were able to occupy themselves with the arts to an extent not dreamed of by their servile descendants or even their white rulers.

And so with the Spanish began the practice of exploiting the land for its mineral deposits. The same economy prevails to-day save that gold and silver have given way to petroleum, copper, tin, nitrates, guano, and other less glamorous products. It is wrong to infer that Peru, Bolivia, and Chile are entirely concerned with their mineral camps, yet the larger portion of their revenue, their foreign trade, and their internal development can be traced to this source. The future of these states, however, depends upon the extent to which each succeeds in attaining to a national well-being founded upon more permanent resources. Chile and Peru have made strides in this direction but Bolivia is inert and helpless.

As late as 1905 Peru was literally standing still—gold, silver, and guano exploitation were history; the nitrate fields had been lost to Chile in the disastrous War of the Pacific ending in 1883; and the country was saddled with a huge debt. To-day, however, Peru has a foreign trade exceeding $200,000,000 annually, and the fact that the export of cotton and sugar equals in value that of petroleum and copper indicates that she is finding a way out. Yet the road is long and hard, for wealth is concentrated in a few hands, there is no middle class, few immigrants are attracted, productive agriculture is confined to the coast, and the development of the interior, the Sierra and the *montaña*, is practically neglected.

The great majority of the 600,000 whites [1] are found along the seaboard, managing haciendas and mines or engaging in trade. With the collapse of the guano industry Peruvian entrepreneurs directed their attention to the alluvial stream beds along the coast. The level lands were irrigated by water that flowed without interruption from snow-capped mountains. To-day great haciendas line the banks of the fifty odd streams. Though embracing only 16 per cent of the cultivated lands they account for half the agricultural produce and half the exports of the country. The great money crops are cotton and sugar. Cotton culture, which is probably indigenous to Peru, has increased from forty thousand bales to 180,000 bales during the last thirty years. Conditions of cultivation are excellent: there is no frost nor hail and no rain to discolor the cotton; the temperature is uniformly high; the dry atmosphere hinders the growth of pest or disease; and irrigation permits a proper application of water to heavily fertilized soil. Thus with only fair methods of cultivation and poor machinery the yield is one and a half bales per acre, higher than that of the United States, and two or three crops result from one planting. Sugar planting enjoys similar advantages. Absence of rain, high temperatures, and perpetual sunshine makes it possible for the Peruvian planter to obtain forty thousand pounds per acre while his Cuban rival obtains only twenty thousand pounds. From three to seven cuttings are had from each planting, and as the cuttings take place all the year round, there is no financial loss from a rushed harvest. The subsistence crops are rice, corn, and various other grains and legumes. Wheat and barley are yielding to rice, which was introduced by the Asiatic laborers, and alfalfa is replacing the native grasses. Fruits of a great variety are grown, as well as tobacco, a favorite of all classes.

Manufacturing, which is confined to the coast, has made considerable progress during the last generation. But in the absence of skilled labor, mobile capital, purchasing power, and a transport system capable of developing interior markets, the industries are confined to simple processes such as the primary preparation of metals, the refining of sugar, the milling of grain, tanning, brewing, and some textile manufacturing.

Exports of crude petroleum and copper still dominate the foreign

[1] Peru has a population of approximately 5,500,000.

trade of Peru. Oil is being exploited in the northwest because of its accessibility, not because it is lacking in other parts of the country. Most of it is exported, but as a fuel in manufacturing and transportation it is important in a country where coal is scarce and where hydro-electric power is relatively undeveloped. Copper, however, is found in the Sierra.

The Sierra contains two-thirds of the population of the country, masses of Indians and mestizos, economically inactive, illiterate, backward, and just able to cope with their environment. There is little variety on the *altiplano;* by primitive methods small patches of land are cleared of rough sod; a little corn, barley, potatoes, and (in favored spots) wheat are planted. Native bunch grass provides thatch for the hut and fuel during the raw winter; and *chica,* a drink made from corn, solace for the soul. Cattle and pigs augment the diet of the more fortunate, and sheep provide wool for clothing, while in certain interior towns the natives find a mart for pack animals and for the wool of the llama. The Sierra produces a fourth of Peruvian exports but all of it is copper. Over 90 per cent comes from three mines, reached at great cost by the Central Railway. Mining is carried on under adverse conditions: the mines are located at elevations exceeding fourteen thousand feet; all supplies, fuel and timber, and much of the food must be imported; and the skilled workers and engineers can work in the rarefied air for only short intervals. Peru enjoys a world monopoly of vanadium, a rare element, and produces a large variety of lesser metals such as tungsten, lead, bismuth, antimony, mercury, zinc, and gold. On the whole the Sierra has no great future, for remoteness and difficulties of transportation are too great even for the most lucrative mining resources to cope with successfully.

More remote is the *montaña* comprising eastern Andean foothills and plains. Here dwell mainly Indians who live by hunting, fishing, and a crude hoe agriculture. Iquitos, the only town, contains a shifting population of from twelve to twenty thousand. Since 1880 the products of the Peruvian rain forest have been brought to Iquitos for shipment down the Amazon. Only goods having the highest value per unit of weight can withstand the heavy transportation charges; *balata,* a diminishing amount of raw rubber, and a little *cinchona.* Westward, to the Sierra, go small quantities of coca, cotton, tobacco, sugar, cacao, and coffee by pack train. The sale is greatest for the coca leaf which gives to its chewers extraordinary powers of resistance to cold and hunger. Not only Peru but Colombia, Ecuador, and Bolivia have an abiding expectancy regarding their eastern lowlands, but centuries must elapse before their extravagant hopes are realized.

Bolivia,[1] lacking a productive coastal desert and deprived of ports, is known to the world for the metals extracted there. In the highlands, the *altiplano,* dwell three-fourths of the population. Centuries ago the Aymara under the direction of the Inca spread southward over the highlands from their homeland about Lake Titicaca. Inca domination was succeeded in time by the Spanish, and the latter's solicitude concerning precious metals is reflected in the fact that seventeenth-century Potosi with 175,000 inhabitants was the largest city in the Americas. To-day from La Paz to Potosi reside the full-blooded descendants of the Aymara and Quichua, and the *cholos,* a large mestizo class. The former are steeped in ignorance and poverty, keeping body and soul together by a meager supply of barley and potatoes, and a liberal indulgence in coca leaves and *chicha*. The soil is stony and infertile, the precipitation precarious, and fuel scarce.

Three railroads connect this isolated land with the coast, carrying 90 per cent of all the exports. A fourth is linked by tortuous routes with Buenos Aires. All of them must climb over thirteen thousand feet to reach the highlands. Tin and copper are the chief metals extracted, and lead, zinc, antimony, bismuth, and tungsten appear as by-products. As in Peru, there is no end of mineral resources, but exploitation depends upon a market price level capable of supporting transportation development. Tin is the index of Bolivian prosperity. Because of the high cost of fuel and the necessity of hauling supplies great distances, the industry labors under a great handicap. Though Bolivia furnishes a fourth of the tin used in the world market, she cannot compete with the product of the Malay Peninsula. Bolivian tin is found in concentrates containing from 55 per cent to 70 per cent tin, but the deposits of British Malay are alluvial and pure, needing no crushing and extraction. Until these deposits and several others are exhausted, the huge stores of Bolivia must wait. The copper industry labors under similar handicaps. Though the deposits of Corocoro are vast and easily worked, full development is dependent upon the exhaustion of native copper in the United States and Chile.

The *yungas* and the eastern lowlands comprise three-fourths of the territory of Bolivia. The *yungas,* lying along the eastern slopes of the

[1] Population 2,900,000.

Cordillera Real, correspond economically to the Peruvian *montaña.* This region supplements the scant food supply of the *altiplano,* sending commodities of small bulk and high value such as the coca leaf, cacao, and brandy. From the pastures is obtained a welcome supply of pack animals and of wool from the llama and alpaca. The *yungas* are a land of huge haciendas supporting a small but powerful group of absentees who live at La Paz. The eastern lowlands are disease ridden and almost uninhabited. The northern portion belongs geographically to Amazonia; it is an unbroken expanse of jungle save for occasional clearings along steaming streams and the source of many "rivers of doubt." With the shrinking of the demand for wild rubber, this region has reverted once more to unbroken solitude. The Chiquitos Highlands separate the jungle from the chaco. Here range huge herds of cattle whose owners in far off Buenos Aires or Paris await the day when speculative bond holders will finance a railway and release this landlocked stream of wealth. Meanwhile self-sacrificing Franciscans minister to the wants of the pastoral settlements. Bolivia shares the *chaco* with Paraguay and Argentina. That the boundaries of this valueless, unhealthy, Indian preserve should be allowed to imperil the peace of Bolivia and Paraguay is a sad commentary upon the state of international relations.

Chile's status as the third wealthiest country of South America is due largely to the exploitation of her mineral resources; nitrate, copper, and iron ore. Of the lands in this mountainous country, over 40 per cent, mainly in the desert north, are dessicated, and over 30 per cent, in the south, are too rainy and too cold to support crops. Only a tenth of the soil fosters any marked agricultural development. The country is far distant from the busiest lanes of world trade, and its peculiar shape is a barrier to unity in that each section looks toward its immediate coastal outlet. Despite the fact that Chilean trade has increased from a mere $25,000,000 to $40,000,000 per annum during the past fifty years, progress toward national self-sufficiency has been very slow. Some of the most lucrative mineral deposits are in the hands of foreign exploiters. Most of the country has no transportation facilities save cart and pack trains; and the internal trade is not sufficient to carry the fixed charges of the Longitudinal Railway. On the other hand the people, unhampered by enervating climatic factors, are energetic. The mestizo element, a fusion of white and Auricanian Indian, is made of sturdy stuff.

Three-fourths of Chile's commerce is concerned with the export of minerals, and half the national revenue is derived from the high export tax of ten dollars a ton upon nitrate. With the exception of the mines of the Braden Copper Company, located one hundred miles southeast of Santiago, and the coal mines located near Concepción (which though not capable of making coke are the largest deposits in South America), the mineral resources of Chile are located in the desert zone between Santiago and the Peruvian border. The nitrates together with the by-products, borax and iodine, the latter a Chilean monopoly, are located between 19° S. and 26° S. on the western margins of the interior plateau. The deposits of nitrate have in places a depth of eight to ten feet, and though the exact manner of their deposition is unknown, the lack of exterior drainage has been a factor in their precipitation. In spite of the richness of the deposits, the industry labors under the usual handicap of poor location. The cost of obtaining the nitrate is high: men, food, supplies, timber, machinery, and fuel must be imported; fresh water must be piped from the Andes, a hundred miles distant; and wells must be dug to obtain salt water for treating the deposits. Nitrate is the barometer of Chilean prosperity. During the World War the demand for fertilizer in Europe was curtailed with the result that fifty thousand men were thrown out of work in Chile and the peso dropped from nineteen cents to fourteen and a half cents in value. In spite of occasional normal years since the war, Chile furnishes less and less of the nitrate of the world; in 1894 her proportion was 73 per cent, in 1928 only 20 per cent. Germany, formerly the largest importer, now produces synthetically twice the amount exported by Chile. Unless economies are effected and unless the government reduces the export tax, so vital to national well-being, the outlook will probably continue dark.

The World War induced the exploitation of low grade Chilean copper with the result that Chile rose to second place among the copper producing countries. Two-thirds comes from the Chile Copper Company, American owned, and the Andes Copper Company, both located in northern Chile, and the remainder from the mines of the Braden Copper Company. The present rate of production, 300,000 tons annually, can be sustained for a hundred years at least. The copper industry also meets with many obstacles: fuel and structural materials must be imported; power is transmitted from the coast along high-tensioned wires; oil is brought from Peru or California; fresh water is piped seventy miles and salt water for leaching, forty miles; labor and food are obtained from Middle Chile and more remote regions. Before production could begin in the mine of the Andes Copper Company at Potrerillos, $40,000,000 had to be spent in constructing a railroad to the coast, erecting pipe lines, providing a fifteen thousand ton concentrator, an electrical generating plant, a smelter, and a model town capable of caring for a population of five thousand. In addition to nitrates and copper there exists at Tofo a huge American-owned iron mine, the foremost in South America, which is exporting annually to the United States a million tons of high grade ore.

In Middle Chile lives nine-tenths of the population. This restricted area constitutes Chile's insurance against the calamity that will result when her mineral wealth is exhausted. The northern portion enjoying a real Mediterranean type of climate, is the more important, though the less fertile southern lands foster a dairying interest built up by thrifty German immigrant farmers. It is indeed unfortunate that one per cent of the population controls two-thirds of the best lands. The owners of the great *estancias* are motivated by gross self-interest, for they not only refuse to impose a land tax upon their estates, but their monopoly serves to perpetuate a feudal system of exploitation. In consequence the agricultural laborers, the servile *rotos,* count as nothing in the national development. The beginnings of a middle class must be sought among the Germans and Dutch, the small farm owners of the south.

The Central Valley Mediterranean area, four hundred miles in length and from thirty to sixty miles wide, is a veritable agricultural paradise and constitutes the richest agricultural development in western South America. On its irrigated lands are grown a large assortment of grains such as wheat, corn, and barley; legumes such as lentils, beans, and peas; fruits of many kinds; and domestic animals, particularly cattle, sheep, and horses. The coastal valleys produce similar crops, while southern lands add oats, potatoes, and dairy products. Middle Chile exports very little, but within its confines there is a lively exchange of goods. There are no iron or steel manufactures, for Chile lacks coking coal necessary for smelting. With the World War, however, and its curtailment of manufacturing, a notable beginning was made in the production of consumer's wares. The milling of grain, the brewing of barley, and the manufacture of

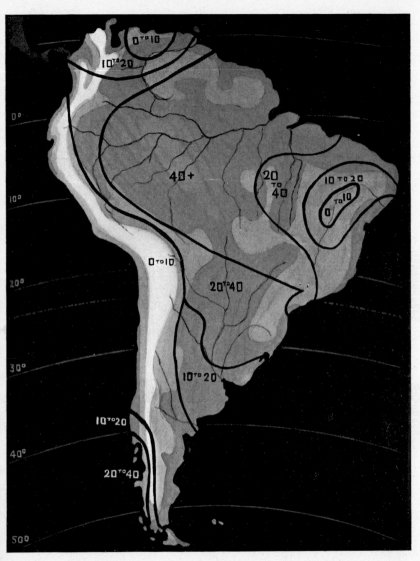

PLATE XII. SOUTH AMERICA—JANUARY RAINFALL
(*After Goode*)

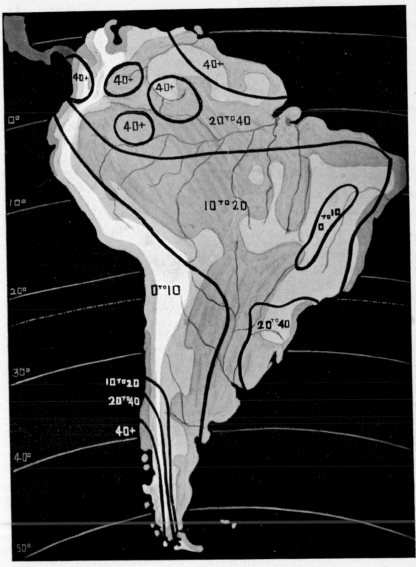

PLATE XIII. SOUTH AMERICA—JULY RAINFALL
(*After Goode*)

wine were augmented by the production of textiles, particularly woolens, leather, furniture, and shoes. To-day some seven thousand factories employ eighty thousand workers. The growth of a class of skilled workers in Valparaiso, Concepción, and Valdivia is a hopeful augury. An abundance of raw materials, hydro-electric power and usable sub-bituminous coal, cheap labor, and the existence of a compact market area presage an important industrial development for Chile, independent of her mineral camps.

Of the bleak southern third of the country little need be said. With its rugged relief, stormy seas, inhospitable climate, infertile soil, and dense forests it will not attract settlers for many decades. Indeed the monopolistic land system and the greater physical attractions of the Paraná basin and eastern Brazil conspire in rendering Chile, as a whole, a land little sought by European immigrants. Magdallanes and the surrounding lands in the far southeast have had an unusual development—one that links Chile with the live stock warrens discussed in the next section. This region is an enviable sheep warren; its incessant rains provide good grazing all year round, and its uniformly low temperatures favor the growth of a fine-texture wool. Here British owners have carved out huge *estancias,* some of them two million acres in size; consequently little available sheep land remains. The herders are Scots, Welshmen, Germans, and half-breeds. Some three million sheep yield twenty million pounds of wool annually. Magdallanes enjoys an international importance, for the product of the sheep warrens of southern Argentina transhipped at this port increases the Chilean export by 50 per cent. At the half dozen meat-freezing plants commercially tributary to Magdallanes more than one million head of sheep are slaughtered annually.

103. The Live Stock Warrens

Live stock has had the same significance in the development of Argentina, Uruguay, and Paraguay that mineral deposits have had upon the welfare of the southern tier of west coast countries. Until the value of live stock as a source of wealth was realized, Argentina and the southern Paraguay-Paraná drainage lands were disregarded by the Spanish. Indeed this portion of South America was approached from the west, from Peru, Bolivia, and Chile, rather than from the Atlantic seaboard. The irrigated oases, nestled in the eastern Andean slopes, Tucumán, Mendoza, and others, were early valued as sources of food for the mining camps and missionary settlements of the Andean Highlands. Indeed the pampas were occupied from Santa Fé, far up the Paraná. Not until the early nineteenth century were these great lands considered valuable enough to wrest from the Indians. From 1850 to 1885 Argentina experienced a frontier movement similar to that of the United States; one which resulted in the annihilation of the Indian tribes and the extension of her border settlements southward to Rio Negro and northward to Rio Bermejo in the chaco. Since then have followed in rapid succession the round-up of wild cattle, the fencing of ranges, the consolidation of holdings into vast *estancias,* the replacement of native grasses by alfalfa, the booming of the meat trade with the introduction of refrigeration (1877) and later, the chilling and freezing of beef.

In the wake of the cattle economy followed two significant developments, one nuclear and one marginal. Within a radius of six hundred miles of Buenos Aires, agriculture has largely supplanted the raising of live stock because of the export value of wheat and linseed in world market. Secondly an extension of the live stock industry has come into areas hitherto unutilized. Not only have the pastoral margins of the pampas been pushed as far as rainfall conditions will permit, but great secondary centers of stock raising have developed in Patagonia and Uruguay. Both trends continue; the "wheat crescent" is displacing the grazing lands within its potential, natural borders, while live stock is being pushed further into available hinterlands. In the sparser lands of western Argentina where pasture is scarce and the terrain rugged, a large goat-raising industry has developed. In the north, with Rosario as a point of concentration, cattle raising has moved eastward into the Paraguay-Paraná, *mesopotamia,* and westward into the Argentine chaco. North of the Bermejo, the advance is limited by obstacles imposed by nature, for the semi-tropical environment is not favorable to the live stock industry. The term "cattle warren," however, symbolizes more than any other term the development and present status of eastern lands lying south of the chaco.

The pampa is the hub of Argentina, now the second largest and the wealthiest country in South America and the tenth ranking commercial country of the world. It is the greatest productive area of the continent, producing 72 per cent of the world's export of flax seed, 66 per cent of its corn, 30 per cent of its hides and skins, 26 per cent of its total of meat and meat products, 54 per cent of its beef and beef products, and 20 per cent of the wheat and flour. From the pampa lands, level and unobstructed, goods move by rail to Buenos Aires and the subsidiary ports, Bahia Blanca in the south and Rosario in the north, whence they are borne to western Europe and the United States. Buenos Aires, in spite of its shortcomings as a harbor, is the queen city of South America. Its growth from a town of ninety thousand in 1855 to a metropolis of 2,500,000 is indicative of the growth of the pampa, and latterly of this portion of South America. In 1850 the pampa contained only a third of the population of Argentina, while to-day over two-thirds of Argentina's eleven million inhabitants live there. Its economic growth represents a phenomenal adaptation to geographical environment.

Physically the pampa possesses many outstanding qualities. It is one of the most level areas of the world; from east to west the rise is only five feet per mile and there are few hills or obstructing stream valleys. The soil though varying in character is of high fertility and much of its loamy quality is due to thick deposits of windborne loess from the Andes. It is literally a stoneless area. In a rough way the amount of precipitation limits the borders of the pampa. From the mouth of the Rio Colorado, the line of twenty-inch rainfall, running north-northwest to the Andes, separates the pampa from the arid plainlands of Patagonia. The mountains limit it on the west, while northward, the Rio Salada tributary of the Paraná, separates it from the swampy, semi-tropical chaco. Most of the pampa lies within a five-hundred-mile radius of Buenos Aires, and in size it comprises hardly a fifth of Argentina. The pampa has an annual rainfall of from twenty to forty inches, most of which soaks into the soil as only three small streams cross the plains to the Atlantic. Fortunately, ground water is easily tapped by means of thousands of windmills turned by the strong Westerlies. The climate is mild: there is no winter drought, no zero weather. The growing season is long, varying from three hundred days in the north to 140 days in the south. Levelness of land has made rail construction so inexpensive that every farm and every cattle warren is within twenty-five miles of the rail facilities.

In 1900 cattle raising was universal on the pampa and cattle accounted for three-fourths of the exports of Argentina. To-day grazing activities are carried on in only a third of the region, yet cattle are almost twice as numerous as in 1900. This economy in area has been achieved through a system of scientific cattle raising whose most noteworthy improvements lay in the direction of supplanting the native by imported breeds and the native grasses by alfalfa. Nearly half the *estancias* are under alfalfa, a cultivated grass that enriches the soil by its nitrogen-fixing capacity and which, because of its deep roots, does not dry up during the heat of summer. Alfalfa not only lives from five to eight years, but it permits of three cuttings a year. It is about four times as valuable as the native grasses, and sends a steer to market a year earlier. Steers have diminished only slightly in numbers during the last few years but sheep have been forced out of the pampa because of the competition of wheat for the land. During the World War, when Argentina was deprived of her supplies of tinned milk and butter, a dairying industry of large proportions grew up in the vicinity of Buenos Aires. There are few hogs in the pampa, for the Argentines do not eat pork and hog raising is difficult because of disease.

Agriculture has made headway at the expense of stock raising in the pampa. Were it not for the traditional land system of great grazing *estancias,* its growth would be more rapid, for it is more profitable than grazing on medium-sized farms. The pampa has three major export crops: wheat, flax, and corn. Wheat can be grown anywhere, but it flourishes best in the outer edge of the crescent where the annual precipitation is about twenty inches. Here environmental conditions are most favorable: mild winters, a moist spring, a sunny ripening period, and a long dry harvest season. The levelness of the pampa permits the use of modern harvesting machinery. Selection of seed in accordance with local climate variations has made possible a yield of twelve bushels per acre, comparing favorably with a yield of fourteen bushels in the United States. A saving of from eight to ten cents per bushel in carrying wheat to the harbors gives the pampa an advantage over the United States in the world market. Wheat is the most valuable crop of Argentina; at present two-thirds is exported, and upon demand the export crop can be expanded 200 per cent. The large wheat farm, so familiar to Americans, is lacking in the pampa, for the average farm hardly exceeds four hundred acres. Most of the farmers are share-croppers or tenants upon grazing *estancias.*

Corn and flax are grown in the warm north where the rainfall varies from thirty to forty inches. This belt, relatively small, suffers from drought and locust invasion. Almost yearly the locust scourge makes its appearance from the nearby chaco and, unless vigorously combated, destroys the young corn. The wheat, which has ripened, and the flax, which has been harvested, escape, leaving the corn at the mercy of the invaders. Pampa corn, in spite of its higher price, enjoys a preference over American corn in the European market for several reasons; its small kernels are better suited for poultry feeding; it is sweeter food for horses; and, since it has a smaller moisture content, it can be longer preserved. Flax from the pampa provides the world with its chief source of linseed for paint making. Much of the flax is grown by tenants upon uncleared fields preparatory to planting alfalfa after three or four years.

Lack of fuel, water power, ores, and timber have prevented the development of primary manufactures in Argentina. Largely for this reason Argentina imports more than three-fourths of her manufactured goods. The manufacturing industry, however, has made rapid strides in recent years, employing 600,000 workers in 61,000 establishments located mainly at Buenos Aires. The majority are engaged in the preparation of the agricultural products for export. Owing to the imposition of high protective tariffs, the meat-packing and milling industries have been augmented by those producing textiles, shoes, leather goods, beer, cigarettes, and other consumers' wares.

In southern Patagonia, a thousand miles from Buenos Aires, has developed Argentina's second great live stock warren. A single small province, Santa Cruz, produces a fourth of the country's exports of sheep, and half the wool export. For reasons similar to those prevailing in the contiguous sheep region of Chile (Magdallanes) Santa Cruz is able to vie with the pampa and with Uruguay as one of the three leading sheep warrens of South America. Grazing is the natural industry throughout Patagonia because, owing to the sparse rainfall, the soil will support only grasses. On the tableland the industry is less profitable because it is essentially nomadic.

Uruguay, though the smallest of the republics of South America, is one of the wealthiest. It is the most concentrated live stock warren in the world for practically all of its soil produces nutritious grasses. Only 4 per cent of its land and 7 per cent of its workers are engaged in agriculture. The pasture lands, owned by 43,000 proprietors are well drained; the temperature is mild in winter; the rainfall is well distributed throughout the year; and the smallness of the country is advantageous in minimizing the cost of carriage to the export center, Montevideo. Cattle and sheep constitute over 90 per cent of Uruguay's exports, and she contributes 12 per cent of the world's beef exports. Other than the preparation of live stock and their by-products for export Uruguay has no manufactures, for she possesses no fuel nor ores whatever. The great prosperity of the country is reflected in her superior transport system, and the small degree of illiteracy among her inhabitants. Incidentally Uruguay has a greater proportion of pure European stock than any other country in the continent. Uruguay, in spite of the good use that has been made of her resources, will grow but slowly. In the south, a beginning has been made in the cultivation of wheat and flax for the Buenos Aires market, but the people of Uruguay prefer life on the range to the raising of crops.

North and west of the cattle warrens the population thins out rapidly, for both the sparsely vegetated mountains and the unhealthy interior lowlands repel settlers. Montane Argentina furnishes just enough fodder for goats, valued for their hides, and in the northern districts for mules and asses, destined for the mining camps of Bolivia. Some forty oases, created by the run-off, break the monotony of this waste land. Once these were regarded as the sole resource of Argentina, serving in Spanish times to furnish food to adjacent mining camps. To-day they supply Argentina with products like sugar and wine which otherwise would have to be imported. North of the pampa the cattle industry dwindles, for as the tropics are approached, tick and other cattle diseases make their appearance. The Argentine chaco is no better than that of her sister republics; much is inundated during a large part of the year, and much of the soil is impregnated with salt because of the lack of drainage. It is the breeding place of malignant diseases and the homeland of poisonous insects and reptiles. Paraguay has been no more successful than Bolivia and Argentina in colonizing the chaco, although with the encouragement of the League of Nations she has made welcome the members of the wide-scattered Mennonite sect. The northern portion of the Argentine *mesopotamia*, situated between the Rio Paraná and the Rio Uruguay, shares in the forest industries of Paraguay.

Here the glossy green leaf of the *yerba maté* is gathered and exported to those parts of South America where Paraguayan tea is esteemed the favorite beverage. In northern Argentina and southern Brazil it has become a plantation crop. Paraguay, with a million inhabitants, largely mestizo and Indian, has little to offer the prospective immigrant. Situated far inland at the very borders of the tropics, it is concerned mainly with primitive forest industries, the gathering of yerba maté and the cutting of quebracho. From the quebracho logs is extracted tannin, so valuable in the leather and dyeing industries. Economically Paraguay belongs to the tropics.

104. Tropical Plantations and Forest Industries

Brazil, Ecuador, Colombia, Venezuela, and the Guiana dependencies lie in the tropics and have many characteristics in common. Concentration of population occurs either on the highlands or along the seaboard. Agriculture, the leading occupation, is confined to the favored highlands or to fertile coastal strips. Extensive lands everywhere favor the production of one or two basic money crops and the direction of effort is in the hands of a few lords of the soil. Marginal always are the herding of animals and the raising of subsistence crops. The interior lowlands are untouched except where conditions permit an easy exploitation of some product of the forest. Tropical South America, then, is a vast uninhabited area save for the human agglomerations clustering upon the highland patches or along the coastal fringes.

Brazil, so vast in extent that it includes nearly half the continent, reveals upon a gigantic scale the characteristics of the tropical South American country: a progressive highland area, a coastal fringe devoted to the tropical plantation, and an interior lowland where the forest products are gathered. In spite of its great size (for it measures 2,700 miles in length and breadth), and its seemingly great population (for it contains half the people in South America[1]), Brazil is a backward unsettled country. Only 3 per cent of the land is cultivated, and half the inhabitants live at the very margin of subsistence. Although her trade ranks second in volume in South America, her per capita trade ranks third from the bottom of the list. On the credit side of the column are her almost incomprehensi-

[1] 39,500,000.

ble resources and her ability to trim her sails, slowly to be sure, to the changing winds of trade and commerce. In colonial times timber cuttings were supplanted by sugar and tobacco plantations; these in turn were disrupted by the discovery of gold and diamonds in the highlands and by agricultural exploitation. Then followed, in the late nineteenth century, an immigration into southern Brazil, while the demand for rubber and other forest products turned attention to Amazonia. Present-day Brazil combines the various sources of wealth discovered in past centuries and is adding new products, new territory, and more modern methods in the exploitation of her rich environment. The highlands to-day are primarily concerned with the cultivation of coffee; the coastal plantations, with sugar, tobacco, and cacao; the interior lowlands with forest products such as rubber, balata, and Brazil nuts. A beginning has been made in the utilization of the vast grazing campos, but the most successful pioneering has taken place in the southeast with the exploitation of new forms of wealth: live stock, yerba maté, and Paraná pine.

The eastern highlands, extending from 15° S. to 34° S. are the heart of the country economically. The land is moderately high, rolling, and well drained, and the soil is deep and fertile. The rain-fall averages about sixty inches, well-distributed throughout the seasons, and while it is hot during the day, the nights are usually cool and pleasant. Latitude has the effect of dividing the Brazil Highlands into two sections, a tropical north and a more temperate south. In the small coastal plain about Rio de Janeiro there are sugar and banana plantations but elsewhere the high mountain barrier of the Sierra do Mar intrudes upon the coast. The ports of Rio de Janeiro and Santos are connected with the highlands by rail and their prosperity depends upon that of the hinterland. Rio de Janeiro is older than Santos, and served first as the port for interior gold deposits and later as the export-import center of the whole country. As the capital of Brazil, it has a political and cultural significance which gives it an advantage. Santos and Porto Alegre are purely distributors of hinterland products. The former serves São Paulo, the Chicago of Brazil. Since 1864 this inland coffee center has grown in population from 64,000 to one million.

The coffee plantations occupy over two-thirds of the cultivated lands of the central (tropical) plateau. Conditions of coffee-growing are exacting, but there is no other area in the world that complies so extensively with them. The plantations are situated about the level of 1,800 feet, for the inverse temperature conditions prevailing in the valleys would be destructive to the crop. On the other hand no coffee is grown above the three thousand foot line for fear of frost. The altitude of 1,800 to three thousand feet is ideal in that no shade trees are needed to protect the bush. The rainfall of spring and summer is heavy enough to induce rapid growth, while its cessation in the fall provides a long season for ripening and drying. Coffee ripens everywhere at the same time so that only one picking is necessary. Ample reserve lands make it possible to open up new lands when soil exhaustion threatens. Brazilian coffee culture, then, is extensive rather than intensive. During the 1880's coffee became the leading crop of Brazil and by 1900 was the leading export of South America. Until recently Brazil practically controlled the world market, a market rapidly expanding because of the increasing popularity of coffee in the United States and to a less extent in western Europe. To-day, however, Brazil furnishes only 65 per cent of the world's supply, and unless reforms are carried out, her hegemony will be in danger. Overproduction upon the *fazendas* as early as 1906 led to price-fixing, and a recurrence of the evil in 1917, 1921, and 1922 brought about the organization of the coffee industry under the government-supervised Institute for the Permanent Defense of Coffee. The withholding of the supply in order to make a profit had the effect, however, of stimulating competition in the Far East. To discourage competitors, it is not enough to regulate the size of the crop, but it is also necessary to reduce drastically the cost of production. The easy-going *fazenda* methods have been too expensive. To preserve her place in the world markets Brazil must reduce labor costs by introducing machinery, and she must curtail the monopoly of the São Paulo Railway. Careful inspection of crops must be undertaken for the *stephanoderes* plant pest has infested more than 200,000,000 coffee trees. Finally, diversified agriculture, of which this productive region is capable, must be developed. Cotton, which can be grown as a secondary crop in the coffee groves, and sugar, which flourishes upon sunny slopes of abandoned coffee lands, offer the best possibilities. The subsistence crops are beans and corn (grown everywhere), rice (introduced by Japanese laborers), and to a less extent cassava, potatoes, and wheat.

In southern Brazil, recently developed by hard-working Italian,

German, and Polish colonists, a system of mixed farming has grown up. With the advantage of all year round grazing this section now supplies 30 per cent of Brazil's cattle and hogs and 75 per cent of her sheep. The quality of the beef is not high and at present the cattle are either converted into jerked beef or employed as draft animals. The eastern section, with access to the sea, is devoted to general farming, with wheat for export. In the west, where forest industries predominate, both yerba maté and Paraná pine provide lucrative resources.

Mining and manufacturing are important occupations in the Brazilian Highlands. Minas Geraes, long the center of the gold and diamond production, has recently attracted much attention because of its manganese and hematite deposits. The extraction of the former is carried on so extensively that Brazil ranks as a competitor of Russia, India, and the Gold Coast in the world market. Most of the export goes to the United States. The iron ore is estimated at twelve billion tons which, if correct, is the largest known reserve. Unfortunately Brazil, though producing nails, screws, chains, and like objects, lacks the coking coal essential to the development of a primary iron and steel industry. Practically all her iron and steel goods are imports, and this situation will long prevail unless there is an important development of hydro-electric power and electric smelting. Scarcity of fuel is the greatest handicap to manufacturing in Brazil, for, despite the fact that the southern mines produce a sixth of her needs, native coal costs as much in Rio de Janeiro as the best Cardiff or Pocahontas coal. Coal and petroleum constitute 12 per cent of Brazilian imports. Nevertheless Brazilian manufactures have attained first place in South America. The industry is concentrated in Rio de Janeiro, a district which needs an outlet for its surplus capital, and whose large population is important both for consuming capacities and as a source of labor. The government zealously encourages manufacturing industries by the imposition of high protective duties. Production is almost entirely concerned with consumers' goods such as cotton and woolens, boots and shoes, hats, beverages, and tobacco. Many of the factories depend upon wood for fuel and, in addition, the manufactures are handicapped by lack of experience and lack of skilled labor.

The coastal plantations, in colonial times more important to Brazil than at present, extend from 3° S. to 18° S. The city of Bahia was once the leading sugar depot and slave market of South America. To-day, with over 300,000 inhabitants, it ranks third among Brazilian cities, while Recife [1] which is further north is fourth in population. The southern part of the plantation area is distinctly a Trade with Ample Rain area, with plentiful rainfall and high humidity and temperature. Throughout the coastal region, conditions are adverse to progress, for nature (though providing food in plenty) has placed a premium upon work of any sort. Hence the plantations are carelessly cultivated and only with difficulty do their products maintain a status in the markets of the world. In the south, cacao is by far the leading crop, while sugar and tobacco supply a large proportion of Brazilian wants. Cacao production began in the eighties in the far south and although hard pressed by the West African plantations, still flourishes because of ideal environmental conditions. At present there are a half million acres under cacao. In the north sugar takes the leading place, but cotton shows great promise. The vast interior of Northeast Brazil, lacking facilities to the coast and subject to severe drought, is an unpromising region.

Interior Brazil is divided into two parts, the Amazonian rain forest and the campos. Both are backward regions in every sense. Man simply subsists here and seems incapable of modifying his environment. The forest products of Amazonia have always exerted an attraction for adventurers able to organize the energies of the reluctant natives living along the stream banks. Indeed, were it not for the fact that this region, as large as all the United States east of the Mississippi, is drained by the tributaries of a single great river, little commercial intercourse could take place. The Amazon has made Pará the port not only of interior Brazil but of eastern Bolivia, Peru, Ecuador, Colombia, and much of the Guiana Highlands. Pará,[2] with a population of 250,000, is concerned mainly with Amazonian shipments. Because the Amazon is truly "Rio Mar," the sea river, with a width of two miles at the Peruvian border, Manáos, a thousand miles up stream, is able to rival Pará in accommodations for ocean-going vessels and to support a population of 75,000.

The physical characteristics of Amazonia have already been surveyed. Though the fish of its rivers and the luxuriance of its fruits and vegetables make food easy to obtain, the climate is enervating

[1] Pernambuco.
[2] Belém.

and disease abounds. Nature's paradise is hardly an Eden for the million and a half people who live there. The economic possibilities are very few though the resources are great. Owing to the high cost of transportation over long distances and the difficulty of exploitation only a few products have any commercial value. The more important are timber, the oil of nuts and seeds, balata, and wild rubber.

Timber exploitation is not promising; the best species are found far inland; few stands of a single wood are to be found; and most of the hardwoods do not float. The Brazil nut enjoys a growing popularity for food purposes. Though found upstream, it requires merely collecting in baskets prior to shipment. The Brazil nut exports are second in value to those of rubber. About a fifth of the world's supply of balata gum comes from the source lands of the Amazon. From this same region, not all within Brazilian borders, once came the major portion of the world's cacao. This forest industry, unable to compete with the plantation system, has suffered the extinction that now threatens the wild rubber industry.

Pará rubber, once enjoying a monopoly of the market, is derived from the species *hevea brasiliensis*. With the inauguration of the tire industry, Amazonian production rose from ten million pounds in 1870 to 93,000,000 pounds in 1912. Until 1909 it enjoyed practically a monopoly position. The production of 6,500,000 pounds of plantation rubber in that year, though a mere 5 per cent of the world supply, soon caused a break in prices. Though Brazil still accounts for forty million pounds of rubber a year, the plantation industry of other lands has far outstripped it. Plantation rubber is cleaner and more uniform in supply, and because of the superior organization of the industry it will supersede Amazonian rubber except in times of unusual demand. Brazil cannot develop the plantation system principally because of the great shortage of dependable labor in Amazonia.

Southward from Amazonia are the campos, vaunted as the most extensive grazing grounds in the world. Owing to the dry season which occurs in Subequatorial regions in latitude from 10° to 17° from the equator, two-thirds of the great stretch from the Paraguay River to the heart of the Brazilian Highlands is covered with grasses. Only forest galleries along the stream beds and the rocky upland areas break the herbaceous expanse. Here, of course, cattle raising is the leading industry. It is, and will long remain, an industry of small proportions. In spite of its natural covering this region must overcome many difficulties before a successful cattle industry is developed. Remoteness is a first handicap. These lands are 1,400 miles from Buenos Aires, their natural outlet. Secondly, no transport facilities exist. Both the Paraguay in the south and the Amazon tributaries in the north are unnavigable. Railway building is out of the question, even though the best lands are in the Goyaz Plateau, not far distant from the rich eastern agricultural districts. Finally, the more accessible grazing lands are capable of further expansion. Thus it is likely that the campos will long, perhaps forever, remain a land of open ranges producing a poor variety of cattle, commercially useful only for their hides.

The northern fringe of South America includes three small countries, Ecuador, Colombia, and Venezuela, and three smaller colonies, British, Dutch, and French Guiana. Of these political divisions Colombia has the largest population,[1] but here, as everywhere, the people cluster in favored spots, highland and coast. The adaptations of Brazil are reproduced in miniature in these northern tropical lands. Each of the states contains humid tropical coastlands like Bahia, dank interiors like Amazonia, and attractive highlands like the Brazilian Plateau. The llanos, shared by Colombia and Venezuela, bear comparison with the campos, while the inaccessible Guiana Highlands are similar to the sparsely inhabited inner reaches of the Brazil Plateau.

Man's progress in these northern regions seems slower than in Brazil, but this is largely because the favorable plateau lands of the latter are more extensive. In reality, considering the gross area of Brazil, that country as a whole is in about the same state of progress as any of the other tropical states. In Ecuador, Colombia, and Venezuela, the physical units are smaller in scale but the relations are the same as in Brazil. The contiguity of coastal plantation, coffee hacienda, and cattle warren has had the effect of accentuating economic sectionalism and political unrest in the smaller states, which, until recently, Brazil has escaped because of her very extensiveness. The dominance of the coffee growers of São Paulo is being challenged by other elements in Brazil to-day, but this is an old, old story in the northern tropical lands.

Most of the people of Ecuador live in the Andean Highlands where Quito, the seat of government, is situated. The Sierra has

[1] Colombia, 5,885,000; Venezuela, 2,412,000; Ecuador, 2,000,000; the Guianas 485,000.

been styled "the granary" of Ecuador because at an altitude of from seven to eleven thousand feet temperate grains and vegetables are grown. Agriculture is the only occupation; there is no mining and little manufacturing. The crops are poor and the methods of agriculture wasteful. The tropical lowlands are the source of wealth, but the highlands furnish a refuge for the masses, the politicians, and the landowners. The highlands of Colombia serve a similar purpose in the economy of the country. Here are located the principal cities—Bogotá, the capital, and Medellín, and here dwell most of the inhabitants. The Magdalena-Cauca basin furnishes a tedious commercial connection with Puerto Colombo on the Caribbean coast. The Western Cordillera, facing the steaming coastal rain forest, is sparsely inhabited and economically unimportant, but the Central Cordillera fosters a wide variety of agricultural and mining enterprises. Coffee and sugar haciendas dominate, but at altitudes above 6,500 feet, cereals and domestic animals contribute to the prosperity of this section of Colombia. More gold is mined here than elsewhere in the continent, and fair reserves of iron and coal, unexploited as yet, are reported. The density of population approaches sixty per square mile, thus permitting Medellín and other large towns to engage in the manufacture of consumers' wares. The Eastern Cordillera, in which lies Bogotá, is sparsely inhabited as yet. The highlands of Venezuela are most favorably situated; they are near the coast and parallel it for six hundred miles. Here is concentrated most of the population, and here are situated Caracas, the capital, and most of the towns. The money crops are coffee, cacao, sugar, and cotton; the food staples, corn and beans. Like Colombia, Venezuela manufactures consumers' goods, and the existence of nearby deposits of coal and iron, so rare in South America, augurs well for the future of manufacturing. The Guiana Highlands are too inaccessible to be of value as a refuge for the exploiters of the Guiana coast.

The lowland coasts of these countries, where the plantation system has developed, are apt to be of some economic importance; otherwise they merely share with the lowland interiors the transitory status of providers of forest products. About the Gulf of Guayaquil, in Ecuador, where the coastal plain has a breadth of one hundred miles, lies the richest tropical area of western South America. Here are the vast cacao haciendas which for a period of fifty years provided most of the revenue of Ecuador. To-day, however, the country suffers from over-specialization, and no longer do the six thousand hacienda owners, exploiting masses of ignorant and servile *cholos,* reap a profit of 25 per cent on their cacao lands. Scientific planters in other parts of the world have been quick to take advantage of Ecuador's weaknesses: careless labor, political unrest, and inability to cope with the witch broom disease. Thus in spite of ideal conditions of cacao-growing the heyday of Ecuadorian prosperity is passing, and the profound inertia to change is proof that no lesson has been learned. From the Gulf of Guayaquil to the Isthmus the coast is physically unattractive owing to the incessant rainfall, high humidity, and the disease-breeding mangrove swamps. Here dwell wild Indians or Negroes who have reverted to a state of barbarism, and here the forest industries flourish: the gathering of *tagua, toquilla, caucho* rubber, balata, and kapok. The seeds of the *tagua* palm possess all the essential qualities of ivory and are in great demand. *Toquilla* is the palm fiber that is used in the manufacture of panama hats. Kapok is the product of the silk cotton tree.

The lowland coasts of Colombia present the same physical appearance. The scattered mulatto, Negro, and Indian population is engaged in gathering forest products, or in working low grade cattle warrens or sugar plantations. In the far east, where the coast rapidly ascends, the plantation system reappears. Under the direction of the United Fruit Company, the export of bananas has increased from eighty million pounds in 1908 to 500,000,000 pounds to-day. This section of the country attracts labor from the Magdalena valley and the West Indies. A phenomenal production of petroleum has advanced Colombia to second place among the South American states, but political restlessness has greatly hindered the exploitation of the oil fields. Placer mining for gold and platinum in the Atrato Valley is a far greater attraction to the forest dweller of Colombia than the gathering of forest products. Until recently the platinum was thrown back into the stream as valueless, but a world-wide demand has led to the introduction of the dredging technique. To-day the Atrato supplies half the world production, and the chief obstacle to the industry is the climate, for only the Negro can withstand the fevers fostered in this unhealthy valley. The Venezuelan coastland, with the exception of the Maracaibo basin, is very narrow and is dominated economically by the nearby highlands. Formerly the Maracaibo district was a sleepy, unhealthy tropical coast. The deluge of oil in

1926 raised Venezuela to the status of second oil-producing country of the world and dislocated the economy of the entire country. In 1929, 136,000,000 barrels of oil, more than half the exports of the entire country, were shipped. Maracaibo Port became a bustling city of 100,000. The fields, like most exploiting enterprises in South America, are controlled by foreign interests—Anglo-Dutch and American. Attracted by high wages, the laborers have rushed to the oil fields, and with the decline of agricultural production has come a régime of high prices, and consequent political unrest.

The Orinoco delta lands are uninhabitable and so unhealthy that the Port of Spain on nearby Trinidad serves as the port of the river hinterland. The plantation system reappears along the Guiana coast. In prosperity, British Guiana is first, Dutch Guiana second, and French Guiana, once notorious as a penal colony, a poor third. None could survive were it not for the solicitude of the mother countries. The whole region is swampy and extremely unhealthy. Sugar is the leading plantation crop, but its export is rapidly declining owing to the development of better sugar lands. To-day in British Guiana there are forty plantations; a century ago there were more than a hundred. The land is cut up by drainage canals, thus prohibiting the use of machinery. After the abolition of slavery, labor was imported from the East so that the population is made up largely of East Indians, Hindus, and Chinese who cultivate rice as a subsistence crop. The forest products are balata and hardwoods, and some gold is panned by the ferocious descendants of slaves who dwell in the forest recesses. Diamonds are mined and, more recently, bauxite, which yields aluminum.

The continental interiors of the northern countries belong either to the Amazon or Orinoco systems. In the *oriente* of Ecuador, an equatorial rain forest, live some eighty thousand Indians who, if occupied at all, are engaged in gathering rubber which finds its outlet through Amazonia. The vast llanos of Colombia and Venezuela are scarcely more valuable than the rain forest of Ecuador. They have been heralded as the great reserve cattle warrens of the world, but as yet there is little fact to sustain such an extravagant fancy. Though the llanos embrace 100,000 square miles of level grassland, the low elevation of the plains makes possible widespread inundation during the rainy season. The hot blazing sun of the dry season induces a coarse, unnourishing bunch grass. Here roving *llaneros* tend herds of low grade cattle, estimated at three million head. Long distances must be traversed before the markets can be reached, and the business is so unprofitable that most of the trade is in hides. South of the llanos, in southern Colombia and Venezuela and along the margins of the Guiana Highlands, feeble forest-gathering industries are carried on. A little *hevea* and balata are extracted during the wet season, and tonka-beans, a base of perfumes, are collected during the dry season. The llanos and rain forests of northern South America have no more hopeful future than the campos of Brazil and the forests of Amazonia.

CHAPTER XIII

CARIBBEAN LANDS AND MEXICO: TRADE WIND LANDS

105. Geographic Basis of Life

Tropical North America is small in area, but it reproduces in heightened form the physical environment and the human responses found in the vast tropics of the southern continent. Very impressive, moreover, is the close relation between physical and social environment in this physically variegated area. Many flags are flown in northern tropical lands, and several of the major races, not to speak of admixtures, are represented; let the manner of living—in large, the culture —is to a surprising degree the reaction of human beings, not states or races, to the environment provided by nature. The basic elements of human existence—food, drink, shelter, clothing as well as the higher economic pursuits, trade and manufacturing—are influenced by the physical environment. The diffused or borrowed elements of the general culture, government, religion, and even the tools of modern industry, are matters of indifference to the masses so far as daily existence is concerned. Democracy has had no great success in these regions, nor indeed any marked failure; simply, the experiment has not touched the masses. Religion, no longer conducted under the auspices of inquisition, has lost much of its authoritarian character. Catholicism, the dominant form in these lands, takes on many hues and shades. Often just beyond the pale of the metropolitan cathedral, its pristine practices become distorted. Religion is picturesque always, necessary always, but it varies from place to place in accordance with the leaven provided by provincial heritage and imagination. Thus, in parts of Mexico, that which is ostensibly Roman Catholic is in reality a strange blend of Maya-Aztecan and Christian practice.

These tropical lands are valued by Western civilization for their products; hence it is along economic lines principally that the pressure of change is felt. Railways and ports must be built, plantations and mines erected, machinery and mills set up, disease and pests fought, and scientific agriculture forwarded. Were it not for the profits to be had from sugar, coffee, bananas, cacao, oil, and other staples, material development here would be exceedingly slow. Like all other parts of the world, Mexico and the Caribbean lands have, by virtue of their resources, been drawn into the orbit of the industrial civilization of Western Europe and the United States. To the extent that their products are valued will their culture continue to be actively influenced by Euramerican civilization. Yet because most of these lands import far less than they export and, more important, because the consumers' markets here are small, the masses are little dependent upon the outside world. Hurricane, drought, flood, disease affect man's life far more than transient business depression.

106. Topography and Climate

Tropical North America lies almost entirely between 10° N. and 30° N. so that part of it is affected, for some of the year at least, by the Northeast Trades.[1] Trades blowing over land are drying winds. In Mexico, for example, most of that region lying between Lower California and the Rio Grande is a desert. Trades which blow over the Atlantic, the Gulf, and the Caribbean, however, have a high relative humidity, and when intercepted by highlands, precipitate much rainfall. Thus, on the mainland, where from north to south a high mountain-plateau runs throughout, there is continual rainfall along the narrow eastern coastal plain. From Tampico to Panama the annual rainfall is very heavy, averaging more than seventy inches during the year. The flat lands of northern Yucatan constitute a sole exception. As the interior highland core lies in the distant mountains of Honduras and Guatemala, most of Yucatan receives sparse sporadic rains. Northern Yucatan produces no bananas, no sugar, but only henequin, derived from the drought-resisting sisal. Its inhabitants depend upon the windmill to supply them with water. Southern Yucatan, however, like other parts of the eastern lowland supports dense vegetation, rain forest or jungle. These lowlands, with the exception mentioned, are extremely unhealthy, and even such an important city as Veracruz, the port of Mexico, contains only forty thousand residents. North of Tampico the influence of the

[1] Examine carefully Plates XIV, XV, XVI, XVII.

sea-blowing trades becomes non-existent, and the annual rainfall drops off sharply. Inland also the rainfall diminishes rapidly until the desert is reached. Thus Monterrey, less than two hundred miles from the coast, has but twenty-two inches of rain as compared to Tampico's thirty. The rainfall reveals the seasonal change common to these latitudes. Most coastal towns experience a relatively dry season during the "winter" months. The dry season becomes shorter in duration as the equator is approached. In the West Indies where mountains rise directly from the sea, rainfall is plentiful all year round on the windward coast. Port Antonio, on the windward coast of Jamaica, receives over five inches of rainfall during every month but has a much greater summer than winter total.

Altitude is a factor not only in the watering of the eastern mainland, but in the determination of several distinct agricultural belts. Here as in South America the terms *tierra caliente, tierra templada,* and *tierra fria* are employed. In ascending from the east coast to the interior, the naturalist will observe a change from mangrove swamps and jungle to open lands interspersed with trees, which at altitudes of nine thousand feet develop into fine temperate forests of oak, pine, spruce, and fir. At the highest altitudes, above thirteen thousand feet, alpine flowers and grasses replace the forest. The transition wrought by altitude is found in all parts of the world within the tropics. The changes in agriculture are even more noticeable; from bananas to sugar in the lowlands; to coffee and corn on the slopes; to wheat, potatoes, and other grains and vegetables in the upper levels of the *templada.* In a country like Mexico, considerable trade arises in the exchange of commodities grown at varying altitudes.

The great plateau of Mexico receives less precipitation than its windward slopes. Except in the north the plateau receives from ten to thirty inches of rainfall annually, the larger part during the summer season. Mexico City,[1] at an altitude of 7,500 feet, receives twenty-three inches of rainfall of which all but three inches falls between May and November. In Central America, nearer the equator, the total rainfall is greater. Guatemala City, at an altitude of 4,700 feet, has about fifty-two inches annually. On the leeward (Pacific) side of the continent and of the islands, conditions differ from those on the windward side. Here the wet and dry seasons are sharply marked everywhere. During the dry season rainfall is entirely lack-

[1] Mexico F.D. or F.D. Mexico.

ing and vegetation (excepting the drought-resisting varieties) disappears. During the rainy season grasses flourish on the lee slopes, and throughout such lands live stock raising constitutes the staple industry. Almost daily there is a sea breeze, resulting in an afternoon shower on the slopes. The run-off frequently turns to flood as there is little tree growth at lower levels to check the flow. For agriculture to flourish, irrigation is necessary.

Throughout Mexican and Caribbean lands the uniformity of temperature is remarkable. On the island of Grenada in the Lesser Antilles, the yearly temperature is 79°, with a seasonal range of only 2°. On the mainland plateaus, though the yearly average is less than in the lowlands, a similar condition prevails. Mexico City with an annual average temperature of 60° has a seasonal range of only 11°, while Guatemala City with a temperature of 65° has a range of less than 7°. Everywhere the daily range is greater than the seasonal range, and the drier the district, the greater the daily range. The low temperature and the low relative humidity of the highlands earmark them as the dwelling place of the majority of the population. Speaking of Central America, Ellsworth Huntington remarks: "It seems a curious reversal of what we are wont to call normal conditions when one sees rich, fertile plains along the coast almost uninhabited, then finds the population fairly dense on the steeply sloping, stony mountain-sides at altitudes of three to five thousand feet, and finally on the hilly plateau at eight thousand feet see little thatched houses clustering thickly everywhere, and every available bit of land almost as carefully and industriously cultivated as in China." Indeed every capital and almost every leading city upon the mainland is located in the highlands.

107. Shortcomings of the Trade with Ample Rain Environment

The chief export commodities of the North American tropics are raised either in the lowlands or upon the windward slopes of trade wind lands. They are bananas, citrus fruits, sugar, cacao, and coffee. We are likely to regard these lands of sunshine, fertile soil, and ample rains as ideal agricultural areas. On the contrary, productive agriculture is a precarious undertaking. Drought, floods, hurricanes, and storms annually take their toll. Plantations continually engage in fighting some plant disease or parasite, and the workers of the lowlands are harassed by the inroads of malaria, hookworm, and other tropical maladies. Let us survey the course of events over a span of less than two years in the British West Indies.

The British West Indies had a difficult time of it during the years 1929–1931. The period is characterized as "one of acute anxiety for those interested in tropical agriculture." All the staple crops were in a serious position because of the depression and because of the ravages of pests and plant diseases. The cocoa industry of Grenada and Trinidad was suffering from overproduction and the competition of other tropical lands. In Trinidad the witch broom disease had become a serious menace to the cocoa industry. The demand for coconuts and copra was small. The banana industry of Jamaica was threatened by the Panama disease. The lime industry of Dominica, suffering continual diminution over a ten-year period owing to disease, was almost ruined by the hurricane of September, 1930. In September of 1929, the worst hurricane in the memory of the inhabitants visited the Bahamas, damaging much property and destroying the small craft engaged in sponge fishing, the leading industry. This catastrophe, states the official report, was unfortunate as the colony was just recovering from the ravages of the hurricane of 1926. The hurricane of 1929 struck Dominica also, destroying the dwellings of the workers and peasants together with all their crops. The combination of hurricane and tidal wave practically wiped out Belize, the capital city of British Honduras, killing and seriously injuring many, and rendering thousands homeless. During 1930, the Barbados experienced crop failure owing to a prolonged dry season. British Honduras suffered an abnormally dry season, followed by an abnormally wet season which brought the highest floods in twenty years. Good rainfall restored agriculture in Montserrat from the effects of the hurricane of 1928, but St. Kitts and Nevis had not yet recovered. The Bahamas in 1930 experienced an eight-months dry season followed by hurricane and floods in late September which wiped out all vegetation and ruined the citrus fruit trees. Jamaica during the same year had only sixty-two inches of rainfall, fourteen inches less than the average of the last fifty years. Serious drought occurred on the north coast, injuring banana and pimento production, and withering the cattle pastures. Antigua during 1930 and 1931 experienced the worst drought in sixty years, the rainfall in

1930 being twenty-five inches in comparison with forty inches for a normal year. Sweet potatoes and yams, the food staples of the natives, failed, and public relief became necessary. Drought and the falling market resulted in a 30 per cent decrease in income in Grenada. Such are the circumstances under which agriculture is carried on in a Trade Wind with Ample Rain zone. One is tempted to advance the proposition that drought, hurricane, and plant infection are normal hazards here. Still, when a locality fortuitously escapes such calamities, a bumper crop generally results.

During the past fifty years the United States has been visited by as many as one hundred cyclones originating in the West Indian area, a fifth of them of hurricane intensity. Two of the latter variety experienced during the past fifteen years have caused property damage, mainly in Florida, in excess of $150,000,000. The damage wrought by hurricanes in the West Indies, however, cannot be measured in terms of dollars and cents. In 1928, and again in 1932, Porto Rico was devastated by hurricanes whose whirl was estimated at two hundred miles per hour. Crops were utterly destroyed, homes and buildings were uprooted, and hundreds of lives were lost. Florida can protect itself from the shock by erecting buildings capable of withstanding the onslaught of winds traveling at 125 miles an hour, but in the West Indies crops are more important than buildings, and against damage to crops there is no remedy. The West Indies average six tropical cyclones per annum (the China Seas average twenty-two) ; and practically all occur during the late summer, in August, September, and October. During those months the quiescent doldrums have advanced far north of the equator, hence are subjected to the earth's rotational deflection. The doldrums, augmented possibly by the Southeast Trades, move forward in a northeasterly direction. These winds encounter Northeast Trades blowing to the southwest and the interaction of the two sets up a revolving whirl. "After the wind circulation is once started, there is a plentiful supply of energy from the latent heat set free in the process of condensation and precipitation of moisture in connection with the heavy rainfall that always accompanies tropical cyclones, so that the cyclonic circulation is not only maintained, but greatly increased, both in lateral and vertical ascent." [1] The whirl of the storm is thought to attain a

[1] "West Indian Hurricanes" by Charles L. Mitchell, principal meteorologist of the U. S. Weather Bureau, Washington, D. C. in the Scientific Monthly, December, 1930.

velocity of as much as four hundred miles an hour upon the open sea, while the rate of movement averages from twelve to fourteen miles an hour in a generally westerly direction. Modern communication has made it possible to warn shipping and settlements of the direction of the storm. During the great hurricane of September, 1928, there was no shipping loss on the high seas, and shelter and relief were prepared in many areas in the van of the storm.

Plant pest and disease are particularly difficult to combat because the humid tropical environment seems to abet the rapid growth and spread of all forms of plant and animal life, destructive as well as beneficial. An "ever watchfulness" must be maintained by the authorities. Where the governmental authority is highly coördinated, as in the British West Indies, it assists the planters in their fight, but where such conditions do not obtain, the planters themselves must maintain laboratories and agencies for combating disease. The Panama disease, a banana wilt, has time and again forced the banana companies to seek new locations. Indeed this blight, together with soil exhaustion, has made the banana industry a migratory one. The sugar planter has to confront a host of ravages: gumming disease, mosaic disease, root disease, dry top root, the frog hopper, and others. To develop a variety of cane immune to these attacks is the constant purpose of the sugar interests. Cacao growers must fight off the witch broom disease and monilia; cocoa planters the cocoa beetle; coconut planters, the wilt disease; lime growers, the wither tip and the red root disease; and cotton planters, the pink boll disease. Many regions have attempted to break away from the economically unfavorable system of monoculture that prevails in these tropical lands, only to have their most promising ventures frustrated by the appearance of blight that never accompanied the enterprise in other lands.

Human disease is another major handicap to activity in the North American tropics. Yellow fever, which once visited cities as far north as Boston, had been all but eliminated in Caribbean areas. Virulent as it is, yellow fever can be readily checked because it has no human carriers and because it runs a short course. The greatest drain upon the energies of tropical peoples is caused by hookworm and malaria, both of which infect the majority of the natives of the Gulf-Caribbean lowlands. Hookworm causes progressive anemia, digestive and nervous afflictions, underdevelopment, and loss of initiative. Much of the laziness attributed to tropical peoples is due to the effects of this disease. Those stricken suffer from it for years on end and reinfection may occur repeatedly. The larvæ find their way into the human body through the skin, generally by way of the foot, and lodge ultimately in the intestines. Investigation in various areas has shown that from 44 to 84 per cent of the inhabitants have hookworm. The disease can be treated successfully by drugs, especially chenopium and carbon tetrachloride, and communities can be kept free of the disease by preventive measures such as wearing shoes, and the installation of toilet facilities. In seven years, two-thirds of the inhabitants of Porto Rico were successfully rid of this plague, and the efficiency of the workers increased in the same proportion. With the aid of the Rockefeller Foundation, the campaign has been actively waged in many other Caribbean areas; and the elimination of hookworm is said to be a matter of time, dependent only upon the coöperation of the local health officers and the response of the natives to educational aids.

Against malaria, far more dangerous and insidious than hookworm, little progress has been made. This disease saps the energies of hundreds for every one it kills, and affects the economic vitality of whole areas. On the coastal plain of the Caribbean practically the whole laboring population is infected. While yellow fever is carried by only one variety of mosquito, malaria is carried by twenty-odd, and a mosquito once infected can transmit the disease for a period of three months. Some of the malaria-carrying pests travel widely, while the yellow fever carrier does not. Human beings may serve as malarial carriers for three years and are not immune to further attacks. In limited areas, where the mosquito land can be drained, malaria can be eradicated. This was accomplished in the Canal Zone but at a tremendous cost. Unfortunately drainage is out of the question in most of these damp lands so that it is unlikely that it will ever be possible to eliminate the carriers. The United States Public Health Service, the Rockefeller Foundation, and the United Fruit Company are in the van of the struggle against malaria. The fight is carried on upon individual plantations and in the most highly infected local areas by the use of preventive health measures. The infected are dosed with quinine or with a new, more efficacious drug, plasmochin, and if they do not respond, they are segregated in hospitals. The discovery of a preventive medicine will certainly come, to the relief of some hundred million sufferers scattered throughout the world. Such a discovery will rank among the greatest of scientific achievements.

108. Population

The distribution and density of population in the North American tropics is the result of historical circumstance, which, in turn, is grounded in fundamental geographical bases. Both in the islands and in the mainland, the aboriginal population has clung tenaciously to the highlands. The great Maya-Aztec civilization was predominately a highland product. With the coming of the whites, the leading economic development in the islands was that of the lowland sugar plantation. This type of work the Carib Indian could not endure, and in a very few years he practically disappeared. The Spanish, after toying with the idea of enslaving mainland Indians, turned to the importation of African Negroes. Thus in the West Indies, whereever the plantation system prevailed, the Negro soon constituted a majority of the population. Curiously, the settlers who went to Porto Rico and Cuba were few, and, as they engaged in stock raising and mining rather than sugar growing, no preponderant Negro element developed. Both Porto Rico and Cuba show a white population, liberally construed to be sure, of about 75 per cent. The other islands are predominantly Negroid. The West Indian population increased enormously after slavery emancipation, for under the harsh servitude of the sugar planter, the average life of the worker had been about ten years.

The Negro, immune to many of the white man's ailments and better able to acclimate himself, can carry on the unskilled work that the white is incapable of performing and at the same time subsist at a much lower standard of living. His fecundity under the most adverse conditions is remarkable, and to-day the West Indian Islands rank among the densely populated areas of the world. Jamaica has two hundred persons per square mile; Hispaniola, 250; the French Islands, 350; while Barbados supports a population of one thousand per square mile. Recently, population saturation has led to a run-off and the presence of the *jamaiquino* [1] has given rise to some thing of a race question throughout the Caribbean area. Cuba and some of the Central American States have attempted to place immigrant

---

[1] Migratory Negro laborer from Jamaica.

Negro labor upon a seasonal status, yet these laws are not rigidly enforced for obvious reasons. The white man and the mestizo of Central America have no liking for the type of work that must be done upon the lowland banana plantation. Resentment against the Negro seems to be based upon his lower standard of living and the money that he takes out of the country rather than upon his race. Cuba and other islands as well as the Central American countries encourage the white immigration, but the flow on the whole is negligible. Cuba during the sugar boom of 1923 to 1927 attracted over 75,000 European immigrants, mainly Spanish; yet with the decline of prosperity, emigration has set in. Nor has the curtailment of immigration into the United States led to the anticipated augmentation of the white stock in the Caribbean. Central America and Mexico are sparsely populated in proportion to their area. With the exception of the small republic of Costa Rica, which boasts 80 per cent white stock, these regions are composed almost entirely of mestizo and pure Indian groups. In Guatemala and Mexico the full-blooded Indian stock is over 60 per cent.

Throughout the whole area, racial discrimination is less sharp than in the United States. Social lines are drawn by the whites, particularly among the upper classes, but differences of education and wealth have much to do with the barrier of race; certainly intermarriage is not regarded as carrying any stigma. Even in the West Indies there exists a large mulatto element; in Jamaica it is 20 per cent and in the Dominican Republic, 50 per cent. In political life there is little discrimination, though in Cuba and some of the other islands the foundation of a "black" party is frowned upon. In the British West Indies limitation of race is no barrier to participation in public affairs. Of Jamaica, Cudnall writes, "There are coloured men who sit side by side with their white brethren on the judicial bench and attain to high rank in Church, Politics, Medicine, Law, and Commerce."

109. The West Indies

For the West Indian native who accepts drought and disease as acts of God, life offers few problems. He possesses or rents a little piece of ground, *conuco,* about which his life revolves until the soil is exhausted. The ground is cleared and kept clear with the aid of a long knife, a *machete.* During the drier season the small trees and brush are burned, and the larger trees are felled with the aid of axe and fire. The patch of ground, less than an acre in size, is then ready for planting, for it is free of sod. A sharp stick, or a hoe, serves to scratch the rich humus in preparation for the seed. Plentiful rainfall and a little cultivation bring forth bountiful crops. The staples are largely indigenous to America; sweet potatoes, yams, corn, beans, pumpkins, and the cassava (yucca) of the manioc plant. The small banana is eaten raw, while the large banana or plantain is cooked. A little tobacco, a few chickens, occasionally a goat, complete the ensemble. There is no variety in the food staples. Those favorably situated, or more important, favorably inclined, will raise a cash crop such as coffee or sugar, to be sold at the local mill. The *conuco* is not an orderly garden for the various plants and vegetables are scattered about at the whim of the owner.

The palm, of which there are many varieties, provides most of the remaining wants. The house consists of poles stuck in the earth, and the walls and roof are made of palm leaves. The binding is done with palm fiber. Both are exceedingly tough and will last for many years. If a dirt floor does not meet the occasion, one is constructed of the outer surface of the palm. The gourd tree supplies buckets and bowls. Palm fiber also furnishes the raw material for hats, baskets, and hammocks. Dishes are unnecessary, for food is conveyed from the common pot to the mouth with the hand; shoes are still considered a luxury and little clothing is required. The children run naked, while the adults at best indulge themselves with homespun or cheap factory-made garments. A dress for the woman, a shirt and overalls for the man, suffice. The consumers' market has no place here, for only a half dozen imported articles, at most, are desired; a *machete,* an axe, a skillet, and a few iron pots and cheap cotton goods would account for most of the purchased articles. Thus only a little cash is needed and this is obtained either by selling a few loads of produce or by working for a few days on the plantation. Altruistic planters have had the experience of raising wages only to find that the beneficiaries much preferred to work a fewer number of days than to reap a greater harvest of cash. Life here, unlike that in the temperate zone, is neither an obstacle race, nor a life-long quest. Each moment is valued for what it brings, and little time is lost either in day-dreaming or worrying about the morrow. To follow the example provided by nature in viewing life as an endless chain of birth, life, and death, and to accommodate one's self to such whims as storms, drought, disease, above all without effort, seems to be the accepted philosophy.

In the world industrial machine, regulated largely by Euramerica, the West Indies play an important part. Many of their products are essential and much foreign capital has been invested in the development of their resources. Great academic interest has been aroused in the United States concerning the methods of economic imperialism in the West Indies and the attitude of our government toward these islands. The wealth created is large but little of it reaches the masses. The profits are split principally among three groups, the foreign planter, the clique that runs the native government, and the native plantation owner who is generally the recipient of favors from the governmental class. Here the "trickle down" theory works badly, for even the necessities of civilization such as public sanitation and education are lacking. Where an island is in possession of a foreign power, the people usually fare better, for a few precautionary health measures and a modicum of education make administration easier. Moreover, nothing commands the favorable attention of the money market so much as a well ordered paternalistic régime.

In the final analysis, however, geographical factors are likely to determine the relative economic standing of any tropical territory. A brief survey of the various physical environments will explain the economic dissimilarities in the West Indian islands.

Little need be said of the Bahamas, for while climatic conditions are ideal from the standpoint of health, the soil is too thin and rocky and the rainfall too scanty for tropical produce. These islands, together with the Florida Keys and the northern third of Yucatan, have only recently, geologically speaking, emerged from the sea. Their elevation is not sufficient to cause the trades to precipitate moisture. What rain does fall drains quickly through the thin limestone soil cover into the porous coral base. In consequence, the Bahamas with an area of 4,400 square miles maintain a population of only 55,000. Any surplus quickly drifts off to more favored places. The principal industry is sponge fishing. Recently the Bahamas have turned their attention to the cultivation of sisal, an innovation from Yucatan, and with the disappearance of the harvest provided by illicit liquor traffic, the enterprise will probably take root. Northern Yucatan was once the glory of America, for there was matured the

Mayan civilization. Even to-day with its scantier rainfall, it provides an environment far superior to that of the adjacent damp mosquito-ridden jungle. In northern Yucatan, monoculture prevails in the cultivation of sisal, which yields henequin, the raw stuff of binder twine. As the sisal plant requires four to five years' growth before there is a yield, the enterprise is a capitalistic one. Mayan peons provide the labor.

The Greater Antilles—Cuba, Hispaniola, Porto Rico, and Jamaica —all possess a Trade Wind with Ample Rain type of climate; hence they are blessed with tropical abundance. In the production of sugar Cuba leads the world. Sugar accounts for over two-thirds of all Cuban exports; even her famed tobacco is hardly a rival. No state can hope to rival Cuba in sugar production, for she combines ideal climatic conditions with an inexhaustible supply of land. During the last thirty years she has far outstripped Java, her most tenacious rival. Thanks to her sugar production, Cuba is queen of the Antilles. With less than half the total population of the West Indies, her commerce is five times as great as all the others combined.

With the exception of the mountainous region in the far east the whole island is excellent sugar land. Much of it has yet to be brought under cultivation. The country from north to south can be characterized as rolling, and is sufficiently high to yield an annual rainfall of forty-five to sixty inches. Because there is no central mountain backbone, the rainfall is evenly distributed; hence Cuba is lacking in dry leeward lands common to the other islands of this group. The seasonal distribution of the rainfall is perfectly suited to the maximum production of cane. The rainier season corresponds with the summer growing period, while the dry season is propitious for the concentration of the sugar and for the harvesting of the cane. During the sugar season, thousands of seasonal laborers converge upon Cuba from all the other islands to assist in its cultivation, transportation, and milling. Much of the cultivation is still done by hand, for though the ground is plowed and harrowed by teams of oxen, the shoots are planted by hand, and the fields are kept free of weeds by the *machete*. After the first harvest no further cultivation is necessary, for the discarded leaves keep down the growth of weeds throughout the period of second, third, or fourth cuttings. The large corporations that mill and market the cane have not yet reached the stage of buying large holdings and cultivating by mechanized agriculture. At present a large proportion of cane that reaches the mill is produced upon the *conuco* of the small land holder. In 1929 Cuban sugar production reached its peak, over five million long tons. Unfortunately the planters had overshot the mark, for the export price of raw sugar dropped from 2.4 to two cents a pound and much of it could not be marketed.

For the tremendous development of the country in the last thirty years Cuba owes much to the United States. The guarantee of freedom from internal disorders attracted the capital necessary to develop the sugar industry. Because of Spanish misrule the land had hardly been scratched. Even to-day, Cuba, with sixty-five people to the square mile, is scantily inhabited. An agricultural frontier is still being pushed eastward into the virgin lands. American capitalists have invested in the neighborhood of one billion and a half dollars in Cuba, gaining control of a seventh of the lands and erecting and operating the several hundred sugar mills scattered about the island. Although the exigencies of war and too rapid expansion has dislocated the industry during recent years, sugar on the whole has paid handsome dividends. With a preferential tariff advantage, Cuban sugar has dominated the cane market in the United States. Though the American possessions enjoy a duty-free advantage, the United States still consumes over three-fourths of the Cuban export.

The population of Cuba exceeds 3,500,000, more than double that of 1899; yet its density is only sixty-five per square mile. If Porto Rico can support four hundred per square mile, Cuba can certainly support twice that number. The sugar crop occupies only 5 per cent of her cultivable soil, while 80 per cent of her land is excellent for purposes of scientific agriculture. Cuba could easily produce the entire world's sugar supply if she controlled the market. Cuba is now making an effort to develop agricultural resources other than sugar. A successful beginning has been made in fruit and vegetable-growing. Though the export of bananas and pineapples has not expanded rapidly because of the competition of the other islands and the preference shown in the United States for the citrus fruits, the increase in the export of winter vegetables has been rapid. The American market has welcomed the fresh tomatoes, eggplants, cucumbers, peppers, and potatoes of Cuba. The export value of fresh vegetables increased nearly 20 per cent in 1929. Tobacco has always been an important subsidiary crop owing to the undoubted excellence of the Cuban leaf. Most of the tobacco is produced in a small area of less than a thousand square miles in western Cuba. Here in the Vuelta Abajo district, under an intensive system of cultivation and land fertilization practised by immigrant farmers from the Canary Islands, crops worth as much as $200 per acre are produced. Two years of slow curing are required to produce the best-flavored Habana tobacco. The reputation of Cuban tobacco is such that manufacturers actually import tobacco to satisfy the demand for Habana cigars. Until the depression in the steel industry, there was a considerable export of hematite ore, which, because of its accessible location in the neighborhood of Santiago, could be shipped cheaply to Baltimore and New York. Undoubtedly, with the revival of industry, Cuba will find a steady market for her iron ore as well as for her copper, chromium, manganese, and asphalt.

The island of Hispaniola contains two backward states, Haiti and the Dominican Republic, at present under American oversight. The Haitian Republic, little more than a third of the size of her sister state, contains a population almost three times as large. In Haiti the density of population is 250 per square mile; in the Dominican Republic, forty-five. The Haitians are composed largely of Negroid stock, the Dominicans, of white stock. Compared with Cuba and Porto Rico, economic and social progress here has been very slow, owing undoubtedly to the unhappy political experiences of both countries.

The plantation system of agriculture has not made much headway in Hispaniola because of the risk of investing capital. In consequence most of the produce that finds its way to market represents the surplus of the *conuco*. Indeed the ease of making a living on this island makes it difficult to transform the small landowner into a wage earner. So free is he of the acquisitive instinct that the merchant must frequently furnish the donkey transportation necessary to bring the goods to market. Most of the population is concentrated in the wet trade wind valleys on the east or west coasts. Here nature is prodigal and little or no effort is required in attaining food or shelter. The woods provide fruits, and where sprouts are stuck in the ground, bananas, plantains, melons, squashes, cassava (here called yamie), and sweet potatoes are produced in abundance. About the palm-leaf shelter hogs and chickens put in appearance. If money is required, it can be secured easily; in Haiti, by planting a little coffee or cotton (either may be gathered wild) ; in the Dominican Republic, by growing a little sugar. In the less rainy interior where few people live, the complexion of existence changes a little, but nature is, as usual, lavish. The native grasses support hogs, chickens, and goats whose skins are marketable. Here the palm-leaf house gives way to walls of basketwork, or to mere sticks plastered over with mud. Life on the uncleared north coast reproduces a type of tropical nomadic life comparable to that of the wild tribes of Borneo.

Hispaniola has immense economic possibilities if ever orderly government develops. Though the topography of the island is not as favorable as that of Cuba since the four lateral ranges reduce the amount of arable land, it favors a more diversified type of agriculture. The alluvial valleys of the east and west coasts, with ample rainfall all year round, are especially adapted for cacao, sugar, and tobacco. The south coast of the Dominican Republic, with a rich alluvial soil and a sufficient dry season, is an excellent sugar-growing region. Higher lands suitable for coffee and cotton are limitless. In the drier interior live stock will flourish, and in the drier lowlands in the south sisal growing is an excellent prospect. But all this is a mirage, for here man's work will not be done for decades, if ever. The export trade of Haiti and the Dominican Republic together is but a seventh of that of Cuba, despite the larger population of Hispaniola.

In the Republic of Haiti the trend of business is largely determined by the yield and price of coffee. Subsidiary cash crops are cotton, cacao, and sugar, with sisal and tobacco gaining in prominence. A few hides and skins, some honey and logwood complete the export list. Almost the entire coffee crop is exported, and it represents 77 per cent of the value of Haitian exports. France is the leading coffee customer. The Dominican Republic is less given to monoculture than Haiti, for sugar, the leading crop, comprises only 55 per cent of the total value of the exports. Cacao, tobacco, and coffee are the rivals of sugar. At one time Haiti was a sugar producer, exporting during the last year of French rule (1791) nearly ten thousand tons. Under native rule, however, the French mills fell into ruin, and the jungle has reclaimed the sugar lands. At present there is a revival of sugar growing; in 1928, ten thousand tons were exported by the single company in business.

Porto Rico, traversed by a high range, reveals the characteristic climatic features of a trade wind island. The windward northeastern side has ample rains throughout the year, forcing the sugar planters to construct drainage works to prevent the cane from being drowned out. On the south side of the island, however, the fields are watered by irrigation systems that draw their supply from reservoirs constructed on the windward side. Tunnels through the mountain ridge conduct the water to the lee side, a method used in trade wind islands such as the Canaries and Hawaii. During the dry season, the south side of the island is brown and parched and even the rivers indicated upon the map are missing. Only the irrigated sugar patches are green. Porto Rico has rich soils, volcanic in structure and overlaid with limestone deposits. Though the steepest slopes are under cultivation, Porto Rico is unable to feed itself and must import large supplies of rice and beans.

American occupation gave the impetus to Porto Rico's development. A system of fine roads was developed, making possible the extension of agricultural lands and the marketing of crops. The greatest benefit, however, was American tariff exemption which confers upon Porto Rican sugar an advantage of a cent or two a pound in the American market. Little wonder that Porto Rico, Hawaii, and the Philippines have expanded their sugar lands feverishly during the past thirty years! Porto Rican sugar exports have increased from sixty thousand tons to 600,000 tons from 1900 to 1928, the bumper year. Farmers on all sides poured cane into the mills built by American sugar interests. The millers, in recent years, have found it an advantage to own their own lands, with the result that the majority of sugar workers are landless men, hired at a wage and purchasing food from the company store. This situation will cause trouble when there is no employment for the laborer.

Porto Rican tobacco production has increased tenfold during the American occupation. It, too, is fast becoming a plantation industry because it requires intensive cultivation, far too expensive for the *conuco* owner to undertake. The crop is planted in November and harvested in March, principally in the northern interior valleys and slopes. Tobacco culture requires much work; the ground is plowed in July and during the summer must be repeatedly limed and harrowed. To increase the humidity as well as to protect it from the wind and the beetles, the tobacco is grown under a cotton cover. Under this treatment the finest cigar wrapping tobacco is produced.

Most of it is raised upon lands, owned by American corporations, that have risen in value to $500 an acre. Coffee is grown upon the higher windward slopes under the shade cover of the plantain or some other tree. This crop is the mainstay of the independent *conuco* owner and supplies the whole family with work. After the picking is over, the coffee farmers seek work in the lowland cane fields. Porto Rican coffee, like all Caribbean coffee, is distinguished for its mild aroma. Its production, however, has not greatly increased in recent years because of the encroachment of sugar lands and because of the difficulty of competing with the favorite, Brazilian coffee. It is difficult to create a demand for a new variety of coffee. In recent years Porto Rico has undertaken with considerable success the export of grapefruit, pineapples, and oranges.

Porto Rico is a crowded land. Its area is small, less than 3,500 square miles; it is ninety-five miles from east to west and thirty-five miles from north to south. The population is 1,500,000, over four hundred per square mile. Prosperity depends entirely upon the tariff advantage, and agriculture, under the direction of American capital, is turning more and more to sugar. There are 800,000 landless men and women on the island, over half the population. The government encourages crop diversification, but most of the newly irrigated lands on the leeward side are in possession of the sugar interests.

The Lesser Antilles extend like a chain for eight hundred miles between Porto Rico and the South American coast. Most of them are British owned. They vary much in appearance. Martinique is a huge volcano of 380 square miles; Dominica boasts of a new stream for every day in the year, while in many of the islands the well is the most important factor in life. A number of them experience such irregular rainfall that they are entirely uninhabited. Except for Trinidad, which produces oil and asphalt, these islands are small copies of the Greater Antilles. Sugar, cacao, coffee, cocoa, coconuts, and limes are the principal exported products. The British government works hard in the interest of scientific agriculture and crop diversification, but it is difficult to keep these islands afloat economically, for they are marginal in the marts of trade, wholly dependent upon the vagaries of world commerce. The development of a new preferential market for their fruits and winter vegetables in Canada, together with the usual Imperial trade favors, enables them to face the future with less apprehension than formerly.

110. Central America

The economy of the Central American republics is quite similar. Their activities conform strictly to the agricultural possibilities afforded by climate and physical resources. Manufacturing is limited to the primary preparation of raw stuffs—the processing of coffee, the grinding of sugar cane, the preparation of cacao, the distilling of liquor, and the sawing of lumber. On the humid east coast the cash crop is invariably the banana. Sugar is unreliable for in time of stress its profits shrink rapidly. In Honduras the sugar lands are being converted into banana plantations, and in Guatemala the planters are restricting production to the needs of the domestic market. In the plateau and on the mountain slopes coffee engages the attention of all. In every republic except Honduras it is the leading crop. Central American coffee, like the West Indian variety, is "mild" and though popular in certain places, it is not the favorite in the world market. The lee western coasts experience less rainfall than the windward coasts, and their less extensive lands are relatively nonproductive. All the states are able to combine highland and lowland crops except Salvador, which does not reach the Atlantic and British Honduras, which has no plateau lands.

The density of population of any state depends upon its proportion of plateau land. Salvador, the smallest republic, has a density of 115 per square mile, while Nicaragua, the largest, has only thirteen to the square mile. British Honduras, practically all lowland, has only five per square mile. Economic life has always centered in the plateau, and as the western coast is more accessible than the eastern, most of the ports are located on that side. The railway systems are necessarily small since they are but spurs from coast to highland.

Life in Central America is not dissimilar to that in the West Indies except that there the Indian has replaced the Negro. The inhabitants live in little villages of thatched houses and often own land in common in the traditional Indian manner. Their clothing is made of the cheapest undyed homespun and their hats are manufactured of palm-leaf fiber. Every harvest season sees them bearing bags of coffee upon their backs to be sold at the local market. In the more thickly settled regions, as in Porto Rico, the natives terrace the steepest slopes for coffee planting. Their food is that of their Indian forefathers, maize, squash, and tropical fruits. The highlands of Guatemala and Costa Rica attain an altitude of seven thousand feet, thus permitting the cultivation of temperate products such as wheat, barley, and potatoes. Here "the ground is prepared for wheat with a hoe; the crop is cut with a sickle, tramped out by the feet of animals, winnowed by the wind, and ground by hand." Rice, another Old World crop, is now grown in several of the republics.

In many parts of Central America the Indians do not like to work on the coffee *fincas.* In Guatemala, with the connivance of the officials, a system of peonage has grown up. The Indian accepts a loan from the planter to finance his wedding or to spend at a *fiesta,* and by law he is forced to remain upon the estate until he has worked off the debt. Complications are likely to arise when the Indian succeeds in borrowing of four or five planters. This system tends to disappear, for the cost of "capturing" the Indian is often greater than the wage paid during the picking season, about sixteen cents a day. Some of the planters give their Indians a patch of land on condition that they will work on the *finca* during the harvest. In Salvador conditions are better, for the less burdensome transportation charges permit a wage of as much as fifty cents a day.

At present the Central American states are having a difficult time because of the depression in the coffee market. Most of them produced bumper crops in 1928 and find it difficult to adjust themselves to a shrinking demand. For the first time since the World War they have been made to realize that their production is "marginal" in the world market. The failure of coffee means national calamity in Central America for diminishing revenues imperil the national credit. Recently Costa Rica endeavored without success to float road-building bonds in the money market. To retrieve their position these countries have endeavored to open up new banana lands. But, as the planters of British Honduras have learned to their sorrow, banana lands under wasteful methods of cultivation are impermanent. As the plantations recede into the interior, the crop cannot bear the increased costs of transportation. Sooner or later the corporation must shift its location to another country. In 1929, for example, the United Fruit Company abandoned its plantain plantations in British Honduras and moved to northern South America.

111. Mexico

Mexico is a relatively large country, ranking fourth among the states in the New World. Yet in the present industrial scheme she occupies a very small place in proportion to her size and population. Canada, with half the population of Mexico,[1] imports seven and a half times as many goods and exports four times as much. Even Cuba with only three million inhabitants can boast of a larger foreign trade than Mexico. Both depend largely upon the United States in their foreign trading, Mexico importing 70 per cent of her wares from the United States and Cuba 60, while each sends 70 per cent of its exports to the United States.

Mexico, because her physiography and climate are essentially the same as those of the Caribbean area, offers much the same wares to the world market. Chief among her non-mineral exports are bananas, chicle, vanilla beans, (*guayle*) rubber, *garbanzos* (chick peas), other beans and lentils and, in increasing amounts, winter vegetables, especially tomatoes. Mining products are more important than in the Central American states where the deposits are too small to be worked profitably. Mexico ships sizable exports of copper, lead, zinc, and graphite, and is the largest silver producer in the world. The recent drop in the price of silver has had the effect of closing down many mines working on a small margin of profit. Mexico contains one of the most extensive oil deposits in the world, and it is estimated that only a hundredth part of her oil lands have been exploited. Oil, because it furnishes a large proportion of the national revenue (in 1922, 30 per cent; to-day less than 10 per cent) and because its development is largely in the hands of foreign industrialists, has been the source of much trouble. Possibly oil has hindered rather than aided in the development of the country, for unrest is not conducive to foreign investment. In 1921 oil production reached its peak with the extraction of 193,000,000 barrels. In 1929, Mexico, though fourth among the oil producing nations, being outranked by the United States, Venezuela, and Russia, produced only 45,000,000 barrels. In 1931, production fell to thirty million barrels, and Mexico was seventh in rank. The reasons for the decline are several: the increased production of the United States; the shift to Venezuela where the fields are new and the taxes lower; the appearance of salt

[1] The population of Mexico is sixteen million.

water in the Tampico fields, an indication of exhaustion; and finally, the uncertainty of the political situation in Mexico. It is likely that the next center of production will be on the Isthmus of Tehuantepec, whence it is possible to pipe oil to Veracruz for shipment. The largest operators are foreign; the Royal Dutch, the Standard Oil Company of Indiana, the Standard Oil Company of California, the Standard Oil Company of New Jersey, the Gulf Oil Corporation, and the Pierce Oil Company.

Mexico is not a manufacturing nation. Her industries employ no more than ten thousand persons out of a population of sixteen million. Most of the factories are located in Mexico City.[1] Textile and shoe manufacturers, largely of coarser grades, employ the majority of the workers. Protected by high tariffs, these and other consumers' industries have made rapid progress recently, but at the present moment they are suffering greatly because of the reduced purchasing power of their customers, the result of a falling-off of the demand for foodstuffs and petroleum in the world market.

On the whole, however, the majority of the people have little to do with the production of either oil or foodstuffs for export. Nationally these items seem important, but they do not touch the life of the individual. To understand Mexico and the people one must see them in the various localities in which they live. As Mexico presents a variety of physical environments, the manner of living changes from place to place. Since the majority of Mexicans reside upon the central plateau, this region harbors what is "typically" Mexican, and the cultural attributes that are shared by the nation as a whole have diffused from this center. The common cultural heritage is non-Euramerican in two important aspects: it is Indian, and it is non-mechanical. Spanish influences are present, to be sure, but they are superficial. In the sphere of practical everyday affairs and in the more intangible realm of ideas, the Mexican has borrowed only those traits which represented some tangible advance or advantage. Wherever doubt existed in his mind as to the superiority of the innovation, it was rejected. In other words, the core of Mexican culture is predominantly a Maya-Aztec survival upon which neither *pronunciamento* nor statute have had much influence. Passive resistance to change has given the indigenous culture its ultimate victory, and that attitude still persists. Euramerican industrial changes have no more

[1] Mexico F. D.

changed the way of life than three centuries of Hispano influence. Thus the Mexican stands his ground firmly against innovation, and though he may by word of mouth agree with all we tell him, his tongue is in his cheek. For him the problems of life were solved centuries ago and he finds no convincing reason for reworking the pattern. Mexico, not Canada, is our foreign neighbor. Mexico City, with its urban population of nearly a million, has adopted all the trappings of urbanity—advertising, hotels, and factories—but the capital does not in this case typify the nation.

112. Regional Differentiation

Topographically and climatically Mexico is a land of violent contrasts, and these contrasts have much to do with variations in the density of population and differences in the economic structure. The whole country lies within the trade wind zone of the northern hemisphere. Roughly, the northern half, that part extending north of a line drawn from the tip of the California peninsula to the mouth of the Rio Grande, is a desert because the dry trades blow there. In only two districts is any moisture precipitated: along the Gulf coast, and in the high forested Sierra Madre Occidental. In the southern half of the country a Trade Wind with Ample Rain type of climate prevails. The lee part of southern Mexico is much drier, hence less useful and less densely populated except in the *caliente*.

Mexico has two great mountain chains running from north to south, the Sierra Madre Oriental and the Sierra Madre Occidental. which converge in the Central Plateau. Between them lies high basin land which rises in altitude as the Central Plateau is reached. At Jaurez, near the American border, it is four thousand feet high; at Mexico City, 7,500 feet. South of the Central Plateau are the Sierra Madre del Sur and the Chiapas Highlands, separated by the depression of Tehuantepec. The Chiapas Highlands are an extension of the highlands of Guatemala.

The Central Plateau possesses all the excellent characteristics of a tropical highland; uniformly cool temperature, moderate rainfall, level surfaces, and rich volcanic soil. In addition it has rich mineral resources, ample water power, and easy access to the Gulf. The Central Plateau is the heart of Mexico. Comprising but a sixth of the area of the country, it contains two-thirds of the population and two-thirds of the cities. The textile mills, the tobacco factories, and the breweries give the impression of industrialism, but the plateau is, by far and large, an agricultural community. Here a greater proportion of arable land is planted in corn than elsewhere in the world, though little of it leaves the country. The plateau consists of a series of fertile lacustrine plains which receive soil sediment from surround-

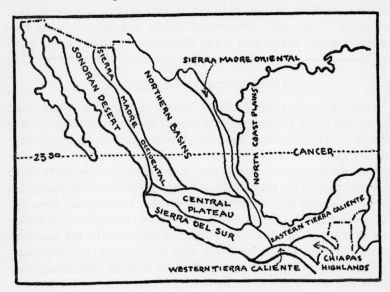

FIG. 13—MEXICO: GEOGRAPHICAL REGIONS
(*After Colby*)

ing volcanic masses. These mountain peaks are capped with snow and act as reservoirs, making irrigation possible for even the poorest farmers. The plateau itself is so high that the monthly temperatures are quite uniform. The daily range is greater than the seasonal range which varies only ten degrees, from 65° in July to 55° in January. Even in July blankets must be used, for it is chilly during the nights and early forenoon. As in all regions of high altitude, the temperature varies perceptibly from sunlight to shadow, making it feasible to have as many sunlit windows as possible. The rainy season, from June to October, corresponds with the growing season, and the precipitation, though far less than that of the *caliente,* is ample enough to support a variety of food crops; corn and vegetables at lower levels, and wheat and barley at higher levels. At high altitudes man has found the climate most suitable for his needs. It is said that the villages located above the level of seven thousand feet are on the average three times as large as those situated at the two-thousand-foot level.

Population density decreases rapidly in every direction from the Central Plateau. Most of northern Mexico has less than ten inhabitants per square mile. The most desiccated region of Mexico, of course, is the Trade Wind Desert that lies in the lee of the Sierra Madre Occidental. So dry is the Sonora Desert that from the Colorado delta to the Yaqui River, a distance of five hundred miles, only two small streams make their way to the sea. In the irrigated lands of the delta and in the surrounding coastlands, Chinese immigrants and other aliens raise winter vegetables and cotton for the California market. In the province of Sinaloa, south of Sonora, irrigation is practised in places where the soil is porous enough to retain the run-off from the Sierra. The agricultural possibilities of northwest Mexico, however, are rather strictly circumscribed by nature.

The Sierra Madre Occidental are precipitous and render the transmontane basin an inaccessible hinterland. In the mountains all economic activity centers about the mining enterprises. Swift mountain streams supply water; narrow valleys, the foodstuffs; and the magnificent forests furnish abundant oak, pine, and cedar for construction. In the northern basin lands the activities of man are handicapped by lack of water. Cattle raising, however, can be carried on, for the cattle tick does not flourish this far north, and the rainfall, from ten to twenty inches, is sufficient to provide nutritious bunch grass. On the other hand, droughts are frequent during the winter season. In the west this handicap is overcome by damming the streams that flow from the mountains and, in Coahuila, by tapping the water table. The northern basin, however, does not provide ideal cattle land.

The state of Coahuila ranks high in importance in spite of its physical handicaps. It contains the most important coal field in Mexico. It produces, in regions having less than ten inches of rain, cotton, wheat, and ixtle, a fiber used in cordage. Cotton, as well as subsistence crops such as corn, beans, and alfalfa, are raised in the Laguna Valley, which derives its soil and water from the nearby mountains of Durango. The Saltillo wheat district also depends upon irrigation and dry farming in making its crop. The Sierra Oriental are less rugged and less elevated than the western mountains, consequently less barren. Rainfall is more abundant, and the valley soils, derived from the limestone slopes, are very fertile. The mountains themselves furnish charcoal, the national fuel, and water power, especially in the south where industry has made some progress. The northern portion of the coastal plain is an extensive lowland with rich agricultural possibilities. The extraction of oil is, at present, the primary consideration and has precluded agricultural development. This coast lies off the beaten path of settlement in Mexico, which in the first place followed the ore deposits to the northwest, and later extended only where coffee and corn could be grown in conjunction. The railways of northern Mexico as elsewhere lead to the capital, with the exception of feeders to Matamoros and Tampico. In the extreme north, the Colorado delta and several other districts are tapped by spurs of the American system, giving them an unusual commercial advantage.

The southern highlands are isolated from the rest of Mexico because of their inaccessibility. Acapulco, the only port for more than five hundred miles along the Pacific coast, has a hinterland that is no more than a coastal border, for within thirty miles of the coast the Sierra Madre del Sur rise to a height of five thousand feet. Guerrero and Oaxaca contain the most highly dissected plateau in Mexico. There is little hope of exploiting their vaunted mineral resources. Chiapas, east of the Isthmus of Tehuantepec, is even more isolated. Indians, whose manners and customs have not changed much since the pre-Columbian period, comprise the bulk of the inhabitants of these southern mountains. It was in Oaxaca only several years ago that Stuart Chase saw the blood of a sacrificial turkey, together with candles, tobacco, and other offerings, placed before a stone monolith. Corn and beans are the subsistence crops and form the basis of the diet. On the Pacific coast a little cacao is raised; on the slopes there is coffee; and high up in the plateau some wheat is grown. In the Chiapas Valley, a dry lee land, live stock is raised. Horses and mules are everywhere, and at higher levels sheep put in an appearance. Spinning, weaving, dyeing, stone-cutting, and pottery-making are the domestic industries, and a crude commerce is carried on by barter.

In striking contrast to the Sierra Madre del Sur is the lowland *caliente* which includes the coastal plain south of Veracruz, southern and eastern Yucatan, the lowlands of Tehuantepec, and the narrow southern Pacific coastal border. These districts have some commercial importance, though it is small in proportion to their size. Sugar and bananas are grown on plantations, largely on the Gulf plain south of Veracruz. There are scattered patches of rice and tobacco, and on higher lands some live stock is raised. From the tropical jungles are extracted a variety of forest products: sarsaparilla, chicle, *castilla* rubber, logwood, mahogany, and cedar. The methods of extraction are exhaustive, for the Indians who push far up the tangled, swampy stream banks think only of loading the boat. The *castilla* rubber trees have been bled to death and none are to be found over wide areas. At present the gathering of chicle and the cutting of logwood are the most lucrative pursuits. The former goes to the United States to be manufactured into chewing gum, and the latter furnishes a dark red substance highly valued in the dyeing industry.

The Indian of the jungle left to his own devices leads a life that is remarkably similar to that which prevails in the tropical forest environment everywhere. His wants are few and easily supplied. From time to time a patch of jungle must be cleared, and this is accomplished by hewing the tangled vines with the *machete* and girdling the larger trees. During the less rainy season the land is burned over and made ready for planting. With the aid of a pointed stick, corn, beans, and pumpkin seeds are planted. The corn is eaten as it ripens, and only at the end of the dry season does the Indian make an effort to gather the ears that have survived the pickings of bird, insect, and beast. Before the rainy season comes again, he must burn over the field or clear a new patch. Only in the dry, flat plain of northern Yucatan, so suited to the cultivation of *yucca* (henequin), do the Indians attain a higher standard of life.

113. Mexico: Geography and Culture

Geographical factors impose certain broad limitations upon the manner of living of any large social group, and in a more subtle fashion geography may condition, in a thousand instances, the general culture pattern. Where the social group is impervious to outside influences and clings tenaciously to the ancient, more primitive ways, as does the Mexican, the geographical influences are more numerous and apparent than in a more sophisticated society because the group, in perpetuating the ancient mores, is preserving a culture that was, of necessity, an adaptation to the environment. Thus, in examining the mode of life among the Indian villages, and, as well, that prevailing among the free villages and the hacienda villages of the central agricultural region, we must realize that their vaunted self-sufficiency rests upon a scheme that harmonizes closely with the physical milieu. Mexican society has not reached that degree of emancipation from environment which permits the communities of industrial America to specialize in a few agricultural or manufactured products.

Mexico contains three racial elements, but the barriers among the groups are so imperceptible that it is difficult to estimate accurately the size of each. In a population of sixteen million nearly 40 per cent is Indian, nearly 60 per cent is mestizo, and the remainder, a fraction of between 500,000 and a million, is white. On the whole, Mexico is rural and agricultural. Excluding the capital, a strange anomaly, fully four-fifths of the people dwell in villages of less than four thousand inhabitants. The Indian lives in the most inaccessible ranges and in the deepest tropical forests, the mestizo is found in the plateau region, and the white in the larger towns. From the American to the Guatemalan border pure Indian stock can be traced along the upper mountain levels. As the ranges in southern latitudes are more hospitable than the northern, and since the tropical forests are more extensive in the east than in the west, the Indian population is concentrated in the south and the east, south of Mexico City.

The Indians do not possess a uniform culture, for they live in regions that vary widely geographically and are comparatively isolated. That there exist to-day among them nearly fifty spoken languages is an evidence of their cultural dissimilarity. Their culture, however, is always primitive and closely dependent upon the environment. They engage in hunting, fishing, and agriculture. In Chichuhua, for example, the Tarahumaras plant two crops annually, one in March on the crest, the other in June down in the *barranca*. After harvesting these crops, they retire to winter quarters to enjoy themselves. Wealth here is reckoned in live stock, for the man who owns three or four head of cattle and a dozen sheep and goats is considered quite wealthy. In the mountains of Nayarit (west central Mexico) live the Huicholes, a nomadic tribe of about five thousand members who secure their livelihood by hunting and fishing. They wear practically no clothes. The great majority of the Indians, however, live in southern Mexico, in the mountains and in the lowland forests. Here the mode of living changes somewhat. The Cora Indians, who live in the lowlands of Nayarit, cut down the tropical trees during the cool season, burn the wood in the spring, and sow their grain with the first rains. As in the eastern *caliente* this operation constitutes the year's work. The rest of their time is occupied in feasts, banquets, and other orgies; their main distraction is dancing with their idols. In Chiapas the hard-working Chamula plant maize and vegetables upon small patches of infertile land.

Most of the Indians, however, have some contact with the mestizos, for they have need of certain commodities that they cannot produce —principally *aguardiente* (a strong drink), sugar, salt, and cheap cotton cloth. Often they will work for short periods upon the haciendas, in the mines, or in the lumber camps. Many visit the villages during the fiesta and sell pottery, blankets, and trinkets of various kinds. They never remain long for they are suspicious of the mestizos. Even where they have established permanent villages, they absent themselves from their homes for long periods of time. In the Sierra Madre Occidental they occupy their houses only on feast days, abandoning them as soon as the fiesta is over to retire to their crags. A large part of the Indians govern themselves according to their own customs with a fine disregard for the law. In an editorial published in 1927 it was stated that the power of the governor of the territory of Quintana Roo [1] was nominal only. The Maya possess this district and obey only their *caciques*. The Indians are very jealous of their lands which they own in common. At Zacatepec, in Oaxaca, the Mixteca Indians refuse to have any dealings with the mestizos. They live under a system of communal ownership and are forbidden to sell or exchange their holdings. Should the cultivator decide to relinquish his land, it is returned to the village. The mestizos and whites who dwell there are regarded very suspiciously. They may build a house in the village but are not given title to the land upon which the dwelling rests. Only the Indian has the right to plant a perennial crop such as cane, cocoa, or bananas; the others are restricted to crops like maize, cotton, or rice, that are planted annually. Throughout Mexico generally the Indian village elects a *guardia detierras* whose function it is to distribute every year a

---

[1] A district in eastern Yucatan.

patch of land to each cultivator. Among some of the tribes the fields are rented to those who wish to cultivate the land. This communal system is found also among some of the free villages, who borrowed it from the Indian tribes.

The majority of the people of Mexico live either on hacienda settlements or in free villages. The latter, though greater in extent and embracing a larger proportion of the peasant population as a result of the recent land legislation, are dominated economically by the haciendas. These great estates possess the best lands and frequently surround the free villages, shutting them off from the ever essential water supplies. Furthermore, in most of the free villages the communal system of landholding has died out, leaving the fields concentrated in a few hands. Consequently, the average worker is usually a cultivator without tools or work animals, and without access to lands sufficient in quantity and quality to enable him to earn a subsistence for himself and his family. Many fill out their economic needs by arts and crafts, by acting as carriers and mule drivers, or as petty merchants. But the greater number supplements its income by working upon the hacienda as laborers, croppers, or renters.

There are twelve thousand haciendas, about 2 per cent of all the farms in Mexico, but they constitute over half the privately owned lands. The small hacienda located upon the Central Plateau in the midst of a dense population is worth far more than the giant hacienda located upon the arid *latifundia* in the north. The owners farm only the best portions of their lands; the poorer lands are worked by croppers, renters, resident laborers, and non-paying tillers of new lands. Viewed in one light, the system of peonage that prevails has resulted from the necessity of keeping a permanent labor force upon the land. The recent revolutionary changes have abolished many of the worst features of the system; debt peonage has been outlawed; wages have been substituted for certain feudal privileges; and the hours of labor have been shortened. These reforms are far more important than the reduction of hacienda lands by a third, because the reduction has taken place largely upon marginal lands, sparsely inhabited. The hacienda still governs the economic life of the country, for through share-cropping or as laborers, most of the peasants are brought into contact with it. It perpetuates a system of backward agriculture, because the exploitation of labor makes it unnecessary to expend large capital sums upon farm machinery. The *hacienda* remains, for the most part, a self-sufficient economic entity, quite in harmony, be it said, with the desire of the individual to be "let alone."

The great mass of Mexicans satisfy their primordial needs for food, clothing, and shelter by availing themselves of the materials that are afforded by the immediate environment. It is the way of life that has persisted since the time of the Maya-Aztec civilization. Corn, the "divine maize" of the Aztecs, is the staff of life of the Mexican peasant. The housewife steeps the hard grain in warm lime water, grinds it by rubbing upon a concave stone, fashions the dough into thin flat cakes, and after baking them upon an earthen griddle, produces the nationally favored *tortilla. Tamales* are made by mixing the meal with meat or *chile,* and *atole,* by brewing a thick corn gruel. All were favorite dishes of the Aztecs. The most popular is still the *frijole,* made of red, brown, or black beans, and seasoned in a variety of ways. For drink, in lieu of water that is neither palatable nor healthful, the peasant depends upon *pulque,* the fermented juice of *maguey* (agave) ; upon the more fiery *mescal,* the concentrated distillate of the century plant; or upon the rich and nourishing *chocolatl.* Fruits and poultry complete the diet. Meat is regarded as a luxury and never reaches the lower classes. The children eat the same heavy meals as their parents, and, judging by the high child mortality rate, the experience is frequently fatal.

Raiment follows the dictates of cool nights and sunlit days. The *zarape* is blanket by night and overcoat by day. The Indians cling to their traditional hand-woven designs, varying from district to district, but in many of the poorer villages has been substituted the cheap factory-made product, "hideous in their travesty on the native appreciation of color." As of old, the *sombrero*—high crowned, broad rimmed, of the finest fabric—tempers the blinding rays of the sun; while *huaraches* or leather sandals serve as the national foot gear. The women folk wear highly-embroidered garments made of cotton cloth spun on primitive looms. The deep blue cotton shawl serves among other purposes as a wrapper to carry babies and other burdens. The women's garments vary in color and design according to district.

Except in the large towns, where a modified form of Spanish architecture prevails, the houses are one-room shacks made of adobe

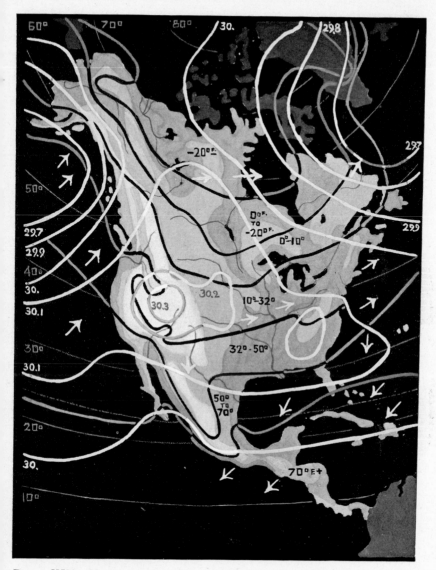

PLATE XIV. NORTH AMERICA—JANUARY ISOTHERMS, ISOBARS, AND PRE-
VAILING WINDS

(*After Goode*)

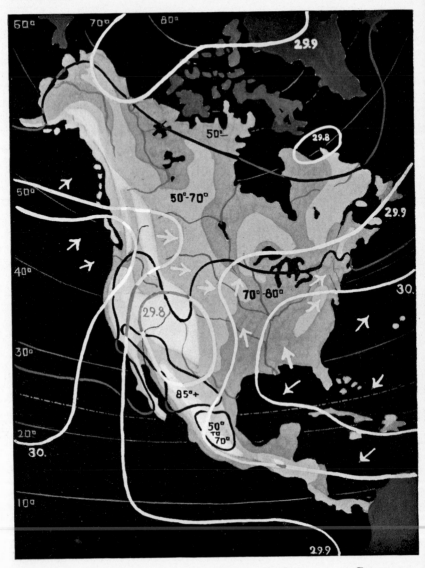

PLATE XV. NORTH AMERICA—JULY ISOTHERMS, ISOBARS, AND PREVAILING
WINDS

(*After Goode*)

in the colder regions and of bamboo reeds in the warmer sections. Where volcanic rock is plentiful it, too, is pressed into service. But, by and large, the adobe hut of sun-baked mud, thatched with *zacate* or shingled with *maguey* leaves, is typical of the *mesa centrale*. Regardless of the diversity of the exterior the furnishings are uniform throughout the country. "There is one room, a griddle, a metate for grinding corn, a huge water pot, brightly painted wooden bowls, a square tin oil can, assorted pottery, hammocks or straw mats to sleep upon, a little shrine with tinsel and candles—not now so frequent as in the Diaz days; two dogs, three hens, four babies; a broom of rushes, and somewhere flowers." Within the cactus-bound compound are various shacks: a cook house, a bath house, a storeroom for maize, and a stable or two. The people live always in villages, each with a central plaza, about which are scattered the church, the town hall, the school, the stores, and the houses of the more prosperous. Within its shaded groves are the bandstand and the well or fountain. Here on numerous occasions during the year are held the fiestas.

The fiesta is the national recreation. At fiesta time the entire population of the locality converges upon the village and all productive labor ceases. Every one is able to indulge his inclination to the fullest. The church is one center, the band plaza another. The rest is a medley of gambling, pageant, fireworks, merry-go-round, and market. In one village thirty fiestas of major and minor importance accounted for one hundred days of the year. The fiesta is an escape from the humdrum of daily existence, not as with us, a transition from organized work to organized play. No one is compelled to listen to long wearisome harangues upon the civic virtues, nor requested to put some drive "over the top," nor strong-armed into sampling the wares of some zealous advertiser, nor even urged to participate in mass singing or prayer. Instead one dances, sings, gambles, gossips, bargains, or, postponing all these exercises until *mañana*—to-morrow or thereafter—one simply naps in the sun.

The peasant works as timelessly as he plays. Until May there is little to do: the hut is repaired, new fences are erected, the tiny fields, *milpas,* are cleared, and the brush burnt. The town, too, is cleared up: roads are tended to, the school-house limed, the church roof repaired, the fountains and wells looked over, and new stones inserted into the public laundry along the stream. In May the rains begin, and what was dusty and barren becomes moist and green. The fields are cultivated with a wooden plow and kernels are stuck into the ground. The rains continue until October, but as little cultivation is required, there is time to work upon the coffee hacienda. By December the corn and coffee are ready to harvest, and the busy season begins. Men, women, and children are in the fields from dawn to dusk, often tenting there at night. The farmer is assisted by neighbors whose corn is not yet ripe, and the completion of the harvest is fittingly celebrated in every homestead. Most of the corn is stored against the winter. The surplus is sold to the factor, the cash being invested in necessities or retained until the Christmas fiesta. The kernels are ground into meal when needed; the husks are used in tamales, and the stalks for fodder or left standing as bean poles.

In the *mesa centrale,* as in other parts of the country, the degree of economic self-sufficiency is remarkable. There is little desire to change the habits of daily life. Food, clothing, shelter, habits of work and even play seem to be closely related to the physical environment. Flagrant abuse is remedied from time to time, usually by violence; but there exists no creed of progress, no obeisance to prosperity. Drought is frequent and disease chronic, but these things are accepted as the normal vicissitudes of life to be reckoned with as they appear. The Mexican village needs little that it cannot supply and, according to one American observer, the only adoptions from the Western industrial world are the discarded tin cans to be found in the homes of the humble; the phonograph, a prized possession seen only in the balconied structures of *los correctos;* and the sewing machine, universally acknowledged as indispensable. Mexico regards the world depression with equanimity; a few white collar men have lost their jobs in the capital, but there is still corn—for sixteen million people.

CHAPTER XIV

THE UNITED STATES

114. Introduction

The United States lies wholly within the temperate zone. Even the Florida Keys, which cross the 25th parallel of north latitude, do not extend to the Tropic of Cancer. The term *temperate zone* may in a very general way be significant in setting it apart from the so-called *tropical* and *frigid* zones, yet it tells us very little of the geographical responses that prevail within its broad bounds. It merely indicates that the temperature is subject to seasonal change and that the rainfall and the remaining climatic factors are subject to wide variation. Within the temperate zone exist climatic differences that are as far reaching in their influence upon the inhabitants as are those that aid us in distinguishing the temperate from the tropical zone.

The United States affords a rare example for studying the effects of the various temperate types of environment because it includes them all within the bounds of a single political state. In Europe, with its multifarious political divisions, geographical influences are obscured because the political boundaries bear little relationship to the natural divisions. Economically we have escaped many of the evils that arise from a dependence upon others for resources that we do not possess. In a rough way, until recently entirely unregulated, certain staple crops are produced in those parts of the country most fitted to produce them. On the other hand, this movement appears to have gone too far, for in our survey of the various geographical divisions of the country it will be shown that certain regions have specialized to their own detriment. Drought, flood, overproduction, pest, and blight have often reduced normally rich areas to a position of actual want. Over longer periods of time "the goose that laid the golden egg" has been unthinkingly slaughtered through careless soil exhaustion, ruthless deforestation, and reckless exploitation of mineral resources. No country, however rich, can proceed with impunity in its economic development, without a due regard for the consumptive capacities of its population, and without the realization that the relationship among the various sections supplying the many needs of a large and constantly increasing population is, at best, very delicately balanced. On the one hand the possibility of crop failure in any one region must be guarded against by duplication, while on the other (and in the United States this constitutes the major problem at present), measures must be taken to prevent the production of goods in excess of the consuming capacities of the domestic and foreign requirements. Russia's economic planning is based upon a desire to produce enough goods to satisfy the primary needs of her vast population, while American planning must proceed in the direction of eliminating the loss and waste that arise from the production of too many goods. Much of the present dislocation in agriculture and industry can be traced to the glutting of the market with goods that Europe, recovering her pre-war status, refused to take, and which America could not use. Economic planning in the United States will bear a very close relationship to geography, for the primary industries are based upon the ores, minerals, and oils that are extracted from the earth; the lighter industries upon the industrial crops; and the food staples upon the products of the soil. Thus far most of our economic planning had been concerned with the acquisition of the tropical industrial products and the few metals we lack. Little attention, however, has been paid to the "domestic balance wheel."

Before the problem can be solved, or even comprehended, one must certainly study in some detail the geography of the country not so much with the view of learning what crops grow in certain sections, but rather with the end of ascertaining why certain crops are best fitted to certain types of environment, and whether a different type of agriculture is either feasible or possible. Thirty years ago the second query would hardly have arisen because economic development was formative and dynamic, and the production of crops and other primary commodities was hardly sufficient for the needs of a rapidly growing population and of a social community that was changing in structure from an agricultural to an industrial pattern.

In Chapter IV the various broad climatic regions in the United States were indicated; hence at this point two things may be assumed: first, the mastery of these divisions, and secondly, an acquaintanceship with the general geographical features of the United States. The very largeness of the subject precludes the use of comprehensive enumeration and statistics which can be obtained without difficulty from current year-books and official publications. We shall examine the most important geographical relationships existing within the various natural regions, then endeavor to establish the relationship of the parts to the economy of the whole.[1]

115. The Maritime Region: Northern Pacific Lands

This region, which, within the United States, extends from the head of the Central Valley of California (*circa* 39° N.), to the Canadian border, has been characterized as "a long string of mountains, a long string of forests, a long string of fishes, and a long string of mines." Laterally it extends from the coast to the Cascade Mountains. The coastal border is narrowly restricted by the Coast Range, but between the Coast Range and the Cascades is a long narrow trough that includes the Puget Sound Valley, the north-south part of the Columbia River Valley, and the Willamette Valley. The southern part of the maritime district, however, is traversed by the Klamath Mountain plateau which merges into the Coast Range in the west and into the Cascades in the east.

The climate of this region has been highly praised as the type most conducive to the expenditure of human energy. As the whole area is subject throughout the year to a succession of cyclones and anticyclones, its climate has great variability, which is highly desirable. The seasonal range of temperature is not great; hence man is never handicapped by heat or cold. The summer monthly average is about 60°, which is believed to be the optimum for physical labor, while the winter average is close to 40°, the optimum for mental endeavor. Seattle has a January temperature average of 39° and a July average of 63°, Astoria has a range from 40° to 60°, and Portland from 38° to 67°. The whole region has ample rainfall for agriculture, while the exposed coastal slopes experience greater rainfall than elsewhere in the United States. A total of 138 inches was recorded during one year. A greater amount of rain falls during the winter than in the summer half year. Olympia, for example, with an annual

[1] In reading the sections following Plates XIV, XV, XVI, XVII should be constantly consulted.

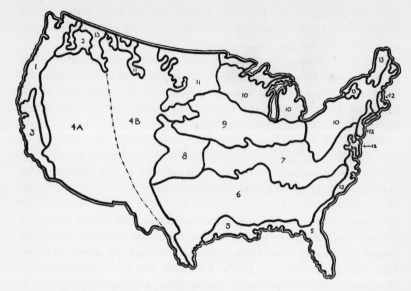

FIG. 14—AGRICULTURAL REGIONS OF THE UNITED STATES

(After O. E. Baker)

1—North Pacific Hay, Pasture and Forest Region
2—Columbia Plateau Wheat Region
3—Pacific Subtropical Crops Region
4—Grazing and Irrigated Crops Region: a—Desert and Mountain
Region; b—The Great Plains Semi-Arid Region
5—Humid Subtropical Crops
6—Cotton Belt
7—Corn and Winter Wheat Belt
8—Hard Winter Wheat Region
9—Corn Belt
10—Hay and Dairying Region
11—Spring Wheat Region
12—Middle Atlantic Trucking Region
13—Forest and Hay Region

precipitation of fifty-five inches, experiences a fall of 9.7 inches in
January and 0.7 inches in July. The precipitation of this region is
strongly influenced by oceanic conditions. It shares with the ocean
the relatively low pressures of winter and the relatively high pressures of summer. Since, under these conditions, more cyclones originate at sea in winter than in summer, the Maritime belt, like the
adjoining ocean, has a greater winter rainfall. Vegetation, particularly

trees and undergrowth, runs riot in this area of high humidity and frequent rains and is most dense along the coast range, some parts of which have not yet been thoroughly explored. The Cascades, too, receive an abundance of moisture, most of which drains off into the inland trough. Although some moisture reaches the high Rockies, far to the east, the vegetation changes perceptibly on the lee side of the Cascades. Here forest gives way to grass, and fruit-growing yields to wheat-growing and stock-raising.

The natural vegetation of the Maritime climate type with its all year rainfall and uniform temperatures is coniferous forest. The Pacific forest extends from the 35th parallel to the 60th parallel, but the finest stands of timber are concentrated in the American states of Washington and Oregon. Further south the dry line extends far up upon the mountain slopes, while in Canada the winter snow line extends far down the slopes. In the American maritime states the timber belt extends from sea level to an altitude of seven thousand feet. From the seaboard to the Cascades, the prevailing species is Douglas fir. In the Cascades region there are excellent stands of spruce, yellow pine, and sugar pine. The conifers are more suitable than the deciduous species for commercial uses because they have a straight tall trunk, with a base diameter often exceeding eight feet. The timber, too, is found in large stands.

In spite of more than eighty years of actual agricultural settlement, the maritime states have not yet lost their aspect of forest. Although the timber has been cut down over large areas—65 per cent of the timber in the State of Washington has been cut over—agricultural advance has been very slow because of the difficulty of clearing the land of stumps. In the Puget Valley region where the forests were remarkably dense, agriculture is confined to narrow coastal treeless borders; the cut-over lands resemble grave yards with thousands of tombstones, ten to twenty feet tall, protruding from the earth. Though Washington and Oregon between them possess the finest timber reserves in the United States, nowhere in the world has there been more ruthless cutting of timber. The Federal government by creating national parks on a large scale has prevented some of the timber from falling into the hands of the lumber barons, but little has been done in reforesting the lands already stripped. Unfortunately, the secondary growth is cedar and other less valuable species. Washington and Oregon are small in population and wealth, consequently Federal aid is needed if the national timber reserves are to be protected. These states have all they can do at present to curtail the ravages of the forest fires. In 1922 as the result of 1,800 forest fires, the state of Oregon lost about 2 per cent of its privately owned timber. During the midsummer when occasionally no rain falls for as long as several months, fires invariably break out.

The lumber industry, needless to say, characterizes the economy of these states. The quays of the towns are piled high with boards, saw-mills dominate the industrial districts, and even the front yards serve as storerooms for the wood that is burnt during the mild winters in lieu of coal. The cutting goes merrily on, for as the smaller reserves are exhausted in various parts of the United States, the price of timber steadily rises. Lumber is now able to carry the freight charges by rail, and much that formerly went through the Canal is now shipped directly to the markets of the middle west and the east.

The mountain regions are sparsely inhabited; the Coast Range section like corresponding districts in western Ireland, Scotland, and Wales, is too wet for agriculture. The mountains contain deposits of many basic ores and minerals, but the mining industry has not developed to any large extent. The Cascades provide ample water for irrigation but the run-off is largely on the western slopes where it is not needed. Washington and Oregon possess a large percentage of the water power reserves of the United States, but there has been no occasion to develop them on a large scale. The mountains act as a barrier, keeping out the winter's cold, but add enormously to the cost of transport construction. The Columbia Gorge aids Portland by facilitating its control of the hinterland, but the cold that seeps through during the winter is harmful to the fruit trees in the valley.

In proportion to their great size, Washington, Oregon, and the maritime district of northern California have but little land under cultivation. A large proportion of the agricultural activity of the Willamette and the less productive Puget Sound Valley is concerned with providing food for the urban population. The Willamette and Columbia districts competed successfully for a time with the California fruit growers, but the greater variety of products grown in the valleys to the south enabled California to forge ahead. The greater rainfall of Willamette Valley makes the plum and cherry crops less certain than in California, and although to-day the northern states enjoy a priority in apple growing and in the berries most suitable for the making of jams and preserves, much of their marketing is carried on through California. Too many stumps and too much rain have retarded agricultural progress in the northern states. The incessant rains leach the soil, washing away much of the essential lime and potash. The necessity of mixing the clayey base with humus adds to the overhead, and yet this must be done, for a clayey soil "puddles" when wet and bakes when dry. The Puget Sound Valley suffers particularly in these respects for the rainfall is heavier than in the Willamette. In consequence the farming community in the immediate hinterland of the great urban districts of the Sound is engaged in the raising of general produce and in dairy "farming," rather than in the cultivation of national staples. East of the Cascades the change from general farming to specialized industry is rapid; here in fertile irrigated stretches are to be found large wheat fields, and along the banks of the Columbia, where bunch grasses grow in profusion and where the winters are relatively mild, the live stock industry flourishes.

The population of the maritime states is urban to a large degree. This seems on first thought surprising for we regard these states as new and pioneer. Yet lumbering is an industry that requires fewer men to cut the trees than to prepare them for shipping. Likewise, fewer men are required in catching than in canning the fish. The same generalization applies to the fruit-growing. Finally, since little of the produce is consumed by the small population of these states, large numbers of people are concerned with the varying functions of export trade. Though the salmon is no longer so prodigal as to provide fertilizer for the fields, the river catch is still important. Furthermore, cities like Seattle and Astoria, because of their experience in canning, have become the pivotal points of the fishing industry of the whole Pacific coast. The bulk of manufacturing is concerned with the preparation of rawstuffs for the market, not in the production of consumer's wares. Thus planing mill products, paper and wood pulp, canned fish and fruits, flour, and packed meats constitute the large majority of manufactured articles. Seattle and Portland are the leading commercial cities; the former is important because upon it converge the growing Oriental trade and the Alaska shipping; the latter, because it controls the vast hinterland leading to the Columbia Gorge as well as the export trade of the Willamette Valley. With the removal of the sandbars at the mouth of the Columbia and the clearing of the river, Portland's position has been much improved for its harbor can now accommodate large sea-going vessels. Other cities, too numerous to mention, are growing rapidly because of their situation in Puget Sound, a drowned valley with many excellent natural harbors. The Maritime region is important in the national scheme because of its lumbering and fishing industries and because of the facilities it affords for trade with the Far East and Alaska; advantages that arise directly from geographical factors.

116. The Columbia Plateau

This is the smallest area in the United States to receive recognition as one of the leading subdivisions in the scheme of American agriculture. It corresponds roughly with the drainage basins of the Columbia and the Fraser rivers (Canada) and lies between the Rocky Mountains and the Cascade Mountains. The Cascades, in robbing the Westerly Winds of most of their moisture, have rendered these lands dry. Much of the land in the river bottoms is covered with sagebrush. Unless this land is irrigated, it provides poor pasture. Where the Snake River joins the Columbia River the annual rainfall is less than six inches. A large area in central Washington and Oregon receives less than ten inches of rain and is regarded as desert land. Many small mountain streams, unable to reach the rivers, flow into interior depressions to create temporary or permanent lakes of a saline character.

The rainfall comes largely during the winter season as might be expected from the proximity of this territory to the Pacific. Fortunately for the farmers, the winter temperature is mild enough to permit the working of the lands; the ground is rarely frozen, and the warm Chinook winds melt the snow and keep the ground exposed. The rainfall and temperature, soil permitting, are ideal for the production of winter wheat. The heavy rains of April, May, and June are most important for the growth of the seedlings, while the almost rainless July and August are ideal for the maturing of the crop. The soil is magnificent in places, being composed of a deep stratum of decayed volcanic lava which the scanty rains can neither leach nor carry away. Such a happy combination of climate and soil enables the Columbia wheat grower to obtain a yield per acre far exceeding that of any other state. The production per acre for Washington is twenty bushels, for Kansas, fourteen, and for Minnesota, 13.5. The misfortune is that such a large part of the Columbia Plateau is too dry to produce any wheat at all. The principal wheat lands lie in a restricted area between the Blue Mountains of Oregon and the Spokane River in Washington. So limited are the good lands that enterprising farmers sow wheat on the hills wherever it is possible for agricultural machinery to perform the necessary tasks.

In this region a type of wheat was developed that would permit the grain to stand for a month after ripening without injury. This artificial extension of the harvest is important in that it permits the employment of fewer men, and thus greatly reduces the costs. All the good wheat land in the Columbia Plateau has been in cultivation since 1900. The earlier farmers raised wheat year in and year out relying on the soil fertility to sustain the crop. Later it was learned that such a system had the effect of robbing the soil of its humus. By 1915, 30 per cent of the wheat lands were lying fallow. Agricultural experts, pointing out the impossibility of single cropping in a region where the annual rainfall did not approximate eighteen inches, recommended changes. Thus began the alternation of wheat with legumes such as clover, peas, beans, and alfalfa. The "frontier" stage was passed when a system of farming that combined small grain farming with stock-raising was introduced. Dry farming, successful for a time because the land does retain the winter rains, has decreased because the soil under such a system is gradually impoverished. This can be prevented only by the application of fertilizer, a financial burden which the crops of this region cannot carry. Irrigation, made possible by capturing the run off of mountain streams, cannot be readily extended because of the mounting expenses of bringing marginal lands into use. The lands now in use are diminishing in fertility owing to soil depletion, and the grazing ranges, too, have a lower carrying capacity than formerly, for over-stocking has made it impossible for the grasses to reseed themselves.

Spokane is the capital of this "Inland Empire." In spite of its vaunted water power resources, it has not developed a great manufacturing industry. It is important because it is the distributing center for a wide expanse of territory. From it are shipped wheat, meat and hides, mining products, and, from the mountains lying east of the Columbia Plateau, lumber.

117. The American Mediterranean: California

California is important not because it possesses the "largest city" and the greatest motion picture industry in the world, nor even because of its resources in timber and oil, for these are transient, but because of its highly specialized agricultural development. For a long period, under Spanish impetus, California, utilizing the rich bunch grasses, raised only live stock. Later, in response to needs of a rapidly increasing influx of miners and settlers, much of the land was turned over to wheat and barley, cereals with small moisture requirements. With the improvement in national transportation which coincided with the introduction of irrigation upon a large scale, California abandoned unprofitable wheat and barley-raising for a more lucrative agriculture, the production of fruits and vegetables. In making this change Californians were, consciously or unconsciously, adopting the mode of agriculture best fitted to their topography and climate—one that had been successfully followed for centuries in the Mediterranean environment of the Old World. California possesses unusual advantages; her membership in a great state, which provides her a market for her specialties, enables her to devote her entire agricultural resources to their cultivation.

The American Mediterranean is situated entirely within the bounds of California. The sections of the state that are not part of this environment are sparsely inhabited and relatively useless to man. The rugged north, the Klamath plateau; the mountainous east, the Sierra Nevada; and the desert southeast, the Mojave, are economically uninhabitable. The remainder of the state is divisible into coastal plainland, coastal ranges, and a central valley; all lying west of the giant Sierra Nevada. The coastal border is very narrow, but embraces two agricultural regions of prime importance: the longitudinal river valleys that penetrate from Monterey Bay and the Bay of San Francisco into the coastal ranges, and secondly, the extensive coastal plain fronting the San Bernardino and San Jacinto ranges in the south. The Great Central Valley is a trough five hundred miles in length, forty or fifty miles broad, comparable geographically to the Central Valley of Chile. It is drained by two streams, the Sacramento and the San Joaquin, both of which flow into the San Francisco Bay indentation. Into the Sacramento-San Joaquin basin flow countless streams from the mountains on either side. The lands on the western side are the less extensive because of the rather abrupt descent of the Coast Range. The Sierra Nevada ascent is very gradual. These mountains, in fact, dominate the Central Valley. As they are snow-capped, they maintain the water supply of the valley until the end of June, long after the winter rainy season has passed. They also protect the valley from the cold of the interior. The Coastal Ranges, too, perform a great service in precipitating the moisture of the Westerlies, which is stored in reservoirs and distributed by means of irrigation.

Topography is more important in conditioning the temperatures of California than latitude. Tropical products like the orange and the olive are grown in the upper Sacramento, in the latitude of New York. The winters are not appreciably cooler than those experienced in the citrus belt of Southern California, four hundred miles to the south. The moderating factors are the ocean and the protection afforded the valley by the northern and eastern mountain formations. Throughout the winter and spring months there is an abundance of vegetation, and though frosts are common in Sacramento from November to April, they do not affect the growth of hardy vegetables and truck crops. Late spring frosts are very rare and little damage is done to fruit crops where the air drainage is good. The citrus-growers evade the bottoms where the cold settles and plant on the foothills up to a 1,200 foot level where the temperature averages from 1° to 5° higher. During the summer the temperatures are ideal for plant growth. The sun shines in a cloudless sky for months on end. The Central Valley is quite hot during the day, often over 100°, but this heat is not stifling to human energy because there is little humidity and because the nights are quite cool. The cloudless atmosphere is important for fruit drying.

California rainfall reveals great variation, from an inch or two annually in the parched Mojave Desert to more than one hundred inches in the Sierra. In general, precipitation increases from southeast to northwest and is less in the basins than on the mountain slopes. On the Sierra, precipitation increases at the rate of 8.5 inches per thousand feet up to the level of five thousand feet. The eastward and northeastward slopes receive less than the others because all the moisture comes from the sea. The agricultural regions receive on the average about eighteen inches of rainfall during the year. In the Central Valley, for example, the rainfall increases from five inches in the south, where Subtropical High Pressures prevail, to twenty-five inches in the north, where the cyclonic season is quite long in duration. On the whole, the agricultural districts receive insufficient rainfall and it must be supplemented. A second disadvantage is that the rainfall is concentrated in the winter months instead of in the growing season. Throughout agricultural California three-fourths of the rainfall falls in winter. At this time of year only are those regions lying between the parallels 31° N. and 39° N. in the belt of rain-bearing cyclones.

Since the water supply must be supplemented from other sources and redistributed, it is clear that California farmers are more interested in the distribution of water than in the ordinary vagaries of the weather. The water comes, of course, from the mountains. In the Sierra, the precipitation is largely in the form of snow, frequently to a depth of forty feet. When thawed out in the late spring, it provides the Central Valley, according to one calculation, with an additional twelve inches of water. During the summer, dependence is placed upon two sources, the reservoirs that dam the mountain streams, and ground water. Throughout much of the Valley, the water table is tapped by artesian wells. On the other hand, where the ground water reaches the surface, it ruins the soil, for it contains alkali deposits. This happens frequently in the lower portion of the Central Valley. The citrus district of southern California depends entirely upon irrigation. Canals, wells, reservoirs, and tunnels are employed. In the Coast Range valleys the rainfall is more plentiful than in the Central Valley, and although irrigation is not necessary in the orchards, the farmers have learned that in employing the pump they can increase their yield perceptibly. As a result, though the crops have increased, the water table is falling at an alarming rate. The temperature, especially near the sea, is cooler than in the Great Valley, with the result that grapes and citrus crops yield to artichokes and apples. The interior valleys, however, produce a great variety of temperate fruits such as apples, apricots, cherries, grapes, peaches, and pears.

The natural vegetation changes gradually from north to south as the rains diminish. In the mountainous north, along the coast, are found the giant redwood; in the interior, the sequoia, Douglas fir, and yellow pine. The pine-fir belt runs the length of the Sierra at proper altitudes. The southern interior is quite barren; on the slopes are woodlands of chaparral, broad-leafed and drought resisting; in the lowlands, desert shrubs, dominated by the creosote. The central, truly Mediterranean region, once supported a good bunch grass, the basis of the early cattle industry. To-day 90 per cent of the surface of California remains unmodified by man. The lands are too rugged and the climate too dry for agriculture. The potentially cultivable lands comprise less than twenty million acres. Because of the increasing costs of irrigation in marginal lands less than half this area is actually under cultivation. The Marshall Plan contemplates the construction of grand canals that will husband all the waters draining into the Central Valley. Not only does it provide a water supply for the towns and power for the industries, but it will also bring much of the potentially cultivable land into operation—at a cost of one billion dollars. The soils of California, yellow and brown, are poorer than any in the United States except those of Florida and the Atlantic seaboard. Agricultural production depends, however, not upon the factor of soil but upon the proper distribution of water. Every available ounce is utilized, even to the extent of covering the viaducts to prevent loss through evaporation.

In order to appreciate the part that man has played in shaping himself to this environment let us not forget the disadvantages that had to be overcome: winter rainfall, insufficient rainfall in many agricultural regions, high summer temperatures, soil that was either too porous or too clayey, barriers of relief, and distance from the great markets. The chief advantages were the abundance of sunshine and freedom from frost, usually for 270 days. Water supplies existed in the mountain reservoir. In some of the Old World Mediterranean regions, Syria for example, the inhabitants have not succeeded in overcoming the disadvantages imposed by nature—the short growing season (March to May), the limited water supply, the enervating summers, and the rainfall that comes either too late or ceases too early. Even the northern Mediterranean lands situated in Europe cannot rival California.

In eighty years this state has developed an agricultural economy whose outstanding characteristics are the variety of its crops and the intensity of its cultivation. California combines the following types of agricultural activity: fruit and nut-growing, vegetable production, sugar-beet cultivation, grain-growing, dairying, beef-cattle ranching, sheep-grazing, and poultry-raising. The value of its crops is greater per acre than that of any other section of the country except possibly the Corn belt; and its exports are larger, in proportion to area, than those of any other section in the United States. Over a third of the winter vegetables of the country are grown in California; nearly three-fourths of the oranges, fully three-fourths of the grapes, prunes and figs, and practically all the lemons, apricots, and almonds. None of these are native to the state. Although 60 per cent of the arable lands are given to live stock raising, 90 per cent of the value of the produce arises from the crops. This circumstance signifies intensive agriculture. During the past thirty years the yield per acre has increased three fold, while the total area under crops has shrunk from seven million to 5,500,000 acres. The average size of a farm has decreased from ninety-five to forty-two acres. These results have been achieved first, through the development of irrigated lands and secondly, by the employment of efficient labor and, wherever possible, mechanized agriculture. Over fifty thousand tractors are now in use. In 1890 only one million acres of land were under irrigation, about 20 per cent of the arable crop land; to-day 4,200,000 acres or over 60 per cent of the arable lands are irrigated. Irrigated lands are more profitably cultivated because they are level lands, lending themselves to mechanized agriculture, and because they are far more fertile than unirrigated lands. The system of agriculture that prevails in California, together with the delightful climate, explains why the population of the state has increased 65 per cent (from 2,200,000 to 5,600,000) in the decade from 1920 to 1930. Future progress no longer depends upon the increase of production within the state but upon the capacity of the country to consume more of its goods.

118. Desert and Mountain Lands: The Great American Desert

This great area which extends south into Mexico and north into Canada is difficult to classify. Its uniformity rests in its high altitude and ruggedness, in the dearth of its rainfall, in the sparse character of its vegetation and human habitation. It extends from the Cascade-

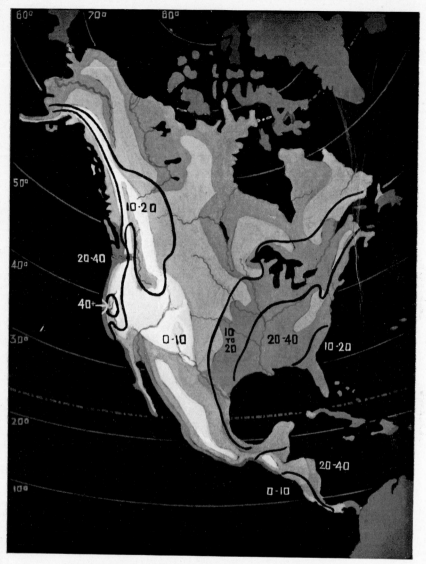

PLATE XVI. NORTH AMERICA—JANUARY RAINFALL
(*After Goode*)

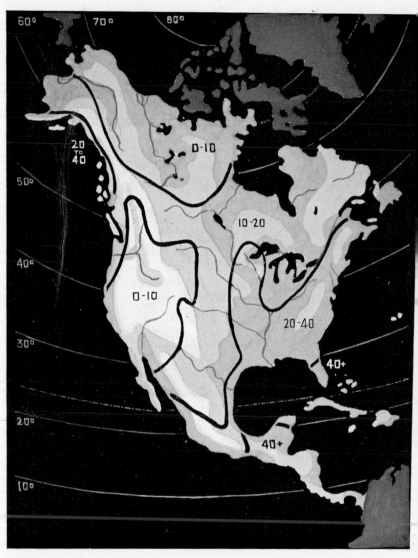

PLATE XVII. NORTH AMERICA—JULY RAINFALL
(*After Goode*)

Sierra Nevada line to the eastern slopes of the Rocky Mountains. In the east its borders pass through the series of small ranges that face the American steppe, the Great Plains. The most important are the Lewis Range and the Big Belt Mountains of Montana, the Big Horn Mountains of Wyoming, the Frontal Range of Wyoming and Colorado, and the Sacramento Mountains of New Mexico and Texas. East of this region lie the Great Plains, whose rainfall is of the steppe type.

The term *Great American Desert* is a loose expression used in designating the great belt between the Sierra-Cascade Mountains and the Rockies. Though most of this region receives less than ten inches of rainfall annually, much of it, as a glance at a precipitation map of the United States will show, has rainfall approximating that of the Steppe type, between ten and twenty inches. Aridity is more marked in the south than in the north; southwestern California, western Arizona, and most of Nevada are especially dry. Two climate types are represented—in the south, Trade Wind Desert; in the north, Continental Desert. Each region lacks rainfall but the reasons for the deficiency are different. The Trade Wind Desert, which includes the borderlands of California, Arizona, and New Mexico, receives little precipitation because it is in the zone of Subtropical High Pressure all year round. The Continental Desert receives little precipitation because it lies in the rain shadow of the Sierra-Cascade Mountains. The visible distinction between the two climatic zones is seen in the prevailing types of natural vegetation. The Trade Wind Desert is characterized by the creosote bush; the Continental Desert by the sagebrush.

Desert rains are irregular and are likely to come in torrential downpours. Little of this precipitation ever reaches the sea. In general, it drains off, frequently underground through porous soil to interior basins. These basins contain amazing deposits of salt, soda, borax, alkalies, and other salts, the residue of waters that have evaporated through the centuries. Searles Lake contains huge stores of borax and potash which were utilized during the World War but which normally cannot compete with the solid layers of potash salts found along the Elbe and the Rhine. Settlements are found in this vast unproductive region only where it is possible to obtain a water supply. It contains, nevertheless, prosperous cities, fertile agricultural districts, forest-clad mountains and rich mineral deposits. Some districts make use of the run-off of nearby mountains; others depend upon ground waters that are pumped to the surface; and others are located along "through" streams which flow from other regions. Along the "master" streams, such as the Colorado, the number of inhabitants is greater, especially where the land is level and the soil suitable for cultivation.

The waters of the Colorado River originate in the Rocky Mountains of Wyoming and Colorado and the Wasatch Mountains of Utah. For nearly five hundred miles not a single tributary enters the main stream. In 1922, under the guidance of the secretary of the interior, Mr. Hoover, an agreement was made among five states— Colorado, Wyoming, Utah, Arizona and Nevada—to pool their fluvial resources and to develop them with the aid of the Federal government into feeders of irrigation and sources of water power. It is a moot question whether such irrigated lands have a national significance; that is, whether they will ever yield crops that cannot be more easily produced in other regions. The power interests naturally think not. Indeed the agriculture of these lands is not stabilized. Many of the farms were planted in cotton, when cotton brought a dollar a pound. The cotton boom of the World War, however, lasted only two years, and the farmers were forced to resume their dairying. At present most of the arable lands are in alfalfa and Egyptian corn. The latter stands the heat better than American corn. The Great American Desert is hardly another Egypt since the streams do not carry a fertile silt but a coarse-grained sand which must be scraped from the irrigation ditches. The ground water, moreover, wells up alkali and impoverishes the soil. On the other hand, a regulated water supply is of the utmost importance to those states situated in the American Desert.

North of the trade wind zone lie the arid interior plateaus. As they are more elevated, they receive a little more rainfall, thus enabling a few cattle and sheep to graze upon the sagebrush. Here there is no master stream like the Colorado. The Snake, which flows along the northeastern border, is the only large stream. This part of the American Desert includes the Great Basin. Here the streams drain into lakes and evaporate leaving the usual deposits of salt, alkali, and similar materials. Great Salt Lake contains 400,000,000 tons of salt. The leaching of the volcanic soils has given western Utah a lake containing millions of tons of soda. Here also agriculture flourishes by means of irrigation. The products are less tropical than those of the south. Alfalfa, wheat, beans, sugar-beet, potatoes, melons, and vegetables are grown principally for the towns and the mining camps. As in the south, the favored spots are scattered oases in a vast arid land. Huge mining resources enable these northern desert states to hold their own, as they undoubtedly will for many generations, but ultimately a marginal pastoral-agricultural economy will prevail.

The Rocky Mountain region, bordering on the Great Plains from Montana to New Mexico is sparsely inhabited. Its mineral deposits are important but its population shifts as old mines are closed and new ventures are undertaken. The history of the whole region is largely the history of the mining industry. In recent years, the population of many of the counties has decreased considerably. Park City, Utah, is a great mining camp where the world's largest lead and silver deposits are situated. Montana is the great copper storehouse and the leading towns, Butte, Great Falls, Helena, and Anaconda are mining camps. As a source of minerals the Rockies have a real future. The central Rockies are known to contain the world's greatest phosphate beds, and when this scarcest of commercial fertilizers is really needed, Colorado, Wyoming, Idaho, and Utah will offer at least six thousand million tons to the world. The amount of oil stored up in the shale oil deposits is even more staggering in dimension. A Colorado geologist claims that in the northwest corner of the state is an area of 1,500 square miles which contains thirty-six thousand million barrels of oil, about ten times as much as the United States has produced to date. The oil does not gush; hence the shale must be quarried like any other rock and undergo laborious distillation before the oil is obtained.

119. The Great Plains: The American Steppe

The Great Plains, which are three to five hundred miles wide and run the length of the country, constituted a zone transitional between desert and fertile plainland. Its western border is formed by the Rocky Mountains; its eastern border by the 100th meridian, roughly the line of twenty-inch rainfall. The Plains, despite their great range north and south, present uniform characteristics: the land is relatively level; the elevation above sea level is over two thousand feet, twice as high as that of the fertile plains; the surface is treeless; and the rainfall, from ten to twenty inches annually, is sparse. The line of twenty-inch rainfall divides the United States almost in half.

Fifty miles west of that line the farms are relatively large, from six to twelve hundred acres, and the greater part of the lands are unfenced and unplowed. Fifty miles east of the line the farms are small, from three to five hundred acres, and the fields are cultivated and fenced. On one side of the line farm produce is worth only five dollars an acre; on the other it is worth more than fifteen dollars an acre.

The amount and character of the precipitation determines, in large part, the economic status of the Great Plains. Rainfall is both sparse and sporadic. Most of it is derived from cyclones that originate in the Gulf region. The cyclonic rains that reach the Great Plains are necessarily few in number since the prevailing Westerly Winds tend to deflect the Gulf cyclones eastward. During the summer, however, because of intense heating, a low barometric depression forms over the Great Plains and cyclones frequently penetrate inland to this region. Although some rain falls every month during the year, the greater part comes in early summer, usually in June. The actual precipitation is due to the contact of warm rising surface air with colder air at higher levels. The consequent convectional overturnings cause heavy showers.

The average annual rainfall in the Great Plains is about sixteen inches. This amount is not quite sufficient to support agricultural crops even though most of it falls during the growing season, from April to September. From place to place and from year to year there are wide departures from the norm. In the light of historical experience the Great Plains precipitation might be termed *deceptive*. Often for several years the rainfall will exceed twenty inches in certain districts. Montana, for example, during the years 1914 to 1916 experienced abnormal rainfall, and agricultural prosperity ensued. Attracted by the war prices paid for wheat and lured by the current shibboleth that "the country is becoming more seasonable," thousands of settlers piled in from the East. Then came the drought and ruin. The Federal government, acting through the United States Weather Bureau, has warned settlers against gambling upon a crop economy in the Great Plains for the past fifty years, but its advice has been disregarded.

Mr. Walter Webb, author of *The Great Plains,* has given a vivid description of drought in this region.

In the heat of the day, under the glare of the hot sun or the blast of the hot winds, the crops wither, slowly at first and only in the heat of the day. Towards evening the plants revive, and by morning they present themselves erect and courageous to another day. But as the days go by they droop more and more until finally the night fails to revive them, and they start the new day exhausted. The gardens go first, then the corn goes, and finally, if the drought continues, the sorghum and cotton follow. Stock water runs low, the grasses parch up in the pastures, and the cattle begin to suffer. It is a catastrophe that catches everybody in a net. The farmers have borrowed from the banker or run accounts with the merchants, who have borrowed from the banker. The cattleman has used the bank's money to finance his herd, hoping to fatten his "stuff" and sell on a good market. A drought never produces a panic. It comes too insidiously and slowly; the disaster is never sudden, but drawn out over days, weeks, and months. The suffering is no less terrible because it is fraught with the persistent hope of rain. "Every dry spell ends with a rain" is a folksaying which none disputes. And the smallest cloud in the burnished sky offers hope until at last there is no room for hope. One can flee from a flood or a storm, but one does not flee from a drought. In too many cases by the time hope is lost, the means of fleeing have departed.

Seasonal variation of temperature in the Great Plains, as in all continental interiors of the temperate zone, is extreme. The exposed flat surface responds most sensitively to the heating of the sun. Eastern Montana, a part of this region, has experienced some of the hottest and coldest days ever recorded in North America. A July day registered 116°, and a January day registered −69°. Winds of various types sweep through large areas causing great damage. During the summer, when the pressure is extremely low, hot blasts blow in from Texas causing much suffering to cattle, crops, and men. The throat and respiratory organs become dry, the lips crack, the eyes burn, and the people are nervous and irritable. During one season over ten million bushels of corn were destroyed by one of these withering winds. During the winters, however, Texas experiences cold "northers" sent out from the continental high pressure interior. Often, in a few hours, the temperature will drop from twenty-five to fifty degrees, causing much discomfort to the inhabitants and injury to the stock. In the north the infrequent cyclonic conditions are accompanied by blizzards, a mad rushing combination of wind and snow, imperiling both life and property. Persons lost in the prairie are certain to meet death unless they are familiar with the nature of these storms. Even the farmers resort to rope guides to find their way from house to barn. Hail storms add to the damage wrought by the vagaries of nature in the Great Plains, for here such storms are more frequent than anywhere in the country. Those, however, who are fortunate enough to dwell along the Rockies from Montana to Colorado benefit greatly from the effects of the Chinook winds. These warm, moist, winter winds greatly moderate the cold, and melt the snows. Evaporation is so active that the ground dries rapidly, enabling the sheep to take advantage of the sparse pasture.

These adverse climatic conditions taken in the aggregate go far in explaining why the Great Plains are so sparsely inhabited, and why pasturing rather than agriculture prevails. On the whole, longitudinal lines are more important than the latitudinal lines in the determination of the agricultural zonation of the region. There is, however, one factor occasioned by latitude that has important consequences for the grazing industry. In the hotter south the rate of evaporation is excessive and lessens considerably the benefits of the actual precipitation. At San Antonio, Texas, the evaporation from April to September is about forty-six inches, while at Williston, North Dakota, it is only thirty inches. San Antonio, therefore, would need sixteen inches additional rainfall to receive a precipitation equivalent to that of Williston. The southern portion of the Great Plains has, then, a much drier climate than the northern portion. Short grass, the prevailing type of natural vegetation, appears in Montana where the rainfall is but fourteen inches, in Colorado where it is seventeen inches, and in Texas where it is twenty-one inches. Thus in the Dakotas only five to ten acres of grass are necessary to raise a steer, while in Texas from fifteen to twenty-five acres are required.

Three types of agricultural economy are practised in the Great Plains. These are: farm-grazing, grazing-forage, and arid grazing. The farm-grazing belt is an area from fifty to 150 miles wide, lying along the eastern border. In the more fertile parts of this zone crops, when not subject to the ravages of drought, have a greater value than stock. Stock-raising, however, always accompanies cultivation of the soil, for when the crops of wheat and corn do not "make" grain, they are used as hay and fodder. The crops raised here are an extension of those of the more humid region east of the Great Plains. In the north, spring wheat, barley, oats, and rye prevail;

further south, corn; then winter wheat along with corn and sorghum. In the far south, cotton accompanies sorghum. Cotton thrives because the harsh winters and the scanty vegetation are inhospitable to the boll-weevil. The average-sized farm-pasture is about nine hundred acres.

In the grazing-forage area, lying further to the west, stock is more valuable than agricultural produce. Wheat-growing is regarded as a gamble. The farms are larger in size, from 1,200 to 2,500 acres. Crops occupy only 7 per cent of the utilized acreage in comparison with 19 per cent in the farm-grazing belt. The chief crops are corn and sorghum, fodder crops, and wheat. The third zone, the arid grazing lands, embraces the far western lands and the so-called "bad lands" of the other two zones. The farms are of large size, from 2,500 to ten thousand acres being thought necessary to support a family. From twenty to forty acres are required to pasture a cow. In fact, in these sparsely vegetated lands cattle tend to give way to sheep because the latter clip the grasses more closely. The sheep migrate seasonally, spending the summers above the timber line in the Rockies, and descending in the winters upon the plains to feed upon the dry natural grasses or upon alfalfa. Agriculture rises in importance about the mountain base lands, for irrigation makes possible not only alfalfa but also crops of corn, vegetables, and melons.

Every possible scheme for the acquisition of a permanent water supply has been considered, but the problem has not yet been solved. Here there are no master streams; and if all the waters flowing from the Rockies were impounded, no wide irrigated acreage would result. In limited areas, for example in the "triangle" of northern Montana, dry farming has proved practicable. The floods from the melting mountain snows are distributed over the fields and the soaking the lands receive enables the soil to produce good crops. Elsewhere, though there are innumerable windmills and artesian wells, the main reliance for water must be placed in the hands of Providence, and this in spite of the current belief that "precipitation sweeps westward as tillage advances."

The great drought of the summer of 1934, which resulted in a property loss of five billion dollars, affecting twenty-eight million people, was particularly severe in the semi-arid area of the Great Plains. Not only did the early summer rains fail, but no relief came until August, long after the major crops should have matured. From January to July the rainfall of five states, Kansas, Montana, Nebraska, North and South Dakota had fallen to 50 per cent of normal. During July there was no rainfall; moreover this month was the hottest on record. High winds swept away the top soil, the subsoil moisture disappeared, and the trees along the stream banks withered and died. The bed of the Missouri was laid bare, and the Red River of the north became a mere creek. Winter wheat, oats, barley, rye, sorghum, flax seed, and corn perished. What corn was harvested came principally from regions east of the Mississippi. As the drought spread to the southwest, the south, and the middle west, the staple crops of the United States fell to a level not experienced since 1881, a year of crop failure. Many of the leading crops of the country were from 20 to 40 per cent below normal. The Great Plains suffered not only the loss of crops but the destruction of live stock. Pasture and hay withered under the blistering heat, and then the water supplies failed. Thousands of head of cattle perished of starvation.

The outlook for this section is particularly gloomy, not only because the rains have been subnormal for the past five years, but because the water table has fallen so low that ground water cannot be obtained. In September, 1934, Mr. Mead, Commissioner of the Bureau of Reclamation wrote:

Two years ago I attended a conference at Washington to consider what should be done with a certain section of the plains country, where for several years there had been a succession of crop failures and where the inhabitants were being practically supported by seed loans and other aid. The question was whether to continue supporting people in the hope of a good year or to try to create a kind of agriculture suited to the climate. There was local opposition to any change. People who struggled to build a home wanted to remain and the business men of the locality resented discussion of a change. Dry farming (had) swept over the central and eastern sections of Montana. It caused a suspension of construction activities on the Sun River irrigation project near Great Falls because there were a few years of abundant rainfall. And yet the early weather records of this section showed seven consecutive years with an average annual of only 6.4 inches and one year of less than two inches during the growing season. It is one of the best range countries in the United States, and the Sun River irrigation district is going to be one of the most valuable economic developments because of the winter feed for stock it will provide.

120. Basis of Classification of Eastern Agriculture

In discussing eastern agriculture geographers recognize eight general zones: the Humid Subtropical Crops belt, the Cotton belt, the Middle Atlantic Trucking belt, the Corn and Winter Wheat belt, the Hard Winter Wheat region, the Corn belt, the Hay and Dairying region, and the Spring Wheat region. From this classification it is readily observed that, for the most part, the several belts extend from north to south rather than from east to west. In the West, the interaction of topography and rainfall determines the character of the natural vegetation and the nature of the agriculture. In the East these two factors are relatively negligible. Furthermore, with small exception the altitude is less than one thousand feet. The Ozark Plateau and the Appalachian Uplands have little more than local significance. Finally, although two types of climate, the Humid Continental Interior and the Continental with Marine Influences do exist, they do not give rise to varying types of agriculture. Both have sufficient moisture during the growing season to support substantially the same varieties of crops. Although the seaboard experiences more rainfall during the winter than the interior, and although the interior reveals greater seasonal ranges of temperature, there are few important distinctions to be made between agriculture on one or the other sides of the Appalachian Uplands. For eastern agriculture latitude is a more important factor than longitude, and differences in temperature are more significant than differences in rainfall.

Other observations of importance may be made. Some zones are sharply determined; others are mere nuclei indicating that a crop which may be grown throughout the entire East rises to prime importance in a single zone. Throughout the whole East, for example, corn is the most important crop, constituting a fifth of the acreage and a quarter of the value of all crops. It is grown in every region and is important in the Cotton belt and the Corn and Winter Wheat region, as well as in the Corn belt. On the other hand, little cotton is grown outside the Cotton belt, and little spring wheat outside the Spring Wheat belt. Winter wheat, though far from a universal crop, penetrates far into the Corn belt on the north and far into the Cotton belt. The Gulf-Florida region is not dominated by a single crop; nevertheless the very mention of the crops—rice, sugar cane, citrus fruits, winter vegetables—indicates the influence of warm temperatures.

Certain broad differences may be set forth at this point between Eastern and Western agriculture. In the latter section, hay is the leading crop, contributing two-fifths of the acreage and a quarter of the value of all crops. Alfalfa predominates east of the Cascades-Sierra Nevada, while grains cut green are the main reliance in the majority of Pacific coast counties. In the West, the value of pasturage is approximately equal to that of all crops taken together. On the other hand the crops of the West are valued at less than 10 per cent of those of the East. Live stock is important both in the East and the West. In the West relatively few hogs are raised because they must be fed upon grain which is required for food. Sheep, however, which can exist almost entirely upon open grazing, are more important in the West. The distinction between eastern and western stock-raising lies in the nature of the industry. In the West the stock is grazed mostly on the open range, in the East it is fed in barnyards or in fields, with shelter at night. Dairying is most prominent in the Hay and Dairying region, while beef-cattle and swine are largely raised in the Corn belt. In the West, sheep are found in the more arid and cattle in the less arid regions, while dairying appears as a major industry only in the cool moist Pacific maritime region. Taking the West as a whole, only a tenth of the animal units of the United States are found there, although 80 per cent of the area is pasture and range. Less than 4 per cent of the whole area is in crops. For the country as a whole the importance of live stock generally increases toward the north for two reasons: first because the pasturage is better, and secondly because of the necessity of finding employment for the farm help during the winter. In the Hay and Dairying region and, to a less extent, in the Pacific maritime region, the production of milk is the principal farm enterprise.

The size of farms varies greatly between the sections. In the East a farm from eighty to 160 acres is large enough to support a family, while in the West from two to four thousand acres are required. Special conditions prevail, however, in the dry-farming and irrigated sections of the West. An eighty-acre irrigated farm in the Great Valley of California is worth far more than a 640 acre dry farm or a three-thousand-acre stock ranch. In the West a larger proportion of the farms are operated by their owners than in the East. The stock

ranch requires more capital than the average tenant has, and the
fruit farm requires more care than the average tenant is capable of.
In the West scarcely 20 per cent of the farms are operated by tenants,
while in the East 30 per cent are tenants in the Corn and Winter
Wheat belt, 40 per cent in the Corn belt, and 60 per cent in the
Cotton belt. In the Hay and Dairying region, where the agriculture
is highly specialized, the proportion of tenants drop to 16 per cent.

121. The South: Subtropical and Cotton Belts

The Humid Subtropical belt occupies a coastal strip twenty to
one hundred miles wide, extending from Matagorda Bay, Texas, to
Charleston, South Carolina. Practically the whole state of Florida
is included in this zone. The northern and western boundary marks
the beginning of the Cotton Belt. The northern boundary corresponds
with the northern limit of the palm and the orange tree. The greater
part of the lands consists of marsh, forest, and cut-over timber lands.
In Texas the prairie extends to the coast, but in Louisiana the coastlands are very marshy. The Florida and Georgia coasts present the
same appearance of lagoons—dank river swamps. The useless Everglades of Florida occupy a considerable area, and much of the Atlantic back-country consists of sandy soil covered with loblolly, slash
pine, and long-leaf pine interspersed with cypress colored lakes.
The soils, with the exception of the Mississippi delta alluvium, are
either poorly drained, as for example the clayey Texas-Louisiana
prairie soils, or sandy, owing to the receding ocean front. The necessity for fertilizers, together with the swampy conditions and the
prevalence of malaria, have retarded agricultural development. The
climate in large manner has determined the character of the agriculture, but the topography and the soil have sharply influenced the
selection of crops. The temperatures are subtropical, with a range
from 80° in summer to 50° in winter. Frost never occurs along the
coast, but appears in the interior, frequently causing serious damage
to crops. The annual rainfall is plentiful, from fifty to sixty inches
in many places. Its great abundance interferes with haying and precludes the planting of cotton.

In spite of several centuries of settlement this region remains an
agricultural frontier. The cost of draining and clearing the marshes
and forests is too great a burden for the land to carry. Only in a

few favored spots do profitable agricultural enterprises exist. The pine forests and the delta species cover two-thirds of the whole region and furnish approximately a tenth of the lumber of the country and half the turpentine and resin. Stock-raising is the occupation of the "poor whites" who struggle to gain a living in a region of poor natural soils. Corn, peanuts, and velvet beans are used to supplement the diet of the open pasture, the cut-over of forest lands. The stock is classified as semi-wild; the hogs are of the razor-back variety, and the cattle are worth only a third as much per head as Corn Belt cattle.

The fruit and early vegetable industries are situated in central Florida, southwest Georgia, and in the delta south of New Orleans. These industries are examples of farming of the most intensive kind requiring large expenditures for the fertilization of soils and highly organized marketing facilities. Although these industries are more lucrative than any other type of farming in this zone, the market will not permit much expansion. It is extremely doubtful whether fruit-growing can support the draining of the Everglades at a cost of one hundred dollars per acre. The cane-sugar industry of the Louisiana delta lands is a luxury for the United States, and only the imposition of a high tariff prevents its annihilation at the hands of the Cuban planters. Labor costs are relatively higher in Louisiana, and since 1910 cane diseases have destroyed as much as three-sevenths of the annual yield. Rice-growing is the only profitable farming industry west of the sugar district. Warm temperatures, plentiful rainfall, clayey soils that prevent the seepage of irrigation water, and level lands permitting the use of machinery make it possible for the American rice-grower to transport rice to China and Japan and undersell the native product although paying the American worker twenty times as much as the oriental laborer receives. Californians have taken a leaf from this book of experience and are growing rice. Because of the high degree of agricultural specialization in the subtropical belt only 30 per cent of the farmers are tenants, in comparison with 60 per cent in the adjacent Cotton Belt. The cultivation of early vegetables is a highly precarious business with risk from frost and overproduction, and citrus fruit growing is even more dangerous. Negligence on the part of a tenant can do more injury in a year than an owner could repair over a decade. Rice and sugar production require too large investments of capital to allow tenants to participate in these industries.

The Cotton Belt embraces a sixth of the area of the country, and cotton growing is predominant in eleven states. The crop is equivalent to a fourth of the annual value of American crops; the United States accounts for 60 per cent of the world's raw cotton. Corn is raised almost as widely as cotton in this belt but its value is only a third as great. The forests, principally pine, have for the past thirty years been the leading source of lumber and turpentine in the United States.

Cotton culture is strictly limited by climatic factors. The northern boundary is the line of two hundred frostless days where the average summer temperature is at least 77°. In the west, the margins of cotton growing coincide with the line of twenty-inch rainfall, passing through Portales, New Mexico and Uvalde, Texas. The southern boundary, the beginning of the subtropical belt, is marked by an autumn rainfall heavier than ten inches which is damaging to the boll. The destruction wrought by the boll weevil has caused the southern margin to recede forty miles and the northern margin to advance twenty miles beyond the natural limits of cotton growing. From Charleston to Norfolk, where the autumnal rainfall approaches the danger point, cotton is receding from the coast because of the higher value of tobacco, peanuts, and truck. The average rainfall over the cotton belt is between thirty and fifty inches. The ideal climate for cotton-growing combines a mild spring with frequent showers, a warm summer with plenty of rain, and a dry, cool, prolonged autumn. Too cool weather in spring retards growth, while too much rain causes the seed to rot. Drought in early summer kills the shallow-rooted seedlings. A wet summer promotes vegetative growth or "weed," while summer drought causes early maturity, reducing the yield. Abundant sunshine is necessary in June and early July when the plant is in blossom. Rainy weather is undesirable late in August for it retards the maturing of the bolls, then opening; but moderate rainfall in early September favors the production of a large "top crop" of late maturing bolls. Greater daily range of temperature in early autumn is also favorable for it checks vegetative growth and induces fruiting. Early frost, not infrequent in northern Texas and Oklahoma, kills the "top crop" on the upper stalk or causes the bolls to open prematurely. The wonder is that the climate is able to satisfy so many conditions.

The density of cotton production in a particular region depends largely upon the quality of the soil. The most important cotton-growing areas are those of more fertile soil composition; in the east the Piedmont plateau; in the south the Black Prairie of Alabama and Mississippi and the Yazoo-Mississippi delta; in the west the Red River basin, the Black Waxey prairies of Texas, and the newly developing Red Prairies and Staked Plains of Texas and Oklahoma. When the boll weevil was at its worst, from 1919 to 1924, expansion took place in Texas and Oklahoma where the cold dry winters precluded the spread of the weevil and where, owing to the level terrain, machinery could be employed in planting and cultivating. With the introduction of "dusting" with calcium arsenate by airplane, cotton production regained its flourishing condition. Less than half of the forested land has been cleared in the cotton belt, and although higher prices for cotton would accelerate the cutting, they would at the same time tempt other lands to increase their cotton acreage. It would probably be better policy to reforest large portions of the south, subtropical as well as cotton lands, than to attempt to expand the crops of either section.

The rural population is denser in the Cotton Belt than in any section of the country. Furthermore, it is possible to raise other crops without decreasing the acreage under cotton or taxing the labor too greatly. Most of the planters and tenants raise hogs, poultry, and corn for sustenance; and cowpeas or velvet beans for the countless horses and mules that labor in the fields. Cotton for cash and corn for "hog, hominy, and hoecake" characterize the agriculture of the Cotton Belt. The tenant farmer plants as much cotton as he and his family can pick, usually twenty acres, and as much corn as he has time to cultivate in addition, usually from ten to fifteen acres. In the west, grain sorghums such as kafir are more important than corn, and in the north, oats cut green.

The southern plantation to-day includes both wage hands and share croppers. The wage hands, who are paid a monthly wage and furnished with a cabin, wood, and rations are engaged principally in growing feed crops and keeping up the plantation. Croppers, though classified as tenants, are really laborers who receive as wages a share of the cotton they raise. Though usually more intelligent than

the wage hands, they are closely supervised by the owner or over-
seer. Texas has few and Oklahoma, no plantations. Three-fifths of
the farms in the cotton belt are operated by white men. Negro
tenants work 31 per cent of the farms; Negro owners, 7 per cent;
white tenants, 30 per cent; and white owners, 32 per cent. The westward expansion of cotton has considerably redressed the proportion
of white tenants in the Cotton Belt; while the slow but certain increase of Negro owners augurs well for the economic security of that
race.

The agricultural economy of the Cotton Belt is not entirely satisfactory. There is not enough diversity of farming; consequently
when the price of cotton is low, the whole section suffers. The peaches
of Georgia and Texas, the tobacco of the Carolinas, and the truck
farming of the seaboard are important commercially, but these enterprises affect only a small proportion of the planters. The solution of the problem will not be met by increasing specialized crops
where the demand is limited and the competition brisk, but rather
in combining forage with cotton. The South might raise more of
these commodities to advantage, although it could not hope to compete in the national markets because the great regions that specialize in these crops could easily undersell the South. Nor would
an increase of permanent pasture solve the difficulty, for stock-raising
on a large scale is prohibited by the incidence of disease. The temperature conditions are such that cattle suffer from parasites and hogs
from worms. Southern agriculture seems definitely linked to the
fortunes of the cotton market; but in spending less for importations,
it would place itself in a better competitive position.

122. The Middle Country

Between the Cotton belt and the Corn belt lies a great transitional
area, the Corn and Winter Wheat belt. Its westward limit lies in central Kansas and its eastern frontier extends to the Atlantic coastal
plain in Virginia and New Jersey. The region between central Kansas
and the Great Plains, however, presents such a different aspect that
this portion of the Middle Country is designated as a separate agricultural region, the Hard Winter Wheat region, which is treated below. The Corn and Winter Wheat belt extends from west to east
for a distance of 1,100 miles and from north to south from 125 to

325 miles. It includes eastern Kansas and northeastern Oklahoma, southern Missouri and the Ozarks of Arkansas, southern Illinois, Indiana and Southwestern Ohio, most of Kentucky, Tennessee, and western North Carolina, Virginia, and Maryland excepting the tidewater, and a little of southeastern Pennsylvania and western New Jersey. Corn, winter wheat, and hay are grown almost universally, accounting for 35, 17, and 13 per cent respectively of the value of crops worth annually over two billion dollars.

The boundaries of the Corn and Winter Wheat belt present an interesting geographical study. The southern boundary is climatic and begins where it is not profitable to cultivate cotton because the summer temperature is less than 77° and the frostless days fewer than two hundred. The northern boundary is the line where the yield in corn exceeds three thousand bushels per square mile because of more level land and more fertile soil. From Ohio westward through central Illinois its boundary coincides with the southern limit of the latest (Wisconsin) glaciation. In the northeast, however, the boundary is again climatic, for here in the Allegheny plateau, the climate is so cool that corn and wheat must give way to hay and pasture. In the west, in central Kansas, the rainfall diminishes so rapidly that it becomes impossible to grow corn. Along the eastern seaboard where the type of climate changes from Humid Continental Interior to Continental with Marine Influence, truck-farming is the predominant type of farming because of milder, more rainy winters.

Excepting the influence due to altitude, this belt has a remarkably uniform climate. The rainfall increases gradually from thirty to thirty-five inches in central Kansas, to from forty to fifty inches in the valleys of the east. This longitudinal difference in rainfall accounts for the differences in natural vegetation; in the west, tall "prairie" grass prevails; in the east, forests of chestnut, oak, hickory, and pine are common. The rainfall corresponds with the growing season; in the west the maximum is reached in August, in the east in June and July. The seasonal range is from 75° to 77° in the summer months and from 30° to 35° during the winter months. There are more than 180 frostless days everywhere, thus insuring a long growing season.

This belt is characterized, however, by great topographical diversity. The whole region, from east to west, is interspersed with hills and highlands, too numerous to mention. The soils, also, reveal variety of texture and east of the Appalachians must frequently be replenished with fertilizer because of their sandy base. The western soils are characteristically medium to good, except where hard-pan develops. Originally 85 per cent of the whole region was forested, but to-day a third of the forest has been cleared for crops. Almost twice as much of the cultivated land is devoted to crops as to pasture.

The crops, owing to the varying topographical conditions, are more diversified than those of the surrounding belts. Indeed in some parts of the region, the staples disappear altogether; in many counties in the east, tobacco far exceeds the combined value of corn, wheat, and hay, and in many mountainous counties fruit orchards, principally of apple, peach, and small fruits, occupy almost a monopoly position. On the whole, however, the three staples constitute nearly 70 per cent of the total crop value. With the addition of tobacco, potatoes, fruits, and vegetables, seven crops in all, the agricultural produce of this region is fully accounted for.

Corn is grown everywhere, in poor soil and good. In the mountains of Kentucky and Tennessee it is the staff of life, being augmented only by beans, potatoes, vegetables, and sorghum for syrup. Wheat rises to an equality with corn where the land is level and more fertile. In the western portion, when the price is high, wheat farming outstrips corn. Hay, likewise, is grown universally but on the whole is more important in the northern portion. The southern boundary of the Corn and Winter Wheat belt marks also the southern limit of timothy, red and alsike clover. In the far west alfalfa and wild hay replace timothy and clover. Corn is dominant in the hilly areas, wheat in the more level lands, and fruit and vegetables in those hilly regions with access to the cities. The higher value per acre of specialized crops such as fruit and vegetables permits the use of fertilizer, and on the level lands the employment of machinery is profitable.

Live stock raising is very important in the Corn and Winter Wheat region. Horses and mules, dairy cows and beef cattle are of equal importance; hogs and poultry are less common, and sheep and goats relatively insignificant. Dairying is largely a specialized industry near the urban districts. Beef cattle are most conspicuous in the western grasslands, but are absent in the Piedmont and Upper Coastal Plain. Hog-raising is most intensive in central Tennessee and the Ohio Valley where corn production is greatest. Mules, marketed principally in the cotton belt, are famous in Missouri, Kansas, and the lower Ohio Valley. Carriage and saddle horses constitute the especial pride of Kentucky and Virginia. About three-fourths of the crop land is devoted to the production of feed for live stock and farm animals and most of the remainder to the production of food for man. Pasture contributes as much to animal sustenance as corn, providing a large proportion of the summer feed. Most of the pasture in the central and eastern portions is permanent bluegrass pasture, while that of the southeastern Kansas and Oklahoma portion is composed almost wholly of wild grasses.

The farming system of this region is based, then, upon corn, wheat, hay, and live stock. Dairying is dominant near the large cities, beef production where pasture is abundant, hog-raising near the centers of corn production, and wheat on the level lands. Nearly all the hay and corn is fed to the stock, while the wheat is sold. The common rotation is corn for one or two years, hay for one or two years, followed by pasture. Wheat enters the combination in many places. Monoculture prevails in the mountains of Kentucky where corn follows corn year after year, and in eastern Kansas where wheat-growing is paramount. In the west where the crops are mainly grain and hay and where machinery may be used, the farms are much larger than in the east where crop specialization is common. The average sized farm is about one hundred acres. Owners operate about 70 per cent of the farms, and tenants, as elsewhere in the country, are found in those districts where the lands are valuable.

The Hard Winter Wheat region is also a transition area, not however, between north and south, but between east and west. This belt is small being substantially an area three hundred miles square, with indentations into the panhandle of Texas and into southwestern Nebraska. The larger part of it is confined to western Kansas and eastern Colorado. Wheat is the dominant crop, constituting in the central counties as much as 60 per cent of the value of all crops. Pasture land exceeds crop land everywhere, although the value of the product is far less. There are no trees except the cottonwoods along the stream banks, but grasses, long in the east and short in the west, are abundant. An important part of the landscape is the windbreak on the westward portion of every farm, which acts as a protection against the dry, cold, northwest winds of winter and the hot, dry, southwest winds of summer. The western boundary is marked by the eighteen-inch rainfall line, and perhaps more closely by the seven-inch summer (three months) line. Beyond lie the Great Plains where pasture per acre is greater in value than crops per acre. The northern and southern boundaries, for the most part, are climatic limits of corn and cotton culture. To the east, where the precipitation reaches thirty-two inches, in other words where the Humid Continental Interior type of climate is firmly established, wheat gives way to corn. Thus climatic environment is the prime factor in setting the limits of a region that is transitional in every direction. Wheat might be regarded as the dominant crop by default, though in turn it defaults to pasture in the west. The land is unusually level, practically all of it being suited to agricultural machinery. The soils are unusually fertile, and 80 per cent of the surface, a proportion unexceeded anywhere save in the Corn belt, is suitable for crop production.

The selection of crops, as has been mentioned, is severely restricted by climate. The summers are too cold for cotton, too dry for corn or oats, or even hay, except in occasional districts. Thus of the five great American staples, wheat only is left. Conditions are fully as favorable for the cultivation of wheat as they are unfavorable for the other staples. The mild winters and the early moist springs are ideal for the stooling of wheat, while the dry summers not only facilitate harvesting but favor early maturity of a hard wheat with a high gluten content. Level lands permit efficient use of seeding and harvesting machinery. In consequence, wheat occupies about two-thirds of the crop land in this area. In the southern portion of the belt, however, sorghums are grown both for feed and for forage. Sorghums such as kafir grass and milo, imported from the semi-dry parts of Africa, are the most drought-resistant crops grown in the United States. Much of the semi-arid west must of necessity be used for pasture.

On the whole live stock is an important industry in the Hard Winter Wheat region despite the relative paucity of corn and hay. Cattle, hogs, horses, and mules appear on the great majority of the farms. In the production of beef, the Hard Winter Wheat belt ranks second only to the Corn belt, and is self-sufficing with respect to dairy cows, hogs, and all other live stock, except sheep. The western portion of the belt is devoted in large part to cattle-raising, the short grass *latifundia* that once supported the buffalo herds contributing a considerable proportion of the feed. The size of the farms in the Hard Winter Wheat region varies in accordance with the diminishing rainfall; in the east from 250 to 350 acres, in the west from 640 to 3,200 acres and even up to 6,400 acres. In the market, the value of the animal products is not quite equal to the amount derived from the sale of wheat. About 35 per cent of the farms are operated by tenants, principally in the eastern wheat-growing districts. This number is certain to increase as this region is in the process of development. The population of the Hard Winter Wheat region is predominantly rural, and there are scarcely a half-dozen towns in the whole area whose populations exceed ten thousand. Unlike the inhabitants of the Corn and Winter Wheat belt, which represents a group with both northern and southern affinities, the more western belt is founded upon a residual core of New England stock, noted for its unwavering devotion to causes that seem just; anti-slavery and populism formerly, prohibition to-day, and the efficacy of thrift always.

123. The North

The northern section of the United States lying largely east of the Great Plains embraces four distinct agricultural belts: the Corn belt, the Hay and Dairying region, the Spring Wheat region, and the Middle Atlantic Trucking region. The Hay and Dairying region is centered upon the Great Lakes, but in the east, in Pennsylvania and West Virginia, it envelops the Corn belt. The Spring Wheat region lies northwest of the Hay and Dairying belt and extends far into Canada, to Calgary and Edmonton. The Atlantic Trucking region skirts the coasts from Maine to South Carolina.

The Corn belt, though including only 8 per cent of the land surface of the country, may be regarded as the apex of American agriculture. It is difficult to refrain from speaking in superlatives in treating this region. The Corn belt comprises the northern parts of Indiana, Illinois, Missouri, Iowa, and western Nebraska. Minor portions are northwest Ohio, southwest Minnesota, southeast South Dakota, and the northern border of Kansas. It is nine hundred miles long and from 150 to three hundred miles wide. This region produces, in value, one-fourth of the crops of the United States.

The Corn belt raises, on the average, five thousand bushels of corn per square mile; the arid western portions producing one thousand bushels and the most fertile counties ten thousand bushels per square mile. In addition, for each square mile there are produced 2,500 bushels of oats, one thousand bushels of wheat, and ample stores of hay and fodder. The value of crops per square mile exceeds by 60 per cent that of any other agricultural region in the whole country. This belt grows more feed for live stock and more meat for man than any area of equal size in the world. Its grain crop is equal to that of the rest of the United States. Almost half the beef and pork consumed in the United States has been fed on its farms. Its exports of meat and meat products, corn and hay, are without parallel. In summary, the Corn belt produces 50 per cent of the country's corn and oats, 25 per cent of the wheat and hay, and possesses 20 per cent of the cattle, 25 per cent of the horses, 30 per cent of the poultry, and 45 per cent of the hogs. It contains only 10 per cent of the population of the country. If required it could, with ease, feed the entire population of the United States.

Corn is a warm climate crop, and to its rare combination of humid and almost tropical summer, to its level and rolling land surface, and to its fertile soils the Corn belt owes its preëminent status. Where these conditions do not exist, the limit of the Corn belt has been reached. In general its bounds are where corn fails to yield more than three thousand bushels per square mile. In the west, the line is that of the twenty-inch rainfall barrier. In the north, the profitable production of corn ceases where the summer temperature falls below 70°. At this point hay and forage become more important than corn, and dairying a more profitable industry than beef and hog-raising. In the eastern part of Ohio, the land is too hilly and infertile for corn-growing, and hay and pasture for cattle and sheep appear as the dominant type of agriculture. In the south, topography again imposes the limits as glaciated lands give way to unglaciated lands in southern Indiana and Illinois and in the Ozark Mountain lands.

The rainfall of the Corn belt varies from fifteen to forty inches, but where corn is dominant a minimum of twenty-four inches during the growing season, from April to September, is essential. The growing season lasts from 140 to 180 days, but high midsummer temperatures, averaging in July 65° during the nights, are important for the production of a maximum crop. Practically all the land is fit for cultivation and in few portions of the world are there such vast expanses of level land. The soils, a combination of silt or clay loam derived from limestone, are of the most fertile type. Originally, only the eastern portion of the belt was in forest, while the remainder was a vast prairie of tall grass. To-day, there is very little forest, and the fact that about 90 per cent of the land is in farms precludes any large agricultural expansion.

The Corn belt has a better balanced system of agriculture than exists elsewhere in the country, for it includes four great staples— corn, wheat, oats, and hay—and lacks only one, cotton. Corn is planted in more than two-fifths of the acreage, while the remainder is divided almost equally among hay, oats, and wheat. Winter wheat is confined generally to the southern portion and oats to the northern portion of the belt. In the district west of the Missouri River, clover and timothy give way to alfalfa and wild grasses because of sparser rainfall and poorer soils. Barley appears on the northern border and rye in sandy regions. Fruits and vegetables are raised for the urban population, while tobacco is an important crop in four counties of Ohio. The minor crops, however, occupy a very small area and yield, compared with the four staples, a trifling return.

The acreage in pasture is equal to that of corn, the leading crop. The pastures have a much higher than average carrying capacity. Half is in timothy and clover and is rotated with crops; the rest is permanent, of the blue grass variety in the east and of native varieties in the arid west. The pastures, except during drought, which is likely to occur late in the season, furnish most of the summer feeding for stock. One of the features of the agriculture of this region is that 84 per cent of the crop land is utilized to provide animal feed. This situation is reflected in the income of the farmer; three-fourths is derived from the sale of stock, only one-fourth from the sale of crops. Horses are distributed uniformly through the belt as they are used as draft animals. Beef cattle are most numerous in the natural prairie in the west, and dairy cattle prevail along the northern borders and in the urbanized east. Hogs are raised where corn is cheapest and most plentiful. They are relatively scarce within a hundred mile radius of Chicago, for there the bulky corn can better stand the transportation charges. In Chicago, corn is converted into many forms and distributed throughout the country. In the hinterland the corn is fed to hogs which, with a higher value per unit weight, can bear the charges of longer transportation.

As in the Cotton belt, there is here one substantial system of farming. Agriculture is based upon corn, cattle, and hogs. It combines two greatly desired elements: utilization of labor throughout the year, and the maintenance of high productivity of the land. This system yields a larger net income than any other method of farming in the United States. The usual cropping system consists of a cultivated crop, corn, followed by a small grain crop, wheat or oats, in which a hay crop, timothy and clover, is usually seeded. Here, as in the Corn and Winter Wheat belt, the farms increase in size in going from east to west. The Ohio and Indiana farms average one hundred acres in size; the Nebraska and Kansas farms are twice as large. The tendency toward larger farms than prevails to-day is the result of the economy wrought by agricultural machinery. The proportion of tenants is amazing, averaging 40 per cent through the whole belt. The social implications of the tenancy system in the Corn belt differ from those in the Cotton belt where the percentage of tenants is even higher. In the latter belt the tenants are largely Negroes or poor whites who have little hope of achieving ownership. In the Corn belt, to the contrary, most of the tenants are kin to the actual owners, who eventually retire and sell the holdings to the tenants. It is a sad commentary upon American agriculture that these rich farms have to be paid for once every generation, while the purchase price drains away to the cities. Possibly, taking a leaf from English experience, it would be better if the retiring farmer were to spend his declining years upon the farm instead of in the town where his capital is wasted. The sons would profit not only through the accumulation of wealth but also by the rich experience of their fathers.

The Hay and Dairying region extends from the western border of Minnesota to Maine, a distance of 1,800 miles. Most of Minnesota, Michigan, Wisconsin, New York, Pennsylvania, West Virginia, and New England lie in this belt. In this region, where hay and pasture have a greater value than corn and wheat, dairying is the leading agricultural industry. This region includes also those parts of southern Canada—the St. Lawrence Valley and the Great Lakes region—where agriculture is more important than forest industries. The Hay and Dairying region contains more than a fourth of the population of the United States, but three-fourths of the inhabitants are urban, not rural dwellers. The value of the agricultural produce is roughly equal to that of the Corn belt, an area, however, only two-thirds as large. In almost every county, hay and pasture occupy over half the arable land. The hay, used for winter fodder, has as great an acreage as all other crops combined. The pasture lands, even more extensive than the acreage in hay, provide excellent summer feeding. Some corn, increasingly larger in amount, is produced for silage, and oats is a very important crop, especially in the north. Wheat and corn are grown for grain, principally in the southern part of the region. Rye, beets and beans are prominent in subsections. More important, however, are the potato, vegetable, and fruit crops, which, though occupying less than 10 per cent of the land in crops, constitute a fourth of the value of all crops. This trucking industry owes its importance to the presence of many cities.

The Hay and Dairying region has great diversity of topography and soil, but similar conditions favor the production of the same agricultural produce throughout most of the vast area. The southern boundary is approximately the line 69° summer temperature, south of which corn and wheat yield large profits. Because of the hilly topography and the higher altitude, which preclude the raising of large stands of corn, the Hay and Dairying belt is enabled to intrude far south into West Virginia. The southeastern boundary, therefore, follows the Allegheny front from southwestern Virginia to New York City. From that point to the Bay of Fundy, the Hay and Dairying belt, with the exception of the Connecticut Valley, presses closely upon the coasts. The northern boundary for the most part lies in southern Canada. The western boundary, coinciding with the Red River of Minnesota, is the line of sub-humid rainfall. For the region as a whole the rainfall increases from west to east. The moisture, however, is everywhere sufficient for the production of the staple crops; in consequence what differences arise are to be attributed to variations in sunshine, topography, and soils. Thus in the south where the growing season exceeds 150 days, corn is more important than hay. Likewise the Great Lakes, moderating the temperatures especially along the eastern shores, make possible a considerable fruit-growing industry. The northern margins have a growing season of only 110 days; in consequence, agriculture is limited to hay, potatoes, small grains, and vegetables. Cultivation avoids the hills and bluff-lands and is concentrated upon the level plains and plateaus. There is also a marked difference between the agricultural status of glaciated and unglaciated lands. The western Great Lakes states, southern

Ontario, and the lowlands of western New York contain little land that is too rough or hilly for use. Originally the whole belt was forested and even to-day fully half consists of forest and cut-over. About 28 per cent is in crops and 16 per cent in pasture. Physical conditions would permit a doubling of cultivable lands if there were any incentive for clearing. The tendency at present is the other way, for in New England and parts of New York and Pennsylvania, the poorer lands have been allowed to revert to forest, while in the west, with the exception of northern Wisconsin and Minnesota, the farming area is stationary.

Only hay and oats of the five major crops of the United States are produced throughout the Hay and Dairying belt. The climate is too cold for cotton, too cool for corn and winter wheat, and too moist for spring wheat. Two-thirds of the total crops are, therefore, in hay and oats. It is surprising that a larger proportion of crops are not food crops since this region contains half the urban population of the United States. The answer lies in two directions: first, its physical unfitness for raising food staples, and secondly, the low cost of transportation which enables regions further distant, utilizing agricultural machinery on level lands, to meet the competition of the Hay and Dairying region. Transportation charges and middlemen's fees constitute a high protective tariff for the farmer of the Hay and Dairying region; so high that the price of hay in New York State averages 35 per cent higher than the price obtained in Iowa. The competition of the cities for labor is also a factor in the selection of crops, for pasture requires no attention and hay the least of all crops. Fortunately conditions are ideal for the dairying industry. The summers are cool and the milk keeps sweet longer than in regions further south; the winters are cold and long and dairying furnishes a profitable all-year-round employment for the farmers of this region; finally, milk is bulky and perishable, making it impossible under ordinary circumstances to transport it safely for more than one hundred miles. The combination of physical suitability, the impossibility of dangerous competition, and the existence of huge urban markets have marked this region preëminently as the most important dairying center in the United States. In addition to dairy cows large numbers of horses, poultry, swine, sheep and some beef cattle are raised.

The average farm in the Hay and Dairying region is little more than one hundred acres in size, partly because the initial cost of clearing land is high, and partly because the leading industries, dairying, fruit-growing and trucking call for an intensive type of agriculture. A collateral factor lies in the fact that the average owner is able to afford very little help and must confine his activities to a limited acreage of land. In fact, the competition of the cities for labor has led to the so-called "abandonment" of farms in the eastern section. This has not necessarily meant a decline of farming as many think, but rather a concentration of agriculture upon the most profitable lands. The sowing of small, level fields in tobacco and truck is far more profitable than the utilization of hilly lands for staples in competition with the mechanized agriculture of other parts of the country. Over 80 per cent of the farms in this region are operated by owners, the highest proportion of any region in the country. The reasons for this are obvious: first, the necessity of a considerable capital outlay in stocking and equipping a dairy farm, and secondly, the danger of loss to the owner of truck or fruit land in the hands of an irresponsible tenant.

It is true that the farming population in the Hay and Dairying belt shows a tendency to decrease, except in the Wisconsin and Minnesota portion. On the other hand, the number of farm owners is almost stationary, and there has been an actual increase in the value of the produce. Curiously, during the past ten years there has been a notable increase in the number of farmers in New England. This is due to the intrusion of a new type of farmer, the *amphibian,* a man who earns his salary as a factory worker, a business man, or as a member of a profession, but who cultivates enough land to be registered in the census as a farmer. That this tendency is a good one, and indeed one fraught with great possibilities, has been shown by the tendency to do likewise in other sections of the country during the present depression. The land is a certain "safety valve" for the helpless millions who are exposed to the recurring vagaries of finance and industry. The Hay and Dairying region, catering largely to the daily wants of city dwellers, has not been subject to the dislocation in agriculture that exists in the staple crop sections of the country. Possibly this situation explains why the farmers of this region are regarded as unduly conservative by their Western brothers who are engaged in the advocacy of unusual measures favoring farm relief.

The Spring Wheat region represents an agricultural extension of the (Humid Continental Interior) Corn belt and the Hay and Dairying belt into the drier Steppe region northwest. In the United States, western North Dakota, all of South Dakota, and central Montana form part of a wheat-growing belt that extends, in Canada, to the Rocky Mountains. Man, in his search for species of wheat able to withstand drought and accommodate a shorter growing season has developed a system of agriculture that now supports the greatest wheat-growing section in the world. The natural vegetation changes from long grass in the east to short grass in the more arid west. The northern boundary of the belt is the northern forest of Canada where the combination of short growing season and low summer temperatures prohibit wheat-growing. The western and southern boundaries are almost indefinable, for they advance and recede with variations of rainfall, with the success or failure of drought-resisting experiments, and with the prevailing price of wheat. The eastern boundaries, too, are shifting as the Hay and Dairying belt advances into territory once thought too precarious for such a system of farming.

Spring wheat, however, is likely to remain the permanent crop in the region because of its suitability to the peculiar environmental conditions that prevail. Winter wheat cannot be grown because of the freezing of the ground for many months; the growing season is too short for large corn crops, and the lighter rainfall makes precarious the cultivation of the tame grasses and legumes that flourish in the Hay and Dairying region. Spring-grown grains alone are possible and these are limited to those requiring least moisture—spring wheat, flax, and oats. Barley and rye are the lesser crops. Half the wheat produced in North America is grown here—a seventh of the world's production—and of this amount, a third is grown in the American portion of the belt.

The climate is of the Steppe type, and with a rainfall of less than twenty inches and with great seasonal extremes of temperature. Only the fact that most of the rainfall is concentrated into a short summer growing season enables the production of any crops at all. The rainfall averages fifteen inches in Canada, seventeen inches in central North Dakota, twenty inches in central South Dakota, and reaches its maximum, twenty-six inches, in the transitional Minnesota Valley region. The whole region is clamped between climatic pincers. In the southwest, the rainfall is so uncertain and irregular that a large acreage must be left in pasture as insurance against drought. In the north, in Canada, where the growing season is limited to one hundred days, frost is an ever-recurring danger. Generally, however, on this northern border the wheat is harvested before frost. Topographically the land is excellent in the east and bad in the west. In the west, young valleys cut through the level lands precluding the use of machinery over large expanses. The soils are fertile on the whole for the freezing during winter prevents leaching.

The Spring Wheat region was settled rapidly because the prairie sod needed only breaking before planting. Agricultural machinery and railway transportation were the primary agencies in converting this semi-arid belt into farming land. The thresher alone made it possible for one man to cultivate an acreage from twenty-five to fifty times as great as he could with the primitive tools used a century ago, and the addition of the tractor and the combine will double that acreage. Only 60 per cent of the eastern part of the American belt is in crops, and only 35 per cent of the western, semi-arid belt. The best lands, however, are in cultivation and only the poorer remain. Catastrophe has resulted from a too rapid settlement. More reliance was placed upon the rainfall than was warranted, while a proper knowledge of dry farming and farm organization was lacking. The drought years, 1917 to 1920, following several excellent years were responsible for an exodus of large numbers from Montana. The numbers of farms in the American portion of the region has declined.

The size of the farms varies from east to west. In the east the farms average four hundred acres and in the west six hundred acres. The Spring Wheat region was once the summer feeding ground of the buffalo and later the grazing ranch of cattle and sheep-raisers, who still hold dominion around the arid fringes. The great ranges were broken up by the agriculturalist but the number of live stock has not diminished. The farmer, raising feed for stock, is able to get along on a reduced acreage of pasture. The tendency to-day is away from beef cattle and toward dairy cattle. Dairying gives the farmers something to do in the winter time, and butter, owing to refrigeration and high value per unit of weight, is likely to reach the eastern market in increasing amounts.

Tenancy is rare in the Spring Wheat belt because it is a pioneer land and few farmers have been there long enough to have accumulated sufficient wealth to retire to the cities. The recent decline in prices and the drop in land valuation have led to mortgage foreclosures and a condition of involuntary tenancy through large districts. The Spring Wheat belt still retains much of a frontier aspect. It represents not so much a part of the westward movement as a converging of three elements upon unexploited land: the eastward drift from the mining country, the northward drift from the cattle country, and the westward stream of European immigration. The Spring Wheat region possesses the type of democratic idealism that is almost a tradition in other parts of the country. Few are rich and few are very poor; all are optimistically working to attain a status in life more or less denied them in Europe with its stratified society, or in other parts of the United States where economic crystallization greatly limits opportunity.

The Middle Atlantic Trucking section along the eastern seaboard owes its prosperity to the existence of a metropolitan population approximating fifteen million people. This dense population needs fresh vegetables, fresh fruits, and milk. The Atlantic Trucking section is able to provide the larger part of the first two and much of the third, largely because of its physical equipment for the production of such commodities. This belt extends from Portland, Maine to Charleston, South Carolina, a distance of nine hundred miles, but it is limited, on the average, to within fifty miles of the ocean front. It is the smallest agricultural region in North America except the Columbia Plateau wheat region. The crop acreage constitutes only one per cent of that of the United States.

In general the bounds of the region are drawn where fruits and vegetables cease to constitute more than half the value of all crops. In New England, truck presses beyond the coastal plain into the granite uplands. The Connecticut Valley is the most important intrusion into the interior. In the middle section it follows the Delaware Valley, but from Delaware south it retreats from the "fall line" to the lower and sandier portions of the coastal plain. Near Charleston, sea-island cotton and rice attain greater prominence than fruit and vegetables, and here, where the palmetto belt begins, is reached the southern extremity of the Atlantic Trucking area. Because the climatic type is Continental with Marine Influence with an ample rainfall and with mild winters and mild summers, latitude has little influence upon crop variation. The numerous indentations give this region, in effect, an insular climate. The frostless season on Cape Cod and Long

Island extends from April 20 to November 1, giving this northern region a growing season of 190 days. Thus this section enjoys a marketing advantage of three weeks over interior points, while the southern district enjoys a slight, but important advantage over the northern district. The sandy to loamy soils are suited to truck and fruit production because they warm up rapidly in the spring and are easily cultivated. Practically all the soils of this region, however, need applications of fertilizer or manure. The original fertility of the soil plays small part in crop production. The average cost of replenishing the soil, ten dollars per acre, constitutes a charge nowhere exceeded in the United States. Soils, for example, that would scarcely be valued at three dollars an acre in the interior bring, in the Connecticut Valley tobacco lands, as much as $300 an acre. Nowhere in the United States does such precise knowledge exist concerning the application of fertilizer to soil.

In this region, curiously, there is a smaller acreage under cultivation than in most agricultural regions of the country. Fully 60 per cent of the land remains in brush or forest; less than 20 per cent is in crops, and a mere bagatelle, 3 per cent, is in pasture. Much land in the immediate neighborhood of large cities is unutilized for agriculture. The reasons are two: many of the sandy soils cannot be used for truck farming, and more important, only a small acreage is needed to produce the quantity of truck that the population can consume. The Middle Atlantic Trucking district contains enough land to supply the whole country with potatoes, vegetables, and tobacco. Since this degree of specialization is not feasible, it seems expedient to convert a portion of the land into timber.

On the whole, the sphere of agriculture in the trucking region is rather limited. In the realm of fruit, vegetables, and even potatoes, not all that is consumed in the cities is grown on the adjacent farms. The importations of winter and early spring produce from Florida, Georgia, and California are, of course, non-competing. But competition of the other regions is made possible by two factors: superior farm organization and a highly adjusted system of marketing based upon refrigeration and express shipment. Much potential trucking land in the east is utilized for marginal crops such as corn and hay. In the north, the corn is used for silage, but from New Jersey, south, its food utilization becomes more prominent. Hay is grown in the northern districts, where its use for feed, along with corn fodder, enables this section to compete with the dairying industry of the better adapted interior lands. The Connecticut Valley specializes in tobacco, competing successfully in high grade wrappers with the Carolinas. The tobacco farms are small and intensely cultivated. In the Connecticut Valley tobacco is grown year after year on fields whose fertility is maintained by heavy applications of fertilizer and manure. Vegetables, however, are grown from Portland to Charleston and the variation from north to south is largely a matter of taste. Thus New England specializes in potatoes, sweet corn, cabbage, tomatoes, lettuce, and celery; the Connecticut Valley in onions; Long Island in potatoes, sweet corn, and cabbages; New Jersey in potatoes and tomatoes; Delaware in tomatoes and melons; Virginia in potatoes, tomatoes, sweet corn, spinach, green beans, cucumbers and onions; and the Carolinas in white and sweet potatoes and melons. This picture is somewhat misleading, for the crops of one section are represented to some degree in all. Beef cattle have relatively little importance. In the New England section, 80 per cent of the cattle are milch cows. Proximity to the great milk consuming regions enables this section to import fodder from the corn belt and produce milk at a handsome profit. Everywhere the raising of poultry is an important adjunct to farming. On the whole the farms are very small in size, for tobacco, asparagus, cranberries, and peaches require intensive cultivation. In the northern districts, tenancy is almost forbidden, for the owner is an agricultural expert, and knowledge, not land, is necessary for profit-making.

Farming has been almost stationary through the trucking region for the past twenty-five years. The drain to the cities in the north has been balanced by the growth of trucking in the south. New England reveals an actual increase because of the heavy inundation of *amphibians*. The movement of factory employees to the land is spreading through this section and, with the improvement of transport service by means of electric trains and automobiles, will soon be commonplace in the vicinity of all large cities. New York City alone seems to lag behind, possibly because the metropolitan area is too poorly situated to permit access to agricultural lands.

To-day only half the population of the United States is rural. This does not mean that agriculture is declining but rather that American farming is increasing in efficiency. American agriculture has developed to the point of setting free for other work half the population of the country. It cannot be argued, therefore, that agriculture has not contributed its full share in the creation of the leisure essential to the development of any great civilization.

American agriculture employs over ten million workers, more than any other branch of American industry. Cotton is our leading export, and products of the farm account for 35 per cent of our shipments abroad. Agricultural production is not likely to increase greatly in the future, not because of any inability to grow larger crops but because the demand for the staples has been more than satisfied by the American farmer. Crop increases, henceforth, are likely to depend almost precisely upon population increase.

Farming in a country such as the United States is not to be thought of as a simple occupation. Scratching the ground, scattering seed, then awaiting the action of Providence is a means of subsistence in many portions of the earth, but the American farmer cannot thrive by bread alone. Compared with the manufacturer, the farmer is a magician, for not only must he gauge the fluctuation in demand but he must face problems of production more multifarious and intricate than the average manufacturer dreams of. Compare, for example, the problems of the wheat farmer and the shoe manufacturer. The wheat-producer, from sowing until harvesting, is threatened daily with calamities so great and so numerous that we marvel that the crop is harvested as often as it is. In the case of the manufacturer, when any operation in the process of production breaks down, no insuperable damage is done. The price of wheat fluctuates more widely than the price of shoes—proof that it is a better bet to wager upon the manufacturer than the farmer so far as meeting demand is concerned. Yet the farmer, whose business is attended with far more risk, and competition just as severe, receives a smaller proportion of the national income than does the manufacturer. The capital investment of American agriculture, sixty billion dollars, is five times as great as that of American manufacturers. Agriculture's share of the national income, however, is only half that derived from manufactures.

124. Manufacturing and Industry

The United States is one of the leading manufacturing nations of the world. It owes its position in large part to its wealth of resources: timber, soil, minerals and metals, and water power. As a nation it imports relatively little of the vast conglomeration of materials that is grist for its mills and factories. Indeed, not to have supplied the human energy and skill necessary for the development of such amazing resources would have branded Americans as an inferior part of the human race. Few nations possess the stuffs necessary for every phase of the manufacturing industry.[1] Some, lacking iron and coal, the sinews of the primary industries, must confine their manufacturing to the lighter consumers' industries. Others, lacking the capital, raw stuffs, and experience to engage in the lighter industries, must limit their manufacturing to the preparation of agricultural products, timber, minerals and metals, for shipment. Still others, lacking a system of national economy, have developed no manufacturing but have left the exploitation of the natural resources to the foreign entrepreneur. The manufactures of the United States are based upon the heavy metallurgical industries which produce the machines necessary to transform the products of farm, forest, and mine into consumers' wares. With the advantages given by our heavy industries and our power resources, we are enabled, like Western Europe, to reach out to all portions of the world and gather rawstuffs that we do not possess and cannot produce. Thus we manufacture most of the raw silk of Japan and most of the crude rubber of the tropics. This explains why the United States has succeeded in setting-up an industrial machine of world stature; why, also, our share in the world trade is second only to that of Great Britain; and, in great measure, why we have developed such great national strength.

Three-fourths of the wares of the country (by value) are produced in the northeastern quadrant of the United States, a region lying within lines that would connect Richmond, St. Louis, Minneapolis, and Portland (Maine). The fifteen leading manufacturing cities of the United States are situated in this region. Before the World War the dominance of this section was hardly challenged in any of the larger aspects of manufacturing: the preparation of food-

[1] The United States is a remarkably self-sufficient nation. Only twenty-five imports are regarded as necessary: antimony, camphor, chromium, coffee, hides (cattle), iodine, jute, manganese, manila fiber, mica, nickel, nitrates, nux vomica, opium, platinum, quicksilver, quinine, rubber, shellac, silk, sisal, sugar, tin, tungsten, wool. Some we lack entirely, but at least seven we produce in sizable quantities. *The Magazine of Wall Street,* Vol. 50, No. 9, pp. 493 ff.

stuffs and raw materials, the production of consumers' goods, or the production of iron and steel. Since then two areas have risen rapidly to prominence, though as yet they can hardly be said to threaten the hegemony of the East.

The development of manufacturing on the Pacific Coast is readily understandable. The nuclear cities, Seattle, Portland, San Francisco, and Los Angeles, and their satellites, participate in two forms of manufacturing—the preparation of raw materials and in the production of consumers' wares. The west coast produces timber and agricultural products that are more easily treated in the first stages of manufacture before shipment. The coming of power utilization based upon water and upon petroleum has forwarded this development.

The South is a second sectional competitor. Its manufacturing activities center about the Birmingham iron and steel industry and the cotton textile industry, two recent developments. Let us examine briefly the status of southern manufacturing, keeping in mind the paramount importance of location in the establishment of a manufacturing industry. "Modern Industry," to quote the words of the editor of *Economic Geography,* "like all activities of modern man, is extremely sensitive to the critical qualities of location. The slightest advantage in some one quality in a site may bring success; the slightest disadvantage in another, failure. Whether it be an element of climate, an attribute of relief or soil, a feature of the natural vegetation, a reserve of some rich ore, or a source of power, that determine whether the balance shall tip to success or failure, the critical factor is none the less powerful. There is no escape from the inexorable influence of location." At the present time the Birmingham district produces about 10 per cent of the nation's iron ore and about 7 per cent of its pig iron. The rest of the ore and pig, except for a small fraction, is produced in the East; the former coming from the Lake Superior mines, the latter being manufactured principally at Pittsburgh and Chicago-Gary. The southern district, because of superior location, constitutes a rival that has come to stay. The basic factors in the cost of manufacturing iron and steel are the cost of ore at the mine, the cost of fuel at the mine or coke oven, the cost of fluxing (dolomite or limestone) at the quarries, the cost of transporting each of the three to the furnaces, and the cost of labor. Birmingham's advantages arise from the fact that both iron and coking coal, in almost inexhaustible quantities, are found "almost within a stone's throw" of many of the ovens and blast furnaces. The ore is practically self-fluxing. The cost of assembling the basic materials, then, is almost negligible in comparison with that of her Eastern rivals. Because of her situation in a region where labor costs have always been low, another advantage is gained. At present the leading drawback rests in the fact that the market for pig and steel is largely in the East, but with the decentralization of industry which has come with the availability of electrical power the Birmingham district can look forward to an expansion of its iron and steel industry.

In 1900 the southern states produced little more than 20 per cent of the cotton goods of the country. Now, however, this section produces nearly 60 per cent, far outstripping the original textile center, New England. Recently North Carolina took the lead from Massachusetts, while South Carolina and Georgia are pressing closely upon her heels. When the South sought to readjust its economic balance after the Civil War in the direction of diversification, it was only natural for her to manufacture cotton textiles. Her location afforded her several indisputable advantages over New England. First her factories could be built in juxtaposition to the fields; indeed some mills actually grow cotton. The second advantage of location is that the southern mills are situated in a region where labor is plentiful and wages low. Even the greater efficiency of northern labor is not sufficient to offset this advantage. Recently the South has had the experience of labor shortage because of the competition of other enterprises for the wage earners. In the matter of labor the South gains, too, because until recently labor was relatively unorganized and because the laws permitted night work. Location has aided southern industry in another way. Possibly the greatest disadvantage to the southern textile industry was the higher cost of power. With the introduction of hydro-electric power on a large scale, however, the South was enabled to obtain power at a cost slightly under that of New England. This difference is proportionately larger where coarse goods are concerned. The climate of New England, however, is more suitable for the textile industry because of the greater relative humidity. Though the South can obtain ample humidity through artificial means, the stuffiness of the mills affects the efficiency of the labor. On the whole, however, the southern factory is a better place in which to work because it is newer and situated upon high ground, while the New England mill is likely to be small and dark. The southern mills, finally, are located in regions where taxation is very low. At the present time the New England mill owners are uniting in demanding lower taxes and assessments to relieve their industry from the pressure of southern competition. It is generally agreed by experts that their cause is a genuine one.

Many elements enter into the construction of a great industrial society. A large proportion relate directly to the physical environment and most of the others are influenced indirectly by it. The greatest manufacturing regions in the world are situated in the climatically favored temperate zone. A large labor supply is requisite also, and since the cyclonic regions are attractive climatically, it follows that all such regions will in the course of time, barring human interference, support dense populations. The southern hemisphere, for historical reasons, is underdeveloped industrially, but the lead will undoubtedly be taken by cyclonic regions such as northern Argentina and New Zealand. A great manufacturing region must also have coal for power and iron for machinery. Eastern United States and Western Europe are the only regions in the northern hemisphere combining these resources. As the result of these factors, and a host of minor ones, these two alone have risen to the status of first-rank industrial societies.

The United States produces in the aggregate about one half of all the power drawn from mineral fuels and water power in the world. Two-fifths of the coal, more than two-thirds of the petroleum, and a third of all the water power utilized by man have their origin in the United States. In addition this country mines about a third of the iron ore of the world. The eastern quadrant of the United States, by virtue of its location and climate, combines better than any other section the resources and human energy necessary for the existence of a great manufacturing plant. Although possessing only a third of the developed water power resources—necessary for the generation of electrical current—this region produces all the anthracite and all but 10 per cent of the bituminous coal. The petroleum output is relatively small but oil is easily transported by pipe line. The bulk of the iron ore of the United States is mined, literally shoveled, from the Lake Superior deposits. The great centers of pig iron and steel production, in which America leads the world, are Pittsburgh and Chicago-Gary. Pittsburgh at one time was without a rival, combining the best coking coal in the country with nearby iron and limestone deposits. With the exploitation of Lake Superior iron, however, and the invention of ovens that make good coke of mediocre coal, the old adage that iron must come to coal has lost much of its significance. The iron and steel industry tends to-day to locate at a point most accessible to both major elements. Thus any place between Pittsburgh, Buffalo, and Chicago constitutes a favorable location for the iron and steel industry, and the Lake ports have a distinct advantage because one less change of bulk is necessary.

With the introduction of machinery into our scheme, manufacturing branches out into the production of consumers' wares and primary preparation of raw materials and foodstuffs. There are sixteen "billion dollar" industries in the United States. The first, motor vehicles, has an output worth over three and a half billion dollars. The others in order are: iron and steel, foundry and machine-shop products, refined petroleum, electrical machinery, newspaper and periodical printing, women's clothing, motor vehicle bodies and parts, bakery products, cotton goods, lumber, railroad and steamcar repair shops, cigars and cigarettes, flour and grain mill products, and book printing. Special industries favor certain locations and the selection of a site is governed with an eye to commercial advantage. First there must be power. Often the cheapness of power explains the presence of factories far removed from the sources of raw materials. Secondly, there must be access to markets; thus most industries regard the facilities for getting their goods to the largest number of consumers as the most important factor governing location. Thirdly, however, is the influence of access to raw materials, especially those that are bulky and expensive to transport. It seems only natural that flour should be milled at Minneapolis and shoes manufactured at St. Louis; but note that the first two conditions are also satisfied.

Usually there intrudes the historical element in location, involving many and varied factors. Established industries shift slowly and reluctantly. Competitors tend to locate at the traditional centers of production because of the trade facilities that exist. The accumulated experience of an industry is worth more than other advantages, if they are to be had only at the price of isolation. There is a tendency to manufacture the machinery of an industry near the seat of the industry. In the first place it is cheaper to import the materials for making machines than to ship the finished product; secondly repairs and replacements are more easily carried out in the factories nearby; and finally, the users of the machines offer constructive criticism and suggestions for improvements. Thus Akron ranks first in the production of rubber machinery because that town is the hub of the tire industry; and Oregon is the leading state in the manufacture of saw-mill machinery.

New England, with its natural advantages of water power and facilities for shipping, obtained a hold upon many industries that she has stubbornly maintained. We have already noted the tenacity with which New England has clung to making of cottons. To-day Boston is the greatest wool market in the world except London. It enjoys, in addition, a vast trade in cottons, shoes, hats, brass, hardware, and machinery. These are the products of the oldest manufacturing centers in the United States, situated in the many towns of western New England. New England must combat many disadvantages to maintain her position in manufactures. It is said that she is more dependent upon imported necessities than any other manufacturing section in the world. Her exports must be of high value per unit of bulk in order to overcome the handicap of high freight rates to distant markets. The result has been for that section to specialize in goods where a high degree of skill is necessary. Hence she relinquishes the making of coarse fabrics to the South but retains those wherein an expenditure of skill adds considerably to the selling price. The skill of her workers is the result of decades of accumulated experience. Thus, though the South makes textiles and St. Louis shoes, the machinery for these industries comes largely from New England, and to her these sections look for leadership. Danbury turns rabbit skins into fur hats as successfully as ever, and the skins must come from all quarters of the world to this small town because there exists the knowledge and the skill wrought of long experience. The transmission of power through the erection of superpower units at the coal mines of Pennsylvania and the generating devices at Niagara will soon relieve New England from the necessity of transporting coal from distant places.

In New York City centers the clothing industry of the United States. Historical growth has played a large part in its development, for to this city in early times flocked the buyers of foreign cloth. It was only natural for imitators to set up their factories in the vicinity of wholesale establishments where they could watch carefully every change in fashion dictated from abroad. New York was able to maintain its place in the clothing industries long after other manufactures were crowded from the small island as a result of the exigencies of trade, commerce, and finance. Clothing establishments require little space and plentiful labor, and the immigrant laborers could be crowded into small rooms. Since conditions of cigar manufacturing are somewhat similar, this industry also still flourishes in New York. The factories of New York City, on the whole, are found in northern New Jersey. Here land is cheaper while all the advantages of labor supply, transportation facilities, and consumers' market are retained. Few of the manufactures draw their raw materials from the vicinity. Paterson, for example, boasts of producing more silk goods than any city in the world, not excepting Lyon in France.

Philadelphia harbors many manufactures and few have anything to do with proximity to raw materials. Her advantages in trade location and experience are similar but less extensive than those of New York or New England. The deep Delaware with its freedom from ice throughout the year gave the impetus to a great shipbuilding industry. There is, however, no environmental reason why Philadelphia should until recently have been the center of the locomotive industry nor indeed why Wilmington should be the powder-making center of the country. No one industry predominates in Baltimore, another leading manufacturing city, but certain conditions have favored the growth of a clothing industry. Advantages of location have stimulated the development of the fertilizer industry and the canning of fruits, vegetables, and shell fish.

An abundance of coal and water power has given those cities located along the busy highway from New York to the west an advantage in the manufacturing industry. But only historical incidence can explain the location of the knitting industry at Utica, the collar industry at Troy, the glove industry at Gloversville, the electrical equipment industry at Schenectady, and the optical and camera industry at Rochester. Only Syracuse, with its great deposits of soda, derives its raw materials from the immediate vicinity. Buffalo looks both west and east, and as she surveyed the mass of raw products flowing through her gateway, she began with the aid of cheap Niagara power, to transform some of the bulkier materials. To-day iron ore, wheat, and live stock are converted into iron and steel, flour, and meat products. Buffalo has attained the rank of chief rival of Minneapolis milling and Chicago meat-packing. The shift of the Lackawanna Steel Company from Scranton to Buffalo is an indication of the advantage accruing from location.

About Lake Erie and Lake Michigan is centered all that concerns automobile manufacture. Here iron, coal, and a hundred other products can meet cheaply. That Detroit leads in this industry is owing to an historical incident, the employment of standardized interchangeable parts by Henry Ford. In consequence Flint, Toledo, and Cleveland are rivals—for second place. Michigan's one leading manufacturing industry, furniture-making, has yielded to the stampede of the automobile. Chicago is the transportation center of the interior, and threatens to become the largest city in the world. Not only the interior West, but the interior South looks to Chicago. This city is the market center, the supply center, and the manufacturing center of the Corn belt. The facility with which Chicago receives goods from all parts of the Middle West and dispatches all necessary supplies is owing to her location on that part of the Lake system that intrudes farthest into the interior. Many east-west railway lines are forced to run through Chicago and this city is able to route goods by steamer or by rail to any part of the United States. In consequence, Chicago has become the greatest food distributor of the world, and incidentally the center of the mail-order business. Her manufacturing is closely linked to her economic location. The foodstuffs, principally grain and live stock, that she receives are manufactured into consumers' commodities. The milling and packing industries have led to a variety of manufactures. Live stock, for example, entails not only the production of beef, ham, and bacon, but lard, oleomargarine, soap, fertilizer, and bone products. A second group of manufactures has to do with the production of commodities that serve her agricultural hinterland. Agricultural machinery, for example, is a more important industry than automobile making in Chicago. The immensity of Chicago's demands for steel and machinery led to the selection of Gary, a nearby town, by the United States Steel Corporation as its chief production plant. Milwaukee has many of the advantages of Chicago; but as it is not a transport center, her commerce and trade are smaller. Her manufactures, however, are important for she has a wide hinterland to exploit. Meat, beer, machinery, leather, shoes, and knit goods are her prominent industries.

The Upper Lakes are dominated industrially and commercially by Chicago. Duluth-Superior is important not for what it manufactures but for the changes of bulk that must take place in shifting goods from water to land and vice versa. Unbelievable amounts of coal, iron, grain, and other raw materials pass through these small cities. Minneapolis and St. Paul, the "twin cities," are not without significance in the industrial world. They lie at the head of navigation of the Mississippi system, they have immense water power supplies, and they receive the wheat of a vast grain-growing hinterland. In consequence they have erected a milling establishment that manufactures more flour than any other city in the world. It was only natural that other industries suitable for the hinterland, should arise. The manufacture of agricultural machinery is important as well as a host of smaller industries that produce consumers' goods. No large city industrially important appears south of Chicago until St. Louis, near the juncture of the Mississippi and Missouri rivers is reached. St. Louis, by virtue of her location at a pivotal point, was from earliest times the distributing center for the southwest. This position she has retained. She is also a large receiver of live stock. It was only natural for her to attempt to manufacture some of the wares she was obliged to procure for her hinterland. In consequence St. Louis, though on a smaller scale than Chicago, engages in two of the three forms of manufacturing—the preparation of rawstuffs for shipment and the production of consumers' goods. Boots, shoes, agricultural implements, tobacco, and a number of smaller industries engage her attention. Kansas City (Missouri), once the head of navigation on the Missouri and with easier access than St. Louis to a large hinterland, has become a great railway center attracting from all directions grain and stock. Millions of animals pass through Kansas City *en route* to the Corn belt. Many, however, are ready for slaughtering, and as it is cheaper to perform the function in Kansas City than elsewhere, this city boasts a slaughtering industry second only to that of Chicago. Refrigeration has made possible the expansion of an industry that formerly was confined to eastern cities. In 1923 the stock yards of Philadelphia were abandoned, for Philadelphia was receiving not live stock but chilled beef.

Pittsburgh, in competition with Chicago, Cleveland, and St. Louis, struggles for the dominance of the Ohio Valley. With her fuel resources and primary industries she has an advantage in the making of machinery and has attained a respectable place in the textile world, especially in the manufacture of silks. Her fuel riches have given her the national leadership in the manufacture of glass. On the other hand, her iron-ore resources are practically exhausted, and her magnificent coal deposits are neither so plentiful nor so accessible as formerly. The steel industry is shifting elsewhere. In addition, water transport yielded to rail transport before the Ohio could be fashioned into a really important traffic lane. In consequence, Pittsburgh's dominance of the densely populated Ohio Valley is dubious. For the same reason Cincinnati, the most northern of southern cities and the most southern of northern cities, has failed to capture the valley markets, much less the vast southern hinterland. But Cincinnati, with nearly a half million inhabitants and a great variety of manufactures, cannot be denied a rank of importance in the national workshop.

125. Transportation and Commerce

The East is splendidly equipped with the physical facilities necessary to move goods. Its relatively level expanses made rail building a simple problem and enabled it to construct countless canals. In addition this section possesses the Great Lakes System, especially valuable in transporting commodities of great bulk and of relatively small value per unit to the centers of manufacturing and consumption. Finally the East has a number of great harbors such as Boston, New York, Philadelphia, and Baltimore, through which most of the foreign trade of the country flows. As the habitat of the largest population, as the manufacturing and distributing center, and as the import and export market of the nation, it goes without saying that this section has the most intricate transportation system in the country.

The United States has a far greater railway network and more railway traffic than any other country. It possesses a third of the total rail mileage of the world and transports more than a third of the freight carried. Traffic by rail is twice that of water-borne traffic, but the latter, with the improvement of national waterways, is ascending rapidly in volume. The advantage of price in water-borne traffic cannot be denied. First in the group of commodities handled by rail are the products of the mines, which account for approximately half (in tonnage) of all goods moved. Manufactures and merchandise constitute a quarter of the whole. The remainder is made up of agricultural products, which slightly exceed forest products, and animal products, which account for little more than 5 per cent. In tonnage carried and in value of freight the East transports more than the South and West combined.

Water-borne commerce may be conveniently divided into foreign and domestic. Domestic commerce is of several types, coastwise and interior. The quality of an inland waterways system is determined, according to Professor Ellsworth Huntington, upon the basis of seven characteristics: depth and breadth, navigable length, character of course, current, seasonal changes, hinterland, and direction. The Great Lakes-St. Lawrence system, upon the basis of these characteristics clearly ranks third among the internal waterways systems of the world. It is exceeded physically only by the Yangtze system and the German system. The Great Lake-St. Lawrence system is characterized by a broad, deep, relatively straight waterway penetrating 1,700 miles into the interior of the continent. The direction of the Lakes, east to west, is ideal. Its waters unite rich regions contributing manufactured products, foodstuffs, and raw materials. Within its compass lie the coal fields of Pennsylvania, the iron ores of Lake Superior, the grain stocks of the Middle West, and the rich general farming region of New York and southern Canada. The most prominent disadvantages concern its outlet to the sea, the St. Lawrence. The direction of this river is satisfactory for traffic with Europe but it flows through a relatively uninhabited territory. The New York State Canal System was erected to overcome this disadvantage. Secondly, the St. Lawrence freezes over for three months, interfering with the continuous flow of goods. Other obstacles like the Sainte Marie Rapids, the falls of Niagara, and the St. Lawrence channels, man has overcome by means of canals, locks, and dredging operations. Realizing the commercial advantages arising from water traffic, the United States and Canada have recently signed a treaty pledging the coöperative improvement of this waterways system. The new Welland Canal, connecting Lakes Erie and Ontario, has a depth of twenty-seven feet. In 1918, when the traffic passing through the Erie Canal had fallen to little more than a fifth of the tonnage of 1900, New York State began to widen and deepen the old waterway. To-day the Erie Canal traffic is equal to that of 1900 and will soon surpass it.

Four-fifths of the water-borne commerce of the United States is domestic and the larger part passes along the Great Lakes-St. Lawrence system. In fact, this system accounts for half of all American commerce, but its share of foreign commerce is relatively small. Through the Sault Ste. Marie Canals alone passes a tonnage almost as great as that of the entire coastwise traffic of the United States. Bulky commodities like iron ore and coal constitute over 85 per cent of the tonnage, while grain products make up most of the remainder.

The Mississippi River System is utilized far less than the Great Lakes System; in fact, it carries little more than 3 per cent of the water-borne commerce of the United States. The advantages of this system are obvious: the Mississippi-Missouri is the longest river in the world; the channel has a depth of nine feet to St. Louis, nearly 1,300 miles from the mouth; the current is on the whole favorable, and the hinterland includes the most fertile parts of the United States. On the other hand the winding and shifting course of the lower Mississippi is notorious, and the seasonal floods are a menace to commerce. The principal disadvantage, however, is one of direction, for the Mississippi flows south instead of east. Nevertheless, the Federal government, realizing the importance of this system in internal commerce and activated by the hope of increasing traffic with South America and the Orient via the Panama Canal, has increased the capitalization of the Inland Waterways Commission from $5,000,000 to $15,000,000 and extended the Federal Barge Line to the principal tributaries of the Mississippi, excepting the Ohio. This line now serves the Mississippi from the "twin cities" to New Orleans, as well as the Warrior River connecting Birmingham with Mobile and New Orleans. In ten years the Mississippi River traffic has tripled. The Mississippi may again become the artery of trade that distinguished it in early steamboat days. The chief southbound commodities are wheat, barley, rye, and agricultural implements from the upper course, and wheat, corn, steel, cotton, and canned goods from the lower course. In 1929 the canalization of the Ohio River was completed from Pittsburgh to Cairo, thus providing a thousand mile nine-foot channel. A total of fifty locks and dams at a cost of $120,-000,000 was necessary in making possible navigation of the Ohio. The tonnage carried on the Ohio slightly exceeds that on the Mississippi, but the traffic is local rather than sectional.

Ocean-borne commerce necessitates good harbors. The essential qualifications of a good harbor, according to Professor Huntington are: protection, depth, abundant anchorage room, space for docks, abundant level land for buildings, easy lines of communication with the interior, and a rich hinterland. Even the best harbor, from a physical viewpoint, would have little value unless it possessed a rich hinterland. A hinterland is adjudged rich not because of its size, but because of the density of its population and its power to produce and to buy goods. Thus Pará is not an important port because its immense hinterland is sparsely inhabited and poorly developed; but Providence, with a limited hinterland, is relatively important because small Rhode Island is densely inhabited and highly developed.

Eastern United States is one of the world's richest hinterlands, and the competition of the various ports for a share in its trade is very keen. Through these ports flows half the foreign commerce of the United States. Although they do not serve as the sole distributors of American exports because of the distant origin of many products, they act as distributors of the nation's imports. They handle nearly 70 per cent of the imports coming to the United States. The most important of these ports are Boston, New York, Philadelphia, Baltimore, and Norfolk. New York alone handles a third of the nation's imports and nearly a fifth of its exports.

New York's commercial eminence arises from her ideal physical equipment for a harbor and her situation at the entrance of a rich hinterland. Unexcelled harbor facilities have enabled New York to wrest from all rivals the control of this hinterland. New York is the only eastern seaport that can accommodate ships of the largest tonnage. The depth of her harbor is forty feet, while her rivals, Boston, Philadelphia, Baltimore, and Norfolk, have thirty-five-foot channels. New York harbor possesses, too, sufficient room to permit the turning-around of vessels of the largest size. Lack of dockage space congests a harbor and imposes costly delays upon commerce. The congestion of Boston harbor in times past lost her much commerce. New York has the most extensive dockage facilities in the world. If all the small bays and estuaries of the metropolitan district are counted, there is a total water frontage of 770 miles, three hundred of which have been improved. New York possesses, too, level land, but as it is limited, it has been necessary for its manufactures to shift to nearby places. Interior lines of communication lead from New York to all parts of the nation. Her connection with the West by means of the Erie Canal and the railways of the Hudson-Mohawk gateway enabled New York to draw ahead of Philadelphia and Boston at an early date. New York claims the whole United States as her hinterland, a claim that Chicago, not to mention others, bitterly contests. This claim, however, is not without an element of truth, for most of the imports of the country pass through New York, and a large proportion of her exports are drawn from sources far beyond Chicago.

The United Kingdom and the United States between them control nearly 60 per cent of the world's foreign trade. Germany, with 18 per cent, and France with 12 per cent, follow in order. They, too, are part of the industrial machine that dominates the world. The United States is the largest exporting nation, while the United Kingdom is the largest importing nation. Their commerce is about equal, though the latter is a far greater shipping nation than the United States. A large proportion of our imports and exports are carried in British bottoms. Europe—principally the United Kingdom, Germany, France, and Italy—is our largest customer among the continents. Europe takes 46 per cent of our exports; North America, principally Canada, takes 28 per cent; Asia 12 per cent; and South America 10 per cent. Our import trade is more widely distributed: about 30 per cent of our imports come from Europe, 30 per cent from Asia, 22 per cent from North America, and nearly 15 per cent from South America. It is important to note that the industrial states trade more with each other than with other countries. Among them prevails a higher standard of living with its innumerable wants; consequently the consumers' market is very active. The United States sells over 60 per cent of its exports to Western Europe and Canada.

We import principally agricultural commodities that we cannot produce in our climate, and minerals and rawstuffs that we either lack or do not possess a sufficiency of. Our leading imports are, therefore, raw silk, crude rubber, and cane sugar. Copper, tin, and petroleum rank high, and newsprint and paper base stocks have a large importance. The presence of vegetable oils, oil seeds, and fertilizer in the import list is obvious. Our exports are well-balanced, consisting of industrial and food crops, manufactures, and minerals. Cotton heads the list, while agricultural commodities such as wheat, tobacco, fruit, and nuts, rank high. Packing house products are fourth on the list, while leather and lumber are prominent. Relatively little iron and steel are exported because it is more profitable to use the products of the primary industries to manufacture valuable consumers' products. In consequence machinery, automobiles, and iron and steel mill products far outrank our exports of iron and steel. Petroleum and its products enjoy a very prominent place, and copper, coal, and coke appear among the first twenty exports. Trade is a very complicated business, but it is important to note that world trade is more a matter of competition among the producers of Euramerica for markets lying within the bounds of this area, than to control the trade of the rest of the world: hence the intense interest of the United Kingdom, Germany, Canada, and France in the American tariff.

CHAPTER XV

WESTERN EUROPE

126. Europe Among the Continents

Europe is regarded as a continent not because of any geographical individuality, for Europe is a peninsula of Eurasia, but because of its political, economic, and commercial importance. It is the most favorably located of all the continents. It lies in the center of the land hemisphere of the world and no part of the world except Oceanica is further than three thousand miles distant. Less of its area is uninhabitable than that of any other continent. Its polar regions are smaller than those of Asia or North America and none of it is exposed to the debilitating influences of the tropics. Europe's small size is a distinct advantage for only parts of the Russian interior are more than four hundred miles from the sea. Its shape gives it climatic and commercial advantages, for it is more indented by seas, gulfs, and bays than any other continent, and as a large part of the coast is submerged, the drowned river valleys provide a number of excellent natural harbors.

Relief, soil, natural resources, and climate all contribute to the geographical superiority of Europe among the continents. The Great Central Lowlands extending from the Atlantic to Asia between the northern and the southern mountain axes provide, where the climate is propitious, vast expanses of fertile lands. With the exception of northern Russia, the Lowlands are excellently drained by rivers whose sources lie principally in the Alps and the Carpathians. These gently flowing rivers have for centuries been the highways of commerce and of intercourse. The mountain ranges, unlike those of the New World, are not climatic barriers setting up huge rain shadows. There is no counterpart of the Great American Desert in Europe. The Westerly winds bearing the moisture of the Atlantic and the temperatures of the Gulf Stream penetrate unimpeded far into the interior. In fact, not until Odessa is reached, are the severe seasons and inadequate rainfall characteristic of the true steppe encountered. The southern mountains extending from Spain to the Balkans, shelter the inhabitants and crops of Mediterranean lands from the cold winter of the continental interior and afford northern peoples protection from the heat and drought of the subtropical summer. The mountains of Europe are of intrinsic value for their timber resources, water-power reserves, and grazing lands. Europe was originally forest-covered; in the north the coniferous forest prevailed; in the Mediterranean border lands, the broad-leafed sclerophyll forest, and throughout the Great Central Lowlands, the deciduous forest. To-day trees have given way to crops except in the carefully husbanded forest lands of the highlands.

Europe possesses only a small store of the precious metals with the exception of the platinum deposits in eastern Russia. Though large supplies are imported to supplement her industrial requirements, Europe has an abundance of coal, iron, petroleum, copper, and zinc. Tin alone, of the essential metals, is scarce. The soils of Europe compare favorably with those of any other continent. The scientific nature of European agriculture is reflected in her leadership in the production of fertilizers such as phosphates, potashes, and fixed nitrates with which she replenishes her hard-worked fields.

Climatically Europe is the most favored of all continents, for her climate is ideal both for man and for agriculture. The seasons are mild, and the variability of the weather undoubtedly contributes to the efficiency of her workers. The climates—Maritime, Continental with Marine Influence, Humid Continental Interior, Steppe, and Mediterranean—enable Europe to produce varied and abundant crops. Wheat, rye, and barley are the leading cereals, although corn and millet are grown. Great quantities of oats and hay are raised to supplement the diet of the live stock. Cattle, sheep, hogs, horses, mules, goats, and poultry are raised in large numbers. The leading industrial crops are beet-sugar, flax, raw silk, and linseed. Cotton alone of the great industrial crops is lacking. The Mediterranean region contributes grapes, citrus fruits, and olives, and the more northerly lands produce large quantities of temperate fruits.

The glory of Europe, however, lies in manufacturing and commerce. This small continent enjoys a larger proportion of international trade than the rest of the world taken together. The economic hegemony of Europe among the continents arises largely from this extra-continental position. Europe utilizes the resources of the whole world to a larger degree than does any other continent. Goods flow in from all regions for use and consumption. Only the United States among non-European lands plays a similar rôle. The growth of European trade from continental proportions to world proportions is an historical matter, but had Europe lacked the fundamental environmental advantages, it is difficult to see how this small continent could have achieved her position at the head of the world economic machine.

127. Western Europe

The region extending from the British Isles eastward to a line that passes through Stockholm, Danzig, Warsaw,[1] Vienna,[2] and Trieste and including, in northern Europe only southern Scandinavia, and in southern Europe only northern Italy, we shall designate as Western Europe. The remainder of the chapter will be devoted to an analysis of the complex relationship that exists there between the physical environment and man. At the present time, this small region exerts a more important political, economic, and cultural influence upon the world than any other. The very expression "modern world" invokes a vision of an industrial society whose nucleus lies in Western Europe. This most recent of cultures, the Euramerican, unlike any predecessor, attempts to sweep the whole world into its orbit. It is a dynamic culture. Those who are unwillingly forced to conform to its pattern deem it insidious and ruthless. It is insidious because in its demands for raw materials it draws other societies and other lands into a complicated web of relationships that cannot be broken. It is ruthless in that survival sooner or later comes to be dependent upon adherence to its economic, political, and ultimately to its social and cultural mores. So closely has it knit the world that any interruption of its sensitive balance, such as the recent economic depression, turns the whole world topsy-turvy. Resistance to its influences, as practised in India and China, by a rigid adherence to the native culture has failed. The only hope for the preservation of an alien culture seems to lie in the adoption of the European pattern,

[1] Warszawa.
[2] Wien.

as in Japan and in Soviet Russia. Only an industrial society can cope
with an industrial society.

Whether or not the non-European case is hopeless remains to be
seen. It is not an easy matter for other societies to rival the industrial
standards of Euramerica, for even though through experience and
experiment a similar industrial machine and a like industrial environment could be erected, these social groups lack the physical and
environmental advantages that exist in Western Europe and Eastern
United States. We have discussed the harassed attempts of Japan
and the feverish strivings of Soviet Russia to pattern an industrial
society. In each case serious environmental shortcomings and physical
handicaps were everywhere apparent.

Western Europe is an industrial society; the remainder of Europe
is governed by an agricultural economy. Like Mediterranean Europe
and Russia, Eastern Europe is occupied primarily in balancing the
equation between population and food supply. The composition of
society and the economic scene changes radically as one moves east
of Vienna. Only Russia among the non-Western European states is
among the thirty leading commercial nations of the world, while every
Western European state except Austria appears upon that list. Eastern Europe suffers too many geographical limitations to support what
is essentially an extra-environmental economic structure. Isolation
from the sea, poorer topography, inadequate resources, and more
exacting climate, in addition to political handicaps, make it impossible
for this region to do more than maintain a simple agricultural
economy.

128. Population

The population of Western Europe is very dense, probably averaging 250 to the square mile. In those regions that have become industrialized the density frequently rises to five hundred per square
mile or over. The largest of such areas extends from the extreme
northwest corner of France through Belgium to Westphalia, and
from southern Holland up the Rhine to Mannheim. The second
largest centers about Saxony. Great Britain, France, and Italy contain smaller areas corresponding chiefly to smaller industrial regions.
In Great Britain a density exceeding five hundred per square mile is

found in the Scottish lowland, in the Manchester area, in south Wales, and in greater London; in France it is found in parts of the Paris basin, in the St. Etienne district, and along the middle Rhone; in Italy, about Milan,[1] Florence,[2] and along the Ligurian coast. Only about Naples [3] in all Europe is there an agricultural region as densely populated as districts primarily industrial and commercial. Overpopulation in south Italy causes the government much concern. There are few regions capable of supporting a density of five hundred and over in the entire world. Besides the urban districts of the United States and Japan, this degree of density is encountered only in such fertile regions as Java and parts of India and China.

Western Europe is the most urbanized portion of the world. A mere list of cities is apt to obscure the importance of certain urban districts because the term "city" includes only the population living within certain political boundaries, whereas the urban population may overflow far beyond those limits. Thus the overwhelming importance of New York among the urban centers of the New World is not appreciated unless Newark and other towns of New Jersey are reckoned as part of the metropolitan district. Greater London includes the population residing within a radius of twenty-five miles of the center, whereas Newark is only twelve miles from New York. If Duisburg, Essen, and Dortmund are considered separately, they do not rank high in the list of European cities, but if they are regarded as a single urban center, *The Ruhr,* one obtains a true picture of this German industrial nucleus. It ranks ninth among the urban centers of Europe.

In Europe there are eighty-three urban centers, each containing more than 250,000 inhabitants. Twelve of them have more than a million inhabitants. In Western Europe alone are situated more than two-thirds of the urban centers of the continent. All but Munich,[4] Chemnitz, and Stuttgart are within five hundred feet of sea level and all are located along streams or rivers. Many of the streams are small and are of little importance in the present prosperity of the cities, though they were of significance in determining the sites of the towns many centuries ago. A large number of the urban centers are important as ports, but the new type of urban center, drawing

---

[1] Milano.
[2] Firenze.
[3] Napoli.
[4] München.

its strength from iron and coal, is met with as frequently as the port.

Western Europe is considered saturated by many of the population experts, and the bogey of overpopulation has become a popular fetish in many states, especially since barriers to immigration have been erected abroad. Yet it is not impossible for Western Europe, in view of her industrial, commercial, and agricultural leadership, to accommodate many more millions. The reduction of armament burdens and stifling tariffs would probably go far toward solving problems attributed to overpopulation.

129. Topographical Relationships

Western Europe, except on the east, is surrounded by water, and no part of it is over three hundred miles from the sea. The indentations of the Baltic and the Mediterranean emphasize its peninsular character, and the many gulfs and estuaries serve to model the minor divisions after the major. The remarkable alternation of land and water bodies has had the obvious effect of tempting the inhabitants to follow the sea and patronize its arts, fishing and shipping. The relief of the ocean bottom off the coasts of Western Europe is particularly interesting. It is a submerged continental shelf, less than five hundred feet deep, extending from the fiords of Norway, around the Shetland Islands and Ireland, to the Bay of Biscay. The waters of the shelf are relatively shallow, giving rise to high tides and stormy seas. They have long been a boon to man, for they churn about the alluvium from the rivers and streams and distribute food for fish in great abundance. The continental shelf emerges in many places, accounting for numerous islands, the chief of which are Great Britain and Ireland. The British Isles are the most favorably situated islands in the world for they are located at the "center" of the world's land mass. Their commercial position is further enhanced by their proximity to the markets of Western Europe. England especially, with a rich economic hinterland of her own, has enjoyed a distinct advantage over her continental rivals, for she faces the most important trade emporium in the world. Paradoxical though it may seem, the most progressive commercial area in the world is also the most war-like. Consequently England's water barrier must be accounted one of her principal geographical assets.

Western Europe has a great variety of relief and resources. Its most noticeable features are the coastal plain, the rugged peneplain, and the Alpine mountain core. The lands are well drained because of the gentle gradation from the mountainous interior to the sea. The topography, however, is not monotonous, for the mountains contain many fertile valleys and plateaus, and much of the coastal plain is hilly. Everywhere the variety of relief is apparent; indeed within a small radius is found every type of crop and live stock common to the temperate zone. A British geographer writes that the British Isles epitomize the relief of the whole world. This statement could be made of many portions of Western Europe.

The relief of Western Europe has sponsored economic unity. Its variety has had the effect of stimulating trade, for the existence of different products within a narrow radius is conducive to exchanges. In Western Europe opportunities for specialization were afforded such as were presented nowhere else in the world. The products of the interior drained toward the coastal plain, the navigable rivers serving as the first highways of commerce. Even to-day there is a larger volume of river traffic than elsewhere in the world. Where the rivers did not suffice, canals were built. France has five thousand miles of navigable rivers connected by two thousand miles of canals; and Germany, six thousand miles of navigable streams and 1,400 miles of canals. All over Western Europe, long before railways came into existence, there existed a veritable network of inland waterways. Even in remote Ireland, which is not regarded as particularly active commercially, canals connect the Shannon with Dublin and Belfast.

Canals and rivers tend to yield to railways for the time element is an important factor in modern business. The barge canals of Western Europe are rapidly being reduced, as in the United States, to the hauling of sand and gravel. Berlin, however, is admirably situated for inland canal traffic; in consequence this traffic has not diminished there to the same extent as elsewhere. In 1928 more than nine million tons of goods were carried over the Berlin canal system. Western Europe imposes few barriers to the building of railways. Its network is the only one that compares favorably with that of eastern United States in mileage, but a difference between the two is noticeable in the less regular contours followed by the European roads for the terrain is more rugged. In Western Europe hardly a place is situated at more than a ten-mile distance from a railway. There are several

conspicuous differences between European and American railway
service. The European freight cars are smaller in size because most
of the commerce is of short haul variety, from the interior to the
coast. Goods for export are generally favored by lower than normal
rates. Most of the passenger traffic is by daylight because of the
shorter distances. The demand for *de luxe* traffic is not great and the
railroads have had to cater to the pocketbooks of their patrons in
establishing three classes of accommodations. Incidentally there are
fewer accidents than in the United States for grade crossings are
rare. The railways have greatly strengthened the commercial
hegemony of the ports of the North Sea enabling them to establish
relations with Constantinople,[1] Rome,[2] Moscow, and other cities and
regions far beyond the horizon of the water drainage. Largely because of connections by rail, north Italy, a temperate region lying
beyond the Alps, has become a part of industrial Western Europe.

The roads of Western Europe are inferior to those of the United
States because they are not so essential commercially. The automobile
and bus cannot compete so easily with the railroad. In consequence
good roads are local rather than national. The smaller European car
reflects the shorter distances as well as the higher price of gasoline.
Airways, on the other hand, have developed rapidly, and because of
the small distances between important places it is possible to travel
by air almost as cheaply as by rail, first class.

The center of trade could hardly be anywhere but the North Sea.
The rivers flowing through the most densely populated areas empty
into the North Sea or the English Channel. The Thames, the Seine,
the Rhine, the Weser, and the Elbe reach the sea within a few
miles of one another. The commodities of the Garonne and the Loire
early entered into the general trade, and from the east, first through ·
the Danish channels and later through the canals, came an increasing
stream of goods from the Oder and Vistula and adjacent Baltic lands.
There are more large natural harbors in the vicinity of the North
Sea than in any other equal area. Not only do numerous bays afford
shelter for shipping but the rivers themselves provide good ports.
Ports like London, Bremen, and Hamburg are situated far inland.
This fortunate circumstance was made possible by the strong action

[1] Istanbul.
[2] Roma.

of the tides which have carved out long deep estuaries. Ports so situated are afforded protection from the elements, freedom from naval attacks, and accessibility to their hinterlands.

The basic industrial resources of Western Europe are coal and iron. Large deposits of each occur in juxtaposition in Great Britain, Germany, France, and small, but important deposits are found in Belgium, Czechoslovakia, Austria, and Poland. The British deposits are situated in the Scottish lowlands, in the Pennines, and in south Wales. Germany shares with Czechoslovakia and Poland the coal and iron fields of Upper Silesia and with France and Belgium those of the west, in addition to her sole possession of the smaller but important resources of Saxony. Holland is lacking in both, and Switzerland and Italy have small amounts. The development of hydro-electric power has augmented the growth of older industrial sites and, as in Italy, has afforded new opportunities. To these resources Western Europe owes its present commercial and industrial leadership. Without them its commercial hegemony would have declined as certainly as that of Venice[1] at an earlier date. Wherever coal and iron existed, it was possible to reproduce the industrial revolution that had its inception in England late in the eighteenth century. Coal and iron have enabled France to keep to the forefront of the nations; Belgium, to escape the ranks of historical non-entities; Germany, to become a great industrial nation; and Poland, Czechoslovakia, Austria, and Soviet Russia to entertain high hopes and lofty aspirations. Western Europe began to reap the enormous profits that come from transforming goods by means of machinery several generations before the United States. From iron and coal, steel was manufactured, and from steel, machines that produce consumers' wares. Trade was vastly increased, for Europe not only continued to sell to a world market but she offered a much greater volume and variety of goods. It became necessary to import from other lands and other continents much of the raw material of her manufactures. Finally Western Europe became so engrossed in manufacturing that large supplies of food had to be imported to feed her laboring millions. Thus countries, that in a world of provincial self-efficiency scarcely prospered, were enabled to attain a place in the world machine and a position in the political arena. The raw silk of Japan, the beef of Argentina, the wheat and rye of Russia became of great im-

[1] Venezia.

portance as Western Europe was transformed into the workshop through which flows a large portion of the raw materials of the world.

130. Climate

Western Europe has an extremely favorable climate. The conditions of optimum temperature, optimum humidity, and optimum variability encountered there make for a maximum expenditure of human energy. The correspondence of ample rainfall and a long growing season renders this region well-suited to the production of abundant crops. Western Europe enjoys marked climatic advantages over the other temperate regions. In the first place its peculiar configuration gives it the benefit of the moderating influences of the numerous water bodies that touch it on three sides; in the second place the proximity of the North Atlantic Drift off the Atlantic seaboard minimizes the influence of high latitudes; and finally the absence of transverse mountain barriers permits the moderating Westerlies to penetrate far inland. In general it can be said that Western Europe has an annual rainfall ranging on the average from fifty inches along the western coasts to twenty inches in the interior. Because of oceanic influences and favorable relief, it escapes the severe temperatures characteristic of continental land masses. The relief is not sufficiently marked to set up a rain barrier at any place, although the usual allowance must be made for heavier rainfall on windward slopes and less than normal rainfall on the leeward slopes.

In Western Europe there are three types of climate: Maritime in the British Isles and along the coast, Continental with Marine Influence just east of the coastal border, the Humid Continental Interior in the interior.[1] The Maritime type, as elsewhere, is characterized by very mild winters, cool summers, high relative humidity, and more rain in winter than in summer. The Continental with Marine Influence has slightly more rain in summer than winter but it enjoys the equable temperatures of the Maritime type. The Humid Continental Interior type has cold winters, warm summers, and greater rainfall during the summer half year. The Maritime type of climate includes the fiord region of western Norway and a narrow coastal border extending as far south as Spain. The eastward line of de-

[1] Examine carefully Plates XVIII, XIX, XX, XXI.

marcation passes in the vicinity of Antwerp,[1] Brussels,[2] and Paris.
The central portion of the English plain, some distance from the
windward coast, belongs to the Continental with Marine Influence
type. London, for example, has this type of climate. The extension
of the Maritime belt as far north as the Scandinavian peninsula is
due to the proximity of the Atlantic Drift. The open sea is never
frozen along this coast. The mean January temperature of the Faroe
Islands is only 39°, while that of Paris, eight hundred miles further
south is 36°. Snow is a rarity on the coasts of northwest Europe and
is a subject of comment. The mildness of the winters is reflected in
the natural vegetation. In favored portions of the British Isles, typical Mediterranean flora, such as arbutus, myrtle, fuchsia, laurel, and
even the lemon tree flourish. Rainfall is abundant throughout the
year with a marked maximum in winter because of the prevalence of
cyclonic conditions over the ocean at that season. Where the relief
is marked, the precipitation on windward slopes is very heavy. Thus
Ben Nevis (4,400 feet) the highest point in the British Isles, has a
total annual rainfall of 171 inches. In flat, low-lying lands the precipitation diminishes perceptibly, falling in north Germany, the Low
Countries, and in the Paris and Garonne basins to from twenty to
thirty inches annually. Maritime Europe is one of the cloudiest regions on earth. In the south of England, the sky is clouded seven
days out of ten; while in northern Scotland, where the cyclone tracks
are most frequent, there is less than an hour's sunshine a day during
the winter. What a contrast to Mediterranean Europe where sunshine
is absent only during the winter showers! The growing season in
Maritime Europe is brought to a close not by a cessation of rain but
by the arrival of the winter's cold.

The Continental with Marine Influence zone is a narrow transitional belt lying between the Maritime zone and the Humid Continental Interior region. Both its rainfall and its temperatures are
influenced by the Atlantic Ocean. Though revealing a summer maximum, the rainfall is ample and well-distributed throughout the year.
Furthermore the seasonal temperature range is less marked than in
the interior. The winters, like those of the Maritime are mild, while
the summers are not tediously hot. The bounds of this belt are difficult to chart. The Baltic coasts are predominately Continental with

[1] Anvers.
[2] Bruxelles.

Marine Influence. Southward the belt is restricted to a zone hardly fifty miles wide. Cuxhaven has a Maritime, and Paris, by a narrow margin, Continental with Marine Influence. No especial geographical influences arise in the Continental with Marine Influence zone. In consequence, in treating Western Europe it is convenient to contrast the seaboard with the interior. The seaboard is to be regarded as including both the marine belts. The interior of Western Europe has a Humid Continental Interior type of climate, a variety transitional between the Continental with Marine Influence and the dry Steppe belt of Russia. The line of twenty-inch rainfall, however, lies far east of the Danzig-Vienna-Trieste line. It extends irregularly into Russia as far as the upper Volga, but in southeastern Europe it appears along the leeward side of the Carpathians. The chief distinctions between the rainfall of the coastal and the interior zone are the summer maximum and the smaller annual total of the latter. The summer maximum is due to the prevalence of cyclones in the interior at that season. The smaller total is caused by distance from the sea. At the dividing line between Western and Eastern Europe—the Danzig-Vienna-Trieste line—the annual rainfall is about twenty-five inches.

The climate of the interior is characterized by noticeable extremes of temperature. Most of this region experiences zero temperatures during the course of the winter. West Germany has only one month when the mean temperature averages below 32°, while east Germany has three. Ice interferes with navigation along most of the rivers. The Oder freezes over for several months, and the Rhine for several weeks. Though the North Sea coasts are never ice-bound, ice breakers are necessary to keep open river ports such as Hamburg. Stettin, situated some miles up the Oder, is closed by ice for two months every winter, although the coast is ice-free. The summer temperature of the interior likewise is more severe than that of the Maritime summer. The mean July temperature of Valencia is 59° and that of Brussels 63°, but that of Vienna is 66° and that of Budapest 70°. The warm summers of the interior permit the cultivation of grapes along the Elbe as far north as Magdeburg, 52° N. Westward, at this latitude, the vine does not flourish because of the coolness. Eastward the shorter growing season minimizes the effect of hotter temperatures and prohibits its cultivation. Throughout Western Europe climate imposes no barrier to agriculture. Local variations, however, are to be expected in accordance with such factors as length of the growing season, appreciable range in rainfall, differences in altitude, and differences in soil.

131. Agriculture

Agriculture is less natural, that is less a direct response to conditions of relief, soil, and climate, in the continent of Europe than in any other. In the first place Europe is divided into many small states, each of which is intent upon establishing a régime of economic self-sufficiency. Needless to say, adherence to such a principle interferes with land utilization of a scientific character over wide areas. In North America, with practically all of the continent in the hands of three nations, the agricultural zones correspond closely with the various natural environments. Cotton, for example, is likely to be grown in the region best suited to it and corn in that fitted for the combination of corn and hogs. In Europe, and in particular Western Europe, the relation of agriculture to the land is obscured. In the second place urbanization has had an immense influence upon crop distribution and land utilization. Western Europe is eminently suited to the cultivation of the small temperate grains. But such a simple agricultural régime breaks down in the presence of a vast industrial population. "To divide Europe into natural regions upon any basis whatsoever is difficult, and on the basis of its plant and animal industries, particularly difficult," writes Jonasson, the Swedish geographer. "The complexity of physical, economic, and historical factors has led to an intricacy of relationships hard to trace, and still harder to present."

Where a large urban population exists agricultural zones tend to range themselves in concentric circles about the city. The more productive land invariably lies nearest the city. The value of the produce decreases as the distance from the market increases, until only those products able to endure long-distance transportation can be profitably raised. Thus, trucking whose produce is of high value per acre prevails in the innermost zone. Next follows another zone of intensive agriculture for whose products, butter, milk, poultry, and small fruits, there is a continuous, almost daily demand. Beyond lies a zone whose products, though imperishable, are bulky and can bear only limited transport charges. Here are grown the bread cereals, potatoes, and similar crops. Finally the zone of extensive land utilization is reached. Here, because of the lesser land value, grazing and lumbering are possible. Though the agricultural zones about the city are generally well defined, their actual boundaries are frequently quite irregular.

Western Europe with its optimum rainfall, relatively mild climate, and generally low relief is a region well suited for the intensive types of agriculture—trucking, dairying, and cereal growing—so necessary for the support of a dense population. The manufacturing area of Europe is included in a nucleus comprising parts of Great Britain, Germany, and northeastern France. The principal exceptions are the Rhone Valley and Upper Lombardy. This nuclear area is the most densely populated part of Europe. Because of the character of the demand the natural zones give way to an agricultural economy that is quite uniform throughout the manufacturing area. The zone that caters to manufacturing area is designated as the Dairy, Hay, and Root Crop Region.[1] Though divided into diverse sub-regions its sole effort is concerned in meeting the food requirements of a small but thickly populated area. The Dairy, Hay, and Root Crop Region extends somewhat beyond the limits of the manufacturing nucleus because of the ease of transporting the essential food supplies to the cities. Thus Ireland, Denmark, northeast Germany, Normandy, and Brittany, where few manufactures exist, form part of the zone that specializes in feeding cities. Other agricultural zones that intrude upon Western Europe are peripheral or marginal to the Dairy, Hay, and Root Region.[2] This region is larger than all other agricultural regions combined, and as it is concerned in solving the food problem of the majority of its inhabitants, it is by far the most important.

The peculiar importance of land utilization in Western Europe is recognized in the fact that the most highly industrialized countries have under crops a larger proportion of land than some of the greatest agricultural countries. Germany, France, and Belgium utilize about 60 per cent of their total area for crops or for permanent grass. In each of these countries two-thirds of the arable land is under crops and one-third under permanent grass. Land utilization in the United States is about 50 per cent. On the other hand Canada uses only 3 per cent of her lands for agriculture; Australia, 5 per cent; and New Zealand, 3 per cent. Great Britain, regarded as agri-

[1] See Figure 15.
[2] Northern Scotland is a hay and pasture region; southern Sweden and Denmark an oats region; Lombardy and Hungary a corn and spring wheat region; and the more extensive belt including the greater part of France and parts of Switzerland and Austria a central wheat, wine, and fruit region.

culturally retrograde because of her vast food imports, utilizes four-fifths of her lands.

The character of European produce, however, differs from that of

FIG. 15—THE AGRICULTURAL REGIONS OF WESTERN EUROPE

(*After O. Jonasson*)

A—Hay, Dairy and Root Crop Region: 1—Hay, Dairy, Sheep
    Subregion; 2—Two-row Barley and Dairy Subregion; 3—
    Sugar-beet, Wheat, Dairy Subregion; 4—Small Grains,
    Dairy, Three Fruit Subregion; 5—Rye, Potato, Dairy Sub-
    region
B—Coniferous Region—No Agriculture
C—Cold Desert
D—Central Wheat, Wine, Fruit Region
E—Corn and Wheat Region
F—Hay and Pasture Region
G—Polar Barley Region
H—Oats Region
 I—Rye and Buckwheat Region
J—Sugar Beet and Winter Grains Region
K—Spring Wheat Region
L—Subtropical Crops Region

the fields and warrens that cater to the world market. Western
Europe does not hope to export its produce to other countries, but
is content, doubtless gratified, in effecting intra-regional exchanges.

Land utilization is centered upon dairying and associated types of farming, for these are the most profitable in industrial regions. Milk, eggs, fresh meats, and trucking, therefore, compete for the arable lands. Denmark, for example, contiguous to the main industrial area, reveals the influence of urban demand upon agriculture. The growing of wheat, for which she is best suited, has given way to a system of two row barley and oats cultivation because it is closely associated with dairying which yields greater profits per unit area of land than single crop raising. Argentina, with practically no industries, produces wheat and beef for the world market. The value of her principal export, wheat, is $195,000,000 per annum, while that of Denmark's butter is $65,000,000. Yet Argentina is a hundred times as large as Denmark and her acreage of improved land is about eight times as great. It would hardly be good business, therefore, for Danish farmers to engage in wheat cultivation.

In general, the effect of industrialization has been to decrease the amount of land devoted to the growth of small grains, with the exception of barley and oats which are adjuncts to dairying. In place of small grains there has been an increase of pasture and fallow, and specialization in three types of crops. Forage crops such as hay grasses, clover, alfalfa, vetch, and other legumes are raised for the dairy industry. Root crops such as potatoes, sugar-beets, turnips, and stock-beets, which yield high returns upon a heavy capital investment in equipment, fertilizer, and labor, constitute a second class of crops. Truck produce, especially beans, peas, onions, lettuce, and tomatoes, is the most widely cultivated class of the three. These three types of crops together with dairying, poultry raising, and incidental but important sheep-raising characterize the agriculture of Western Europe.

Into this simple picture must be fitted the various boundaries—political, economic, racial, religious, and historical—which, unlike those of North America, interfere with the function of mass feeding. France, for example, by the imposition of a high tariff and subsidies, enables her farmers to compete successfully with the wheat-growers throughout the world, although her physical environment is not adapted for large scale wheat production. Yet because we live in a world that guarantees no political security, France feels justified in purchasing agricultural self-sufficiency.

Agricultural production is uniform only in its major aspects in the Dairy, Hay, and Root Crop Region, for, in spite of the desirability of specialization for the urban market, crop distribution is forced to pattern itself to the gauges set by rainfall, temperature, soil, and relief. These variables have led agronomists to divide the Dairy, Hay, and Root Crop Region into sub-regions, too numerous to be considered in detail here. In those where the rainfall exceeds thirty inches annually more than half the land surface is in pasture, whereas east of that *isohyet* [1] grain, root, and forage crops predominate. Thus most of Ireland, western Great Britain, and Normandy are cattle warrens. The uplands, where the topography is rough, the soil infertile, and the climate chilly and wet, are the principal habitat of sheep, while the more temperate valleys and lowlands are reserved for beef and milch cows. In Great Britain, for example, Wales is a sheep-raising district; the contiguous districts of western England are devoted to cattle, while eastern England is given over to mixed farming. Around the Zuider Zee lie the *Polders* of Holland. These are fertile alluvial lands, rich in organic and chemical content, and especially suited to dairying and floriculture. The Polders are below sea level, but are well drained by means of canals and pumping devices. The lands draining into the Polders are less rich, and here stock-raising is the sole occupation.

About the Wash in eastern England, on the Danish coastal plain of Jutland, in the southern tip of Sweden, and on the German coast opposite, the rainfall is less than thirty inches a year. Here are raised two row barley and sugar-beets, crops essential to a highly specialized dairying industry. Two row barley, which is not a food grain, is used in feeding hogs and in manufacturing malt. The Baltic section is the center of one of the greatest dairying industries in the world, but its status is due to the demand of the industrial regions rather than to superior physical qualifications. The sugar-beet lands, the richest soils of Europe, also support a highly lucrative farming industry. The most important of them are in Upper Silesia, Saxony, and along the Franco-Belgian border. All are located along the southern edges of the ancient continental ice sheet where there were suitable conditions for the deposition of finer sediments over extensive areas. The climate affords high summer temperatures, low winter temperatures which freeze the soil preventing erosion and leaching,

---

[1] An *isohyet* is an imaginary line connecting places of equal annual rainfall.

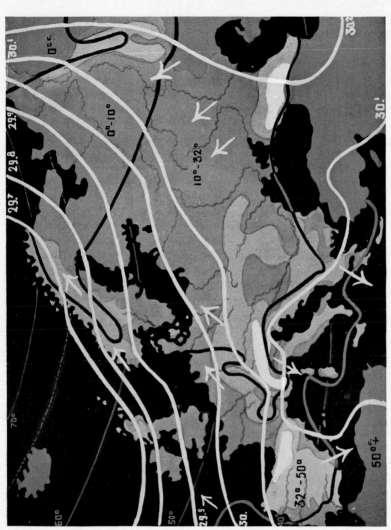

PLATE XVIII. EUROPE—JANUARY ISOTHERMS, ISOBARS, AND PREVAILING WINDS

(*After Goode*)

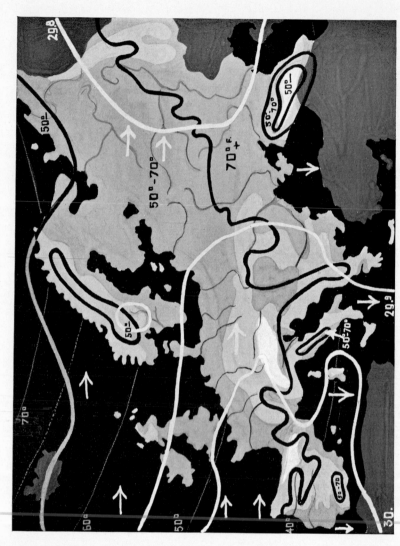

PLATE XIX. EUROPE—JULY ISOTHERMS, ISOBARS, AND PREVAILING WINDS

(*After Goode*)

and evenly distributed rainfall. Thus these lands owe their fertility to a fortunate combination of physical circumstances. They are intensely cultivated, with sugar-beets and wheat constituting the principal crops and dairying the leading agricultural enterprise.

Directly north of the sugar-beet district the emphasis shifts to rye and potato-planting and directly south to small grains and tree-fruits. As in all parts of the Dairy, Hay, and Root Crop Region, dairying forms the hub about which agriculture rotates. The northern interior lands, with their cool climate and their glacial and sandy soils, are particularly suited to the cultivation of rye. In northern Germany, close upon the industrial nucleus, potato-growing is paramount. Potatoes, there, are the counterpart of corn in the United States, being consumed directly or converted into pork. The short distance to market and the cheap water transportation lead the farmers everywhere to combine potato-raising with live stock raising and dairying. South of the best districts, small grains tend to replace the sugar-beets. This is one of the few districts in the world where four grains of equal importance, wheat, rye, oats, and two row barley are raised. Beets, of course, occupy the most favored spots, but as the relief and soils of this district are inferior, their production is minimized. The lands are generally rugged, for this district includes the highlands of the Black Forest, the Vosges, the Bavarian and Swiss Plateaus, sections of the Bohemian basin, and the steep valleys of the Rhine and Moselle. Thus, though the climate and soils resemble those of the typical beet-growing districts, both have a greater variety of crops owing to the diversity of relief. Dairying is prominent since these districts include several industrial areas, principal among them being the Ruhr district, the greatest on the continent.

Of the other agricultural zones that intrude in Western Europe, the Central Wheat, Wine, and Fruits Region occupies the most extensive areas and constitutes the most profitable economic unit.[1] This zone skirts the southern border of the great Dairy, Hay, and Root Crop Region, and the northern border of the Mediterranean zone. The grape is grown throughout. Physically it is an area of rugged relief and includes not only the principal mountain systems of Europe— Pyrenees, Alps, Carpathians, and Caucasus—but numerous uplands. It is in these hilly uplands, extending from the Bay of Biscay to the

[1] See Figure 15.

Caspian, that agriculture is so important. No section in Europe reveals such a variety of agricultural produce. This is undoubtedly due to its location which is transitional between the Subtropical Mediterranean and the temperate small grains belt. The Central Wheat, Wine, and Fruits Region most nearly approaches the Atlantic in central France, and it is here that the crop diversity is greatest. Rye, millet, barley, and buckwheat give way to fruit trees and grape vines as the mountains are approached, but wheat never loses its peculiar importance. In the mountains agriculture is strictly governed by conditions of altitude and topography, and as the mountains of Western Europe are more thickly populated than any others, every resource and every agricultural possibility is carefully husbanded and exploited. The varied location of valleys and slopes, differences in amount of sunshine, and other factors make possible a surprising variety of produce. Vineyards, citrus-fruit gardens, and fields of barley, oats, potatoes, and hay are irregularly distributed. In the Alps barley is cultivated to a height of 7,500 feet, rye to 6,000 feet, and wheat to 4,500 feet. The agricultural products of the Alps, like their timber and water-power resources, are unusually important because of the situation of these mountains between the manufacturing districts and the Upper Po.

132. National Agriculture

Western Europe, in spite of tariff barriers and adherence to the doctrine of economic self-sufficiency, imports much food because it is forced to do so. The governments of the various states are willing to protect agriculture, providing cultivation takes the direction best calculated to serve the industrial population, but they are unwilling to impose too great burdens upon the proletariat. In general, but not always, there is less willingness to protect the great staples which the overseas countries provide so cheaply than to encourage the production of perishable products or necessities that cannot bear the cost of long-distance transportation.

Most of the farmers of Western Europe live in villages and go out each day to work the land. This custom, like many others in agriculture, harks back to the Middle Ages. The American farmer, on the other hand, planted his home upon his land, frequently far in the van of settlements. The village system makes possible a higher standard of living, facilitates the exchange of goods, and furnishes a fuller social existence than the American farmer enjoyed until recently. In Europe, too, many of the workers live outside the towns and cities upon the land, and they derive immense satisfaction from owning and cultivating small holdings. The French farm is very small, usually under twenty-five acres in size, and is frequently scattered about in several parcels. Subdivision, which considerably handicaps French agriculture, is the result of customs and laws whereby the land is divided equally among the heirs. Under such a system there is little agricultural surplus, and owing to the reluctance of the French cultivator to regard his farming as a business, coöperative societies, so widespread in Denmark and Germany, have made little progress. The German farm averages from fifteen to fifty acres in size, while the British farm, owing to the prevalence of pasturing, is nearly one hundred acres in extent. Tenancy is very high in Britain (over 90 per cent), but as the land is held on long-term leases according to the custom of the country, the British occupier regards himself as no less an independent farmer than his French or German neighbor. Thus in Western Europe the farm problem is much less acute than in the United States. Ownership shifts more frequently at death than at the hands of mortgage brokers.

Only seven million people, about as many as in the mining or textile industries, engage in farming in Great Britain. The leading crops are potatoes, oats, barley, wheat, and hay. But because the emphasis is upon stock-raising, especially sheep-raising, fully twice as much land is in permanent grass and pasture as in crops. Both the climate and the national economic policy favor animal husbandry rather than cereal growing. The west, like Ireland, is too cool and too rainy for cereals; consequently mixed farming is limited to eastern England. The persistent rains of the Maritime type of climate delay the seeding of grain and interfere with the harvest. Direction was given British agriculture during the nineteenth century when cheap grain was a necessity for the factory worker. At the same time, the farmer was unable to compete with the factory owner for labor. His response, therefore, was to turn his fields to pasture, for the care of stock required relatively little labor, while there was always a market for wool, fresh meats, and dairy products. With the increasing importation of refrigerated meats the emphasis has shifted latterly to dairy products. Britain, however, still ranks second to Russia as the wool producer of Europe. Since sheep serve both as food and raw material, there are three times as many sheep as cattle. Ireland and Scotland are incapable of engaging in grain growing to the same extent as England. Ireland contributes fine beef and bacon to the British market, but Scotland, handicapped by rugged terrain, is forced to limit her stock-raising to sheep.

Half the leading commodities on the import list of the United Kingdom are food and food products. Meat products such as chilled and frozen beef, ham and bacon are highest in value on the list of food importations; dairy products—butter, cheese, eggs—are second; and grains are third. The United Kingdom imports four times as much wheat as is harvested and imports four times as much wheat as corn, the second grain item. The other leading food imports, cane sugar and tea cannot be produced in the kingdom. The tendency in British agriculture is shown in the increased planting of oats and other feed grains at the expense of wheat and barley. The acreage of sugar-beets has increased phenomenally during the last few years owing to the stimulus of government subsidy. Thus Great Britain has taken a lesson from Germany in encouraging the planting of a crop valuable both as a food and as an industrial commodity. The disruption of the industrial machine, resulting in unemployment on a large scale, may make it necessary to replant the land once more. As one British economist expressed it—it may have been good business to barter away one's agricultural heritage for a cheaper loaf of bread, but, on the other hand, self-sufficiency may well be one of the luxuries in which every progressive nation can afford to indulge itself.

While striving toward a position of industrial eminence Germany has bent every effort to remain agriculturally self-supporting. That she is second only to France in the latter respect is a tribute to the willingness of her statesmen to accept the findings of scientists. Today the yield per acre in Germany exceeds that of every state in Europe except Great Britain, where only the best land is under the plow. Yet the physical conditions of climate and soil are not comparable to those existing in France. The climate is cool and moist with insufficient sunshine. In the north the soils are sandy and light and the land is poorly drained; in the south the soils are better but the terrain is rougher since this region is a dissected plateau. Germany about 1871 embarked upon a system of intensive cultivation involving the widespread use of commercial fertilizer, scientific selection of seeds, careful planning of crops, scientific breeding of stock, and a program of agricultural education. To-day Germany is 70 per cent self-supporting.

As in Britain, forage crops and stock-raising form the basis of agricultural production. Cereals are distinctly subordinated. Yet, as there is much light soil in the north and much rough land in the south, rye can be raised without intruding upon the more valuable forage crop land. Thus rye has become the national cereal, and wheat is restricted to fertile, clayey soils where it is forced to compete with the sugar-beet. More rye is raised than wheat and barley combined. More potatoes are grown, however, than all the cereals. They are the chief item in the German diet and serve other purposes as well. They are widely employed as forage for stock, in the manufacture of alcohol, starch, and potato flour. German scientists have increased the starch content of the potato from 14 to 20 per cent. The potato is grown on the sandy soil of the northern lowland, especially where labor is cheap and abundant. The sugar-beet has appropriated the best agricultural lands in Germany, those about Magdeburg on the Elbe. The sugar-beet also serves many purposes, but is principally used as a source of sugar and as fodder for stock. The tops and the pulp-refuse make the beet second only to hay as a source of food for stock. Germany is the leading sugar producer in Europe and actually exports sugar, while the United Kingdom has a sugar bill of $100,000,000 annually. Hay is the leading fodder crop in Germany. German live stock better approximates the needs of the population than British live stock. The meat bill of the United Kingdom is fifteen times that of Germany. Germany raises relatively few sheep as compared with Great Britain but possesses twice as many cattle and five times as many hogs.

On the whole, however, Germany must go to the world market to supplement her food supply. Butter and wheat are her most expensive food imports. Since the war, because of the high price of agricultural machinery, the absence of protective tariffs, and financial difficulties, there has been a lessening of intensive cultivation and an increase of pasture and meadow. Barley, eggs, fruit, coffee, and potatoes are imported in considerable quantities. But Germany comes nearer feeding herself than the United Kingdom. Her bill for grains and potatoes is only 70 per cent of that of her rival; her bill for dairy products only 50 per cent; and her bill for meat only 5 per cent.

Artificial fertilizers have played a large part in raising Germany to a high agricultural plane. Before the war Germany enjoyed a monopoly of potash, owning the deposits of Staszfurt and Alsace. The German potash syndicate controlled the output and price and favored the German farmer. Sixty per cent of the product went into the German fields. Only the Netherlands used more artificial fertilizer than Germany. Potash, incidentally, aided German shipping in that it provided a bulky commodity, like British coal, to complete the outgoing cargoes. The fortunes of war gave the Alsace deposits to France. France now contributes 25 per cent of the European potash output and the amount of potash consumed in France has trebled since the war. Thomas slag, a by-product of the steel industry, is the main source of domestic phosphate.

France is agriculturally the most favored state in Europe. Though the Great Central Plateau occupies much of the country, more than half the land has an altitude of less than seven hundred feet. The climate provides a long growing season, sufficient rainfall, and the river drainage from plateau to sea is excellent. The Aquitaine basin and the Paris Basin are outliers of the Great Central Lowlands. The former is the richest agricultural region in France and the latter, because of its commercial and industrial importance, dominates the country. On the whole the soil of France is exceedingly fertile and productive. The keynote of French agriculture is diversity. Along the Atlantic coast orchards and pastures prevail; in the warmer and less rainy interior, wheat is cultivated; the vine is grown in favored localities. In the Mediterranean south, a different type of agriculture prevails. France, Italy, and Spain contain 90 per cent of the irrigated lands in Europe, and France has more than any single state. Thus France is able to combine the hardy cereals, root crops, and animal industries of the north with the vine, corn, olive, and mulberry of the south.

France conducts her agricultural economy on a different basis from that of her rivals. This she can do because her industrial population is only 46 per cent compared with 64 per cent for Germany and 80 per cent for the United Kingdom. Industrially, however, France is outranked by the others. French agriculture serves the needs of her people better than does that of Britain or Germany; indeed she is 90 per cent self-supporting. Her imports of wine actually exceed those of wheat, her largest food import. France raises five times as much wheat as she imports, while Britain grows only a sixth of her wheat and little Belgium pays an annual wheat bill of $50,000,000. As foreign wheat-growers could enter the French market at will and undersell domestic wheat, a high tariff was imposed upon wheat and several other food staples, for France does not wish to be dependent upon other states for her food. In 1929 the low price of wheat abroad led to measures increasing the duties upon wheat by a third and prohibiting bakers from using more than a fixed proportion of foreign wheat in their bread.

Oats rank second among the crops; some rye is raised; and in the south, corn. The vine grows best in the warm valleys of central and southern France. The grape industry never entirely recovered from the effects of *phylloxera*—indeed wine production has never since exceeded 75 per cent of the peak year, 1875—although France is still the leading wine maker of the world.

The yield per acre is a third less than that of Germany, for agriculture in France is not mechanized and facilities for agricultural instruction were never emphasized. The World War, however, wrought certain changes in French agriculture. Labor shortage in the fields led to a degree of mechanization. Furthermore, with the need for rebuilding the industries and exploiting new resources urbanization in France has been greatly accelerated. The increased cultivation of oats and potatoes suggests urban consumption. Root crops and forage crops are competing with wheat for the best lands since dairying is likely to assume prominence as manufacturing increases. Other significant changes are the substitution of raw cotton for the native wool and the importation of cheap foreign meats. This shift in agriculture, however, is slower than the process that so transformed Germany a half century before. The French are conservative about their agriculture because of their love of the soil to which they have been so rooted for many generations.

133. Manufactures

Only in Western Europe and in a small portion of the United States are more than a fifth of the workers engaged in manufacturing. Four Western European nations control a third of the world's foreign trade and each of them has succeeded in building up a highly productive manufacturing plant. This has been possible because of the favorable geographical advantages each enjoys. All four states share in common the excellent climate and other natural advantages afforded by Western Europe, and in addition all are endowed with the mineral and metal resources capable of sustaining the heavy industries.

Though possessing only a fraction of the reserves of the United States these countries mine and use more coal than the United States. The British mines produce 230,000,000 tons of coal per year; the Ruhr mines, ninety million tons; the mines of Upper Silesia, thirty million tons; the French mines, thirty million tons; and the Belgian mines, twenty million tons. The mines of Czechoslovakia produce more coal than the Don basin mines of Russia but this condition is not likely to continue long. The coal of the manufacturing states is of high quality, either anthracite or good grade bituminous. The larger portion is located near the tidewater, enabling easy and profitable shipment. The reserves of Europe are sufficient to serve her for several centuries. In fact, Western Europe sells considerable quantities of coal to regions lying in the southern hemisphere where coal is scarce. More interesting is the fact that much coal is imported as well as exported by several of the industrial states.

The mines of Western Europe produce approximately eighty million tons of iron ore per year in comparison with sixty-five millions produced in the United States. Before the World War Germany produced fifty million tons; Great Britain, sixteen million; Spain, ten million; Sweden, eight million; and Luxembourg, seven million. With the acquisition of the Lorraine ores by France and those of Upper Silesia by Poland the formula has undergone considerable change. France produces fifty million tons, and Germany only six million tons. France is now able to supply a fourth of the world's iron ore, while Germany to maintain her pre-war industrial rank must import millions of tons of ore yearly.

The production of pig iron and steel, however, is a better indication of the industrial status of the countries than is the output of the mines. In this capacity the four manufacturing states are distinctly the leaders. Germany, France, Great Britain, and Belgium produce respectively thirteen million tons, ten million tons, seven and a half million tons and four million tons of pig iron annually. Steel production is as follows: Germany, sixteen million tons; Great Britain, ten million tons; France, nine million tons; and Belgium, four million tons. Soviet Russia alone of the remaining European states rivals Belgium, producing far less pig iron but slightly larger amounts of steel. The four European states taken together, do not rival the United States in the production of either pig iron or steel, for the latter manufactures annually forty-two million tons of pig iron and fifty-six million tons of steel. France has not yet had time to develop fully her newly acquired resources, but should she succeed in adapting herself to the heavy metallurgical industries, she would rank second to the United States.

The great steel centers of Western Europe are Birmingham, Middlesbrough, Lille, Essen, Prague, and Breslau. These places owe their prominence to the possession of coal and iron deposits. There are several score lesser centers but their number tends to diminish rather than to increase. Many of the original steel centers have declined owing to the exhaustion of their pig iron. On the other hand, others have increased in importance because they lie near the seaboard and are able to import the ores of Spain, Sweden, or North America. Both Great Britain and Germany bring huge quantities of foreign ore to easily accessible coal deposits.

The United States produces within her boundaries most of the lesser metals and a large proportion of the raw materials essential to the textile industry. The manufacturing establishments of Western Europe must purchase huge quantities of copper, petroleum, tin, lead, zinc, and wool as well as such tropical and semi-tropical products as rubber and silk. Great Britain, Germany, and France are three of the four world's leading cotton importers. Japan is in second place. The leading wool importers of the world are France, Great Britain, and Germany. In addition these countries must import great amounts of food. Yet because their physical environment is such that they have access to large stores of iron and coal, the mainstays of modern industry, and a climate, stimulating to man and productive agriculturally, they have attained a degree of liberation from their physical environment equaled nowhere save in the United States. This is reflected not only in the specialization of industry and in the vast accretion of capital, but in a culture which reveals a reaching out in all directions, which for want of a better name we term modern civilization.

The manufactures of Western Europe are widely distributed, and their location is not entirely dependent upon the steel centers. Some advantage arises in having the steel goods and machinery industries situated in the steel producing districts, and a similar advantage attracts the textile industries to the coal fields. On the other hand other powerful influences are at work in determining the location of an industry or even a single factory. Some corporations consider nearness to raw materials the primary advantage; others, cheap labor costs; others, skilled labor; others, facilities for distribution; and others, a densely populated market. Some are compelled to locate in the ports either because of their dependence upon imported rawstuffs or because the principal part of their wares is exported. Four districts, however, stand out as the principal manufacturing centers of Western Europe. The most important is the district extending from northern France through Belgium to Westphalia. Here are coal, steel, and access to the sea. Second in importance is the British area, less compact, but with each subdivision specializing in a few commodities. The south German-eastern French area ranks high in the manufacture of steel goods, textiles, chemicals, electrical equipment, and highly graduated instruments. The upper German area carries on a highly diversified system of manufactures with textiles, glassware, bookmaking, sugar-refining, and beer-making as the most noteworthy. Lesser areas of intensive manufacturing are found at St. Etienne, Lyon, Marseille, and Milan. The St. Etienne district produces steel and aluminum; the Rhone centers, lace, silk, soaps, and other goods derived from vegetable oils. North Italy is prominent in the manufacture of silk rayon and machinery.

Textiles, second in importance to iron and steel manufacture, are distributed widely, but certain centers stand out in the spinning and weaving of cotton, wool, flax, and silk. The greatest textile centers are the Pennine district of England, Saxony, the Upper Rhine, Valenciennes, Alsace, and Lyon. Both cottons and woolens are important in Great Britain. Woolens are prominent also in Germany because of the long winters, and in France because of the popularity of French light weight woolens in the marts of style. Lyon leads in silk manufacturing, although closely rivalled by Milan. At Krefeld, Germany, is located the only important silk manufacture in northern Europe. Rayon manufacture began in France but the industry is now strongly established in north Italy, Britain, and Germany. The famous Irish linen industry relies on skill alone, for most of the flax is imported from Belgium, which in turn imports more and more from Russia.

Chemicals and chemical products are important among the industries of Western Europe. In the beginning certain places such as Staszfurt, where there were great salt deposits, dominated the industry, but to-day skill is regarded as more important than materials. Hence the industry tends to become more and more widely scattered. The smelting industries likewise bear little relation to the ore deposits as most of Europe's supplies of tin, zinc, and lead have been exhausted. The zinc smelters of Belgium, the largest in the world, now use only imported ores. The smelting of tin is still carried on in Wales owing to the peculiar capacity of Welshmen to withstand high temperatures, but most of the ore is imported. In other words, access to the sea has become the most important factor in the location of smelting works. The refining of oil takes place in seaports such as London, Hamburg, Rotterdam, and Marseille. Cheap power is the largest factor in the manufacture of aluminum and nitrogen fertilizer. Southern Norway has risen to prominence in these industries because of her abundant water-power resources, but Germany with vast stores of lignite is able to compete in the aluminum industry. France, affording the largest market for automobiles, took the lead in that industry, but with the rapidly growing demand throughout Western Europe, the American manufacturer has been quick to establish subsidiaries wherever feasible. Book publishing is important in Great Britain and Germany. The British publishers cater to a market three times as large as the German, but the latter have been doing the more discriminating work since the war.

134. National Manufactures

Great Britain is the most highly specialized industrial society in the world. Unfortunately, with the recrudescence of nationalism following the World War, Great Britain's exports of manufactured products have decreased because of the adoption of the doctrine of economic self-sufficiency by so many of her customers. In consequence, she has suffered severely during the period of readjustment. Unless nations permit their citizens to buy freely in the cheapest markets, it will be difficult for Britain to maintain the huge industrial establishments that have grown up there. Her industrial plant is absolutely dependent upon the opportunity to sell her wares freely in other countries, for she consumes only a fraction of her manufactures. During the nineteenth century, Great Britain consciously sacrificed her agricultural interests in the firm belief that manufactures could always be profitably traded for food. Her population was gradually drawn into the cities, and to-day it is 80 per cent urban. The amount of land under the plow and the number of agricultural laborers have steadily diminished. For food staples Great Britain is utterly dependent upon other regions. Under these circumstances, it is not to be wondered at that British statesmen are preoccupied with matters of trade and are feverishly engaged in welding the empire into an economic unity that will afford Britain the opportunity of exchanging her manufacturing surplus for their raw products. Unfortunately, most of the Dominions have also been bitten by the virus of self-sufficiency so that the effort to maintain her industrial machine has become more and more difficult.

Great Britain must purchase abroad not only her food but most of the raw materials of her manufacturies. All the cotton, rubber, jute, and most of the wool, hides and leather, the chemicals, and the iron ore must be imported. Great Britain's leading exports are cotton goods, woolen goods, iron and steel manufactures, electrical apparatus, and chemicals. Coal is the only raw material exported in quantities. Great Britain's principal customers are the United States, Germany, France, Argentina, the Netherlands, and of increasing importance in recent years, the British dominions and India.

Cotton stuffs including principally piece goods, yarns, and thread account for fully a third of all British exports. A third of the world's spindles are located in Great Britain. Hardly a fifth of the cotton manufactures are consumed in the British Isles. Great Britain, in addition to enjoying the advantage of an early start in the textile industry, is admirably fitted geographically as a textile center. An atmosphere too dry or too cold renders cotton fiber brittle, and in spite of all efforts, artificial humidifiers do not yet approximate the perfect atmospheric conditions that prevail in England. The necessity of maintaining a high temperature in the factories during severe weather has hindered the cotton industry in other temperate lands. In England the factories are located along the west slope of the Pennine Ridge, exposed to moist Westerly Winds that blow all year round. In addition to climatic advantages the looms and spindles are situated near the coal fields. Over 90 per cent of the spindles and looms are in Lancashire, a district only half the size of Rhode Island. Each town or group of towns specializes in the production of certain types of cloth. Manchester is the great warehouse center of the trade. In a sense, the reliance upon skilled labor has made for conservatism in the introduction of new types of machinery. In the United States the labor was of the immigrant type, unskilled and uneducated; hence American manufactures, in order to compete with the British, have had to keep abreast of every improvement that would enable them to increase the efficiency of production. The combination of unskilled labor and machinery is thought to be more elastic in meeting the conditions of a changing demand than a fixed body of skilled labor, especially in the production of coarse cottons, the staple of the export trade. Great Britain is being driven, as New England has been, into the production of finer grade cotton goods, which is essentially a luxury trade catering to a limited market. Foreign competition has hurt the British textile industry. The United States, Germany, France, and recently Japan and India, are large scale cotton manufacturers. British exports to the Far East have declined 50 per cent and the cheap labor and long working hours make it difficult for the British to compete there. Since 80 per cent of the cotton goods are destined for the export trade, an acute situation has developed in the British textile industry.

Great Britain's woolen manufactures are extensive; they employ half as many workers as her cotton manufactures, but the value of the woolen exports is only a fourth of that of the cotton exports. Great Britain, however, provides a large domestic market for woolens because of the damp climate of the islands. The industry is concentrated in Yorkshire with access to the sea, to coal, and to the sheep warrens of the Pennines. Bradford and Leeds are the leading wool centers. Britain's position in the woolen tissue trade is unassailable. The United States has succeeded in meeting British competition only by enforcing a tariff of over 50 per cent upon British goods, but even under this régime of protection over $5,000,000 worth of British woolens are imported yearly. Worsteds are fabrics made of yarn in which the woolen fibers are simply matted together. The tendency of the world trade lies in the direction of worsteds. This phase of the woolen industry requires more specialized and more expensive machinery. After weaving neither the pattern nor the finish of worsteds can undergo change. Domestic producers, the world over, have, therefore, demanded high protection before undertaking the risks of engaging in the worsted industry. The British manufacturers, because of the general nationalist protectionist trends, have also refused to invest in expensive machinery in the face of hostile legislation in other countries. Thus, again Britain is forced to specialize in a single direction, whereas under a system of free trade or reciprocal tariff agreements she could maintain the supreme position in the woolen tissue trade.

The iron and the steel manufactures including hardware and other supplementary metal industries occupy first rank in British manufactures and a place in the export trade second only to that of the cotton manufactures. The industry is fundamental since it provides the machines that produce consumers' goods. Great Britain's chief weaknesses in the metallurgical industry are two: first, the necessity for importing in increasing amounts iron ore; and secondly, the conservatism of the British manufacturers in utilizing new types of machinery. In the United States and Germany particularly, there has been a constant pressure, which is lacking in Britain, to improve the technological processes. The leading iron and steel district of Britain is situated at Cleveland close to the Durham coal deposits and to the largest iron ore deposits in the kingdom. Native ores are almost exhausted at some of the other steel centers, notably at Glasgow and the Clyde, and in South Wales. These districts account for a large part of the foreign ore imports. Lesser steel centers are located at Cumberland, at Sheffield, and in the Midlands.

As has been explained, coal and iron are essential to the development of a great industrial nation. But coal is important to British trade for other reasons. Her Cardiff and Newcastle mines lie near the sea, thus enabling her to sell coal cheaply in foreign regions. The average distance from mine to port is only twenty-five miles giving Britain the advantage of cheap marketing. It costs forty-seven cents a ton to get British coal to the seaboard, but seventy cents to haul German coal 140 miles from the Ruhr to Rotterdam and $1.25 to send coal from West Virginia to Hampton Roads. Secondly, coal, like her leading imports, cotton, grain, and iron ore, is large in bulk, while her manufactured wares are small in bulk. The British shipper in carrying coal is able to sail the seas going, as well as coming, with a full cargo in his hold. This advantage which she enjoys over all others is a factor in Britain's leadership in the world mercantile marine. Foreign shippers find it convenient to stop at Britain to take on coal, a circumstance which has been a great help in making her the commercial center of the world.

Germany's conversion into an industrial plant is very recent. She is not so industrial as Great Britain for only 65 per cent of her population is urban. Germany's phenomenal advance in the industrial world is the result of enterprises planned and subsidized by her government. The whole development, however, rested upon very solid geographical bases. Her Wesphalian coal reserves constituted over 50 per cent of the known coal reserves of Europe. This coal, especially suitable for the smelting of iron, lay within easy reach of the Lorraine iron ores. The war, however, has stripped Germany of these advantages. By the treaty of Versailles, Germany lost 10 per cent of her population, 12 per cent of her land, 26 per cent of her coal, 75 per cent of her iron ore, 70 per cent of her zinc ore, 15 per cent of her rye and wheat lands, and 16 per cent of her potato lands. Lorraine iron, Alsatian potash, and Saar coal [1] have been surrendered to France, and Silesian coal and the eastern grain lands have been given to Poland. Furthermore, under the peace terms Germany was seriously handicapped, at least temporarily, by the confiscation of her merchant marine.

At the present time, Germany depends upon foreign sources for three-fourths of her iron ore. Yet the German industrial position is far from dark, for Britain has to import all the raw materials of her great cotton industry. Furthermore, Germany's food bill is much less than that of Britain in spite of the loss of agricultural lands in the east. The most important factor in Germany's continued industrial prosperity, however, is her retention of the high-grade Westphalian coal deposits. These deposits extend over 1,500 square miles and are only one-fourth exploited. As this district is accessible to the sea, Germany is able to import foreign ores, at no great disadvantage. Her successor in Lorraine must import coal, indeed Westphalian coal, to reap any great profit from the vast, but low grade, ore deposits there.

Germany's industries are well distributed. The emphasis is upon human skill rather than upon subservient dependence upon coal and raw materials, for the transportation facilities are excellent. The bulk of the manufactures are situated in the southern two-thirds of the country. Saxony has developed a diversified system of manu-

---

[1] To be sold to Germany by agreement of December 4, 1934.

facture with textiles, publishing, and the conversion of kaolin into Dresden china as the most prominent. The Ruhr district leads, of course, in the heavy metallurgical industries. Bavaria is a poor agricultural region and lacks any large deposits of coal and iron. On the other hand, there is an abundance of water power and timber. Using her meager resources to best advantage, Bavaria has attained a respectable position in the industrial machine through the manufacture of quality wares. Nürnberg is famous for its toys, Pforgheim for its jewelry, and Munich for its beer. Germany's imports for industrial purposes reveal remarkable diversity; chief among them are hides, cotton, wool, silk, lumber and pulpwood, rubber, mineral oils, ores and slags, copper, chemicals, colors and dye-stuffs. Oil seeds of various kinds head the list.

Measured in terms of world trade, German exports, exclusive of deliveries on account of reparations, are third in rank. At present, her iron and steel exports and her exports of machinery and electrical apparatus account for a third of her export trade. The chemical industry supplies a fifth of all her exports, while paper, leather, and cotton manufactures are very important. Coal is the only considerable raw stuff that is exported. Thus Germany's position in the world trade is still high and she must be accounted, as before the war, an integral part of the Euramerican industrial plant. It is thought that with the development of heavy industries in France, Germany may be forced to specialize in her manufactures. However, it will be long before the other nations are able to command the technical knowledge needed for the manufacture of highly graduated machinery. In the chemical industry and in the production of electrical apparatus Germany is without a rival. Germany disposes of her wares chiefly in the United States, Great Britain, the Netherlands, and France, and imports chiefly from the United States, the United Kingdom, Argentina, the Netherlands, and France.

Less than half the French people dwell in cities; hence the degree of industrialization is not so great as in the other countries of manufacturing Europe. Where Germany boasts of forty-five cities with a population exceeding one hundred thousand, France is able to claim only seventeen such cities. French industry developed slowly for it has always been subordinated to agriculture. Even to-day more than 90 per cent of the manufacturing establishments employ fewer than twenty workers. Skilful craftmanship has been the outstanding

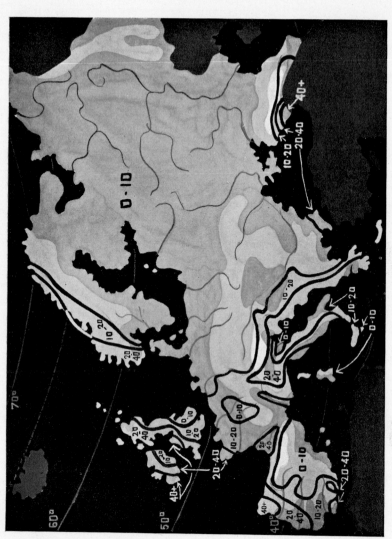

PLATE XX. EUROPE—JANUARY RAINFALL

(*After Goode*)

PLATE XXI. EUROPE—JULY RAINFALL.

(*After Goode*)

feature of French manufacturing. The production of luxuries rather than staples is reflected in the prominence of wines, jewelry, cosmetics, lingerie, laces, gowns, and millinery in the French export list. This trend was due partly to the individualistic taste of the French worker and partly to the scarcity of high grade coal. Changes, however, are taking place in French industry. The labor shortage created by the World War has speeded up the use of machinery, and the acquisition of Alsace and Lorraine has brought to France huge stores of iron ore, coal, and potash. France lost a third of her manufacturing plants during the war, and in renovating them the equipment has been modernized. The acquisition of Alsace and Lorraine has augmented her cotton and woolen plants by a fourth. The country is now in better competitive position in the industrial world. France is first in European silk manufactures, third in cottons and woolens, and third in iron and steel production. To-day the industrial trend is more pronounced than in Germany but this is largely because France is in the process of "catching up."

The great impediment in the development of the heavy industries in France has been the lack of coal. Before the war the Valenciennes basin, an extension of the Belgian coal fields, supplied 70 per cent of the coal mined in France. Valenciennes coal, because of bad rock faulting and a heavy overlay of strata, is difficult to get at. Many of the mines penetrate to a depth of one thousand feet and some to three thousand feet. The price at the mine in 1914 was $4.00 per ton, in comparison with $2.80 for Westphalian coal, and $1.25 for American coal. The other French fields were widely distributed and the coal was not of a high grade. With the acquisition of the Saar until 1935, France was enabled to enter the ranks of the coal exporting nations. Temporarily she controlled 20 per cent instead of 2 per cent of the coal reserves of Europe. On the other hand she imports four times as much as she exports. The trouble is that the Saar coal is not of the best quality for metallurgical purposes and must be used in combination with coke. Even when Germany was exploiting this region, the Alsatian industrialists found it more economical to import the better and cheaper Westphalian coal to run the factories. In addition, coking coal must be imported to supply those industries lying near the seaboard.

Metallurgical industries are usually located near the coal fields. Ore is said to seek coal, but in France a difficulty arises owing to the shortcomings of the ore. The ores of Lorraine are of such low content that they cannot bear the charges of transportation to the coal fields. The conversion of pig iron must take place at the ore mines. Hence, France must continue to import coking coal from Westphalia if she is to develop her heavy industries. To-day only 12 per cent of the coal used in Lorraine is French. Thus, though France controls the ore essential to supremacy in the heavy industries, Germany possesses the better coal. Since the future lies in the hands of statesmen and not in those of the economists, it is uncertain whether a great Continental industry can be developed without regard for political boundaries. French metallurgical production has shown no significant increase since 1913. Pig iron has hardly increased 10 per cent, while steel production and finished products in iron and steel show only slightly greater increases. The German heavy industries, in spite of the diminution of resources, still surpass the French by a wide margin.

By 1913, owing to the attraction of coal, the *Département du Nord* had become the major industrial center of France. Here the density of population rose to 850 per square mile, greater than any *département* in France save that in which Paris is located. Here were situated the manufactures of cotton, linen, wool, and steel. The Nord with its coal supplies and its appropriately damp climate was suitable for the spinning industry. Spinning is especially suited to capitalistic production as, unlike weaving, it calls for no special taste or skill. The Lyon district, however, remains the most important region for the textile industry, since French textile exports are essentially quality goods and it is only natural for the finest cottons to locate near the districts producing silk goods.

Recently, the textile industry has experienced considerable adjustment. The first change, a post-war development, was a shift to the east. With the recovery of Alsace, France advanced to the position of the third largest cotton manufacturing country in the world, being exceeded only by the United Kingdom and the United States. The second adjustment was more difficult. During the post-war years, the luxury market all but evaporated with the decline of the aristocratic class in France, the imposition of heavy taxes upon the English wealthy class, and the shrinkage of the American market for fine imported goods. France, which relied more upon skilled labor than upon

machines in production, had to embark upon a program of moderniz-
ing her textile machinery. Her position was similar to that of the
United States several generations ago. To-day large numbers of
Belgians and Italians work in the mills and thousands of Poles labor
in the mines. France has had to draw upon the labor surplus of other
lands not only to make post-war replacements but to give her highly
competitive textile industry the advantage of low labor costs. Thus
the war brought about a *bouleversement* in industry; France is now
engaged in quantity production, while Germany tends to specialize in
high quality wares.

French imports and exports reveal a similarity to those of the
other manufacturing states of Western Europe. The leading imports,
besides coal, are wool, cotton, silk, and chemicals. Machinery stands
fourth upon the list, and this is significant in showing that the
French during the past ten years have been renovating and moderniz-
ing their manufacturing plant. Textile fibers constitute 40 per cent
of French imports and 43 per cent of the exports. The reliance upon
agriculture for supplying the rawstuffs of industry is lessening. Only
4 per cent of the raw silk utilized is produced in France. All the
cotton, six-sevenths of the wool, and two-thirds of the hemp and
flax are imported. The exports fall into three classes: first, cotton,
woolen, and silk goods; secondly, iron and steel products including
sizable shipments of machinery and automobiles; and thirdly, dyes
and other products of the chemical industry. The imports come from
the United States, Germany, United Kingdom, and Belgium; and the
exports go principally to the United Kingdom, Belgium, Germany,
and the United States. In recent years, trade with Algeria, the leading French colony, has greatly increased.

Belgium has arrived at the same type of environmental adaptation
as Great Britain, Germany, and France. Modern industry has permitted in this small state a density of population that would be impossible in a Western European agrarian community. Belgium's
density, 686 per square mile, is the greatest of any nation in the
world. To be sure agriculture has not been neglected, but it is of the
garden type adapted to the demands of a population that is 78 per
cent urban. Through a system of intensively regulated agricultural
production and marketing Belgium boasts of supplying 85 per cent
of her food requirements. Nevertheless, for the staples she is a de-

pendent nation and is obliged to import vast quantities of wheat, corn, barley, and refrigerated meats.

Belgium, however, is wonderfully endowed to carry on manufacturing. Her rich coal deposits made profitable the importation of iron ore and gave rise to heavy industries that have constantly expanded. The World War threw her into economic alliance with Luxembourg, formerly a member of the German economic union and a state enjoying a surplus of iron ore. To-day the coal production of Belgium is hardly equal to the demand and large quantities must be imported from neighboring states. Her production of pig iron is almost half that of her political mentor, France. In addition Belgium has a flourishing textile industry, turning out quantities of cotton and woolen goods for export. Her chief exports, however, are the products of the heavy industries: iron and steel goods and machinery. Her principal customers are Great Britain, the Netherlands, Germany, and France.

Great Britain, Germany, France, and Belgium constitute the European nucleus of the present manufacturing world. Like the United States each has resources of coal and iron, the *sine qua non* of modern industry. In Europe history and politics interfere with regional development and, paradoxically, economic rivalries have become an increasing disturbance in the relations of states. In large measure it is these economic jealousies and nationalistic aspirations that have made it so easy for the United States to draw ahead. Nationalism has its price, for the costs of economic self-sufficiency are large. Yet running through the warp and woof of the political skein there is everywhere apparent a centralizing, as well as a decentralizing force. Men engaged in the production and distribution of goods are obliged to look beyond the barriers set up by nationalism. Trade is not alone a facility for the exchange of goods; it is infinitely more important in diffusing that which is best in culture and civilization from one group to another. With the growth of trade, Western Europe has been subjected to a quickening of ideas that has tended toward cultural uniformity. All chauvinistic arguments to the contrary, Western Europe shares a social heritage and a social environment that is the common property of all. If there does not come the realization that a common social and economic adjustment with other states is as important as the harmonious adaptation of a nation to its physical environment, Western civilization must surely decline.

135. Commerce

Western Europe carries on approximately one-half of the foreign commerce of the world. Great Britain alone enjoys a volume of trade exceeding that of the United States. Great Britain has 14 per cent of the world's foreign trade; Germany, 10 per cent; France, 6 per cent; and little Belgium, 2 per cent. Brazil and Argentina buy half their imports from Western Europe; Australia and India, three-fourths; and Japan, a third. Four-fifths of the exports of Africa go to Western Europe, as do three-fourths of Australia's and half those of North and South America.

More than 70 per cent of the merchant tonnage of the world belongs to Western European states. The United States, with 21 per cent of the world's tonnage, and Japan, with 6 per cent, are the sole competitors. Nine-tenths of the shipping launched during the past ten years was Western European. The chief carriers of goods are Great Britain, first by a wide margin, with twenty million tons; Germany, with more than four millions; and France, Italy, Norway, and the Netherlands, with approximately three millions each.

The import trade of Western Europe falls broadly into four categories: first, food and rawstuffs; secondly, minerals, especially copper, petroleum, silver, and tin; thirdly, tropical products, such as cane sugar, vegetable oils, copra, coffee, and tea; and fourthly, specialties that could be produced in Europe, yet for some reason or other are not. In the latter class are many commodities supplied by the United States: automobiles, typewriters, victrolas, and radio receiving sets. Silk from the Orient, butter and cheeses from Canada, Australia, and New Zealand are additional imports.

Trading among the states of Western Europe, however, is more important than their foreign trade. Germany's trade with Great Britain is exceeded only by that of the United States and India with Great Britain. Much of the trade between Great Britain, France, Germany, and Belgium is in commodities which any one of them could produce but does not owing to conservatism or some other reason. German dyestuffs, French silks, British cottons, woolens, and mechanical devices enjoy a wide patronage throughout Western Europe. A fifth of the imports of the leading manufacturing states are, oddly, manufactures. Fully half of Europe's imports are European and two-thirds of the exports find their markets on that continent.

Great Britain, Germany, France, Belgium, and the Netherlands normally have more imports than exports—in other words, an unfavorable balance of trade. This, however, is not necessarily an unhealthy condition. All the countries mentioned have sources of income from abroad which compensate for the excess of imports. Great Britain, for example, imports annually a billion dollars' worth of goods more than she exports. The difference is made up from invisible exports such as returns from capital investments, receipts from the merchant marine and from the reëxport trade. Similarly, the other nations profit from their foreign investments, their merchant marine, and their reëxport trade. Britain is a reëxport center for such commodities as wool, tin, tea, rubber, and cotton; the Netherlands for cacao, spices, and rubber; and France, for coffee. Many of the imports and exports of Germany, Switzerland, Czechoslovakia, and Austria pass through Belgium and the Netherlands.

Half the exports of Great Britain and a third of her imports are with the Empire. She purchases from the United States a billion dollars' worth of goods annually and sells to this country a fourth as much. Her textile exports are slowly diminishing, but her iron and steel exports are slowly increasing. Until the World War, the export trade in coal was increasing, but with new competitors and the substitution of oil for coal, exports of coal have diminished from 10 to 6 per cent. Two-thirds of British exports are divided among textiles, metals, and coal. Then follows a long list, for Britain boasts that she is able to supply any demand on the part of her customers. Britain dominates the trade of South America. Only recently, owing principally to the American demand for bananas, has the United States, despite a carefully calculated policy, been able to intrude upon the British monopoly in Colombia and Venezuela. In 1914 Great Britain was importing four-fifths of her food but the German submarine peril served to revive British agriculture. To-day a sixth of the wheat consumed is British wheat. Rawstuffs of the textile industry such as cotton, wool, jute, and flax are largely imported. She is able to obtain 50 per cent of her wool from the Empire, principally from Australia and South Africa. With cotton she has been less successful, for only a fourth of her needs are supplied by Egypt and India. British finished goods are of uniformly high quality and in great demand. Her foreign investments are a stimulus to her trade because much of the exported capital is utilized in exploiting enterprises requiring tools and machinery. The strong foreign branches of the British banking system are able to direct large purchases to the British market through credit devices.

By 1914 Germany had risen to the rank of one of the three greatest commercial nations of the world. Seventy per cent of German trade is sea-borne. The tonnage through Hamburg is greater than that of all other German ports combined. Yet, because of their more favorable location, the Dutch and Belgian ports handle a large amount of the German commerce. The German coast is obstructed by lagoons and deltas, and part of it is ice-bound for several months. The Elbe is a great highway of commerce, carrying more goods than any stream in Europe except the Rhine. The latter stream, however, reaches the sea through the Netherlands.

The trade of France is only 40 per cent of that of Great Britain. Four-fifths of it is in manufactured goods, and the export tonnage is small because the commodities are small in volume and high in value. Marseille is the most important port. It has a continental significance as it is an important gateway leading to industrial Europe. Its immediate hinterland is the Lyon-St. Etienne industrial district. Bordeau is the great wine port; Calais and Cherbourg are passenger ports; and Havre, Rouen, and Dunkirk are freight ports. Havre, at the mouth of the Seine, has a shallow and unreliable harbor. None of the French ports are as important as those which serve the industrial nucleus of Western Europe.

136. The Great Ports

No other port in the world dominates a whole continent as New York dominates North America. In comparison with the trade of New York that of the other American ports seems dwarfed and marginal. With the decentralization of industry the day may come when a real port rivalry will arise in the United States, but at present the outlook is discouraging for the other ports. In Europe, however, the situation is entirely different. There no single state controls manufacturing and finance to the exclusion of the others, nor are the railways and waterways centered upon a single commercial metropolis. In addition to a number of national ports of secondary rank, there are no less than five of world importance situated in Western Europe. On the mainland three great ports, Hamburg, Antwerp, and Rotterdam are engaged in a fierce competition for control of an extensive international hinterland. In the British Isles, London and Liverpool have risen to gigantic stature. London competes with the Continental leaders in the reëxport and tranship-ment business, while Liverpool, firmly entrenched as the port of British industry, endeavors to circumscribe her rival's hinterland.

Geographical factors have played a large part in the well-being of each of these ports. None has such natural facilities for mobile shipping as New York, yet each by constantly improving its harbor has been able to retain a preëminent place in world trade. Size alone is no indication of the efficiency of a harbor. In fact, New York harbor is many times larger than any harbor in Europe so far as physical capacity is concerned, but the European ports far exceed New York in intensity of use. New York transfers 150 tons of cargo for every linear foot of equipped quays, while several of the European ports average 1,500 tons. Yet compared with New York, the Eu-ropean ports are "little dug-out-of-the-mud harbors."

Now let us consider fully the advantages of site and situation, as well as some of the more important minor geographical elements in the prosperity of each of the five great ports. Liverpool, at the mouth of the Mersey, has had a different kind of growth from the other four great harbors. It is primarily a product of the industrial revolution of modern times. For centuries it was no more than a fishing village, and not until the eighteenth century did it advance above a status of local importance. Then Liverpool began to partici-pate in the North American triangular trade dealing in slaves, rum, molasses, trinkets, and fabrics. Yet, because her "Liver Pool" af-forded better facilities for small vessels than other west coast ports, she gradually drew ahead of her rivals. Her harbor, four acres in size, and fourteen feet deep, could accommodate as many as one hundred ships. When the Industrial Revolution transformed northern England into a manufacturing district, Liverpool, prepared to ac-commodate ships of a size that the other ports could not, grew rapidly. At present she has only a single competitor for the industrial hinter-land of England, the artificial harbor of Manchester. During the years 1887 to 1893 Manchester built a canal thirty-five miles long, 120 feet wide, and twenty-eight feet deep from the sea to the interior. This she has constantly improved. Manchester, however, vies with Liverpool only in the importation of wares that can be utilized immediately as food or in manufacturing operations. Thus her trade is largely in bulky commodities like oil, lumber, frozen meat, and grain, whose transit it is expensive to break. Liverpool, in spite of Manchester's more favorable location, retains her supremacy, importing most of the raw cotton and shipping most of the piece goods. The reasons are three: first, Liverpool enjoys a greater choice of shipping services throughout the world; secondly, she has superior warehouse facilities for "in and out" service; and finally, she monopolizes the exchange and brokerage facilities. As the competition in the cotton industry of Lancashire is severe, skilful purchasing may represent a very tangible advantage. Thus, under the prevailing method of "hand to mouth" buying which enables the manufacturer to benefit from fluctuations in price, the commercial function of the port binds the hinterland to Liverpool.

Liverpool's prosperity is absolutely dependent upon that of her hinterland, the textile center of Great Britain. Her imports and exports from year to year constitute a barometer of the status of British industry. Her function is to distribute the raw materials to the hinterland and to export the surplus of manufactured goods. Her trade fell to 55 per cent of the pre-war level in 1918, reëqualed the pre-war level in 1925, reached a new peak in 1927, but thereafter declined. This cycle faithfully reflects the status of industry in the British Isles. Like London, Liverpool has a small hinterland. Its radius, seventy or eighty miles, is minute in comparison with that of Hamburg, Rotterdam, or Antwerp.

Liverpool is prepared to handle the whole merchant fleet of the world, so numerous are her docks and so ample are her storage facilities. Yet she has had to combat a number of physical handicaps in order to attain such a status. Tidal fluctuations have enforced the building of enclosed docks; the silt must be constantly cleared, and the cost of turning large vessels adds to the shipping overhead. In order to afford efficient service, Liverpool has created a Port Authority which is a non-profit public trust. The profits on the warehouses and the pilotage are consumed by the docks, quays, and other necessary services. The Port Authority has been eminently successful, showing an average earning of 3¾ per cent upon a capital investment of £42,000,000. Some see factors developing that will render it difficult for Liverpool to maintain her position. The expense of certain charges, it is feared, will handicap the British

textiles in competition with those of the Continent. Labor is paid
$2.90 a day, 20 to 45 per cent higher than the scale of her Continental
rivals, Hamburg, Rotterdam, and Antwerp. In addition, it is alleged,
Liverpool has fallen behind in not developing a manufacturing industry of proportions. Her manufacturing is of a strictly commercial
character; the refining of sugar, the milling of flour, and similar
operations of convenience. Other causes have intruded to decrease
her volume of commerce. She is no longer "the liner port." Not only
is the emigrant business no longer profitable, but the passenger trade
has shifted from Liverpool to Southampton, whose harbor has a
depth of thirty-four feet. Liverpool has also lost what share in the
transhipment trade she formerly enjoyed. In modern times the
tendency is to ship directly to the port of destination, with the result
that only those ports situated on the great lanes of commerce and
affording unusual commercial and financial facilities are able to retain
this type of commerce.

Liverpool, in conclusion, is a port whose fortunes are definitely
attuned to those of a limited and highly specialized industrial community. Through her quays flow thousands of tons of cotton, wool,
and tin for manufactures and other thousands of tons of grain, flour,
meat, and sugar to feed the workers of her hinterland. From Liverpool depart large stores of cotton goods, woolen goods, iron and
steel products, and machinery. There is little diversity in her commerce in comparison with that of the four other great ports. Though
she caters to the finest industrial machine in the world, it is a machine
which owing to the tariff policies of post-war states can no longer
function at top speed. To-day it is a question whether the British Empire will rally to the support of Britain's industrial plant or whether,
deeming it unnecessary, they will permit it to fall into disuse. Upon
this decision hangs the fate of the port of Liverpool.

If Liverpool is the port of manufacturing Britain, London is the
port of the Empire. Furthermore London harbors the most inter-
nationalized commerce of the world. Liverpool's exports exceed those
of London but the latter's imports are double those of Liverpool and
her reëxports and transhipments are unparalleled. London's site was
precisely determined many centuries ago by the fact that there, over
sixty miles inland, the banks of the Thames were solid enough to permit the building of a bridge out of reach of the tides. The situation of
London for purposes of commerce is superb. For centuries this port

far inland, yet deep enough to accommodate the shipping of pre-modern times, tapped the resources of the most populous and the most industrialized portion of the British Isles. Until the dawn of the Industrial Revolution she had no rival in the British Isles. England's comparative freedom from the political embroglios of the continent attracted traders and merchants of all nationalities to London. Here arose a system of trading and banking which since the seventeenth century has enjoyed an international status. Opposite London lay the great markets of the Continent, and from a vantage point of greater security London was better prepared to accommodate continental needs than many of the harassed ports on the mainland. London, then, for centuries has been not only the commercial center of Britain, but the clearing house of the world.

"London," writes a British geographer, "is an example of a town which maintains its importance from geographical inertia. Its history together with its location at the center of world trade routes, contributed to its overwhelming importance in world trade." Certainly London's industrial importance is not as great as once, for she possesses none of the geographical advantages to be derived from iron, coal, or other staples of modern industry. Yet through London to-day passes two-fifths of British imports and a sixth of the exports. The disparity between imports and exports reveals the low position of manufactures in the London area. Foodstuffs, which can be conveniently distributed all over Britain, and wool, because of London's tenacious hold upon the historic wool market, are her principal imports.

Not only does London control about 50 per cent of the volume of British commerce but a tenth of her traffic consists of reëxports. For Europe, London is the principal distributor of commodities such as tea, tin, hides, crude rubber, and wool. Since 1913 London's foreign shipping has increased 30 per cent while Liverpool's has hardly increased 10 per cent. London's increase is due to British trade and financial stability while Liverpool's relatively small increase reflects the breakdown of the British industrial plant. Raw materials for manufacture or consumption are shipped to London to be warehoused until the world needs them. The shippers are credited with 70 or 80 per cent of the current value of the wares by banks which finance the transaction. After the goods are sold, the balance is paid less interest and commission. The consignment market is possible because of the ease of importing, storing, and reëxporting. Seasonal movements of commodities such as the produce of the harvest cannot move from producer to consumer without financing, warehousing, grading, and marketing; and it is in these functions that London excels. In a recent year half of our huge imports from England were not produced there at all. Some of the items are interesting: $40,000,-000 worth of rubber from Brazil, the Congo, and the Straits; $30,-000,000 worth of cotton, largely Egyptian; $25,000,000 worth of tin, mainly from Bolivia; $10,000,000 worth of Australian wool; and $700,000 worth of Philippine hemp.

The harbor of London labors under physical handicaps, chief of which has been the accommodation of shipping. In 1908 was established the Port of London Authority, which acquired control of all the docks and warehouses of importance. The second step was the deepening and widening of the channel under a single direction. A fourteen-foot channel at low water is now maintained up to London Bridge, a thirty-foot channel with a width of six hundred feet extends as far as Woolwich, and at the Tilbury Docks, far down the river, a thirty-eight-foot channel has been cleared. The necessity of extending the docks and quays to a length of over thirty miles has occasioned huge expenditures.

Britain's Continental port rivals fulfill more adequately the function of the port in modern economy than either Liverpool or London. Hamburg, Rotterdam, and Antwerp combine equally diverse but coordinating rôles. Each has a regional function, an industrial function, and a commercial function. The importance of a port's regional function, that is, the power of attracting the commerce of the hinterland, depends upon basic geographical factors. Geographical advantages, however, have only an initial significance where competition for the hinterland is severe. Unless care is taken in organizing efficiently the port facilities, in reducing to the minimum charges of lading and unlading, in providing regular and adequate transport services for the collection and distribution of goods, a port's business will soon dwindle. The development of the industrial function is comparatively recent. Every modern port makes determined efforts to persuade entrepreneurs to establish factories. Manufacturers, whose business it is simply to transform imported raw materials into exportable wares, are more and more likely to be attracted to the ports because of reduced transportation costs. It is in this regard that London has fallen behind her Continental rivals. The commercial function embraces many services. The port must make an effort to lessen the arbitrary burdens upon the movement of goods and to extend shippers and producers every possible credit facility. Heavy customs drive away business. The commercial function involves the establishing of exchanges for the marketing of specialized products in foreign lands. Since the war, however, the policy has been to eliminate wherever possible the middle man. The organization of horizontal and vertical cartels in France, Belgium, and Germany has enabled giant organizations to operate without the assistance of the commercial facilities of the ports. A large part of the metallurgical shipments from Luxembourg, for example, are shipped directly through Dunkirk instead of being marketed through the commission merchants of Antwerp.

The geographical factor is definitive in the status of a port and only where the advantages of geography are balanced does competition arise at all. Hamburg, Rotterdam, and Antwerp stand out because of certain natural advantages in site and situation which no amount of efficiency on the part of other rivals can overcome. The factor of efficiency, however, enters into the competition of these ports for the hinterland of Western Europe. This struggle goes on in the face of and frequently in spite of all sorts of political impedimenta that stifle the normal geographical relationships of trade.

Hamburg, situated sixty-five miles up the Elbe River, is the leading German port among many, and in some respects is the first in rank on the Continent. The Free City of Hamburg is a member state of the German Republic and like Liverpool has a population just exceeding a million. Hamburg is a newcomer among the important ports of the world, hence its early history is relatively unimportant. Its site like that of so many other Western European ports was determined by the existence of a patch of high ground in a marshy estuary. Hamburg shared the usual vicissitudes, interspersed with occasional successes, of a minor port until 1870. It did, however, during its long existence which dates certainly from the twelfth century, maintain the status of a Free City, and upon that basis it entered the German Union. Since 1870 it has enjoyed an enviable position in world trade, with the exception of the period of blockade during the

World War. Its recovery from the effects of that debacle was exceedingly rapid because Hamburg is not only indispensable to Germany but to portions of the surrounding countries.

The chief factor in Hamburg's prosperity is her rich and economically diverse hinterland. As the larger part of Hamburg's hinterland lies in Germany, she enjoys a marked advantage over Antwerp and Rotterdam, her chief rivals. Antwerp, it is true, has an immediate industrialized national hinterland, but it is small in comparison with that of Hamburg. Rotterdam must penetrate beyond the bounds of Holland before tapping an industrialized hinterland. The German port, too, has the advantage of membership in a powerful political entity that can add through tariffs, subsidies, and reciprocal trade agreements with other nations directly to her prosperity.

Hamburg has highly desirable communications with her hinterland by water and by rail. First of all she controls the commercial drainage of the Elbe, a stream of international importance. Through this river, its branches, and connecting canals Hamburg is linked with the east as far as Posen. The Baltic is reached by a canal that proceeds through Lübeck and the Oder by way of the Berlin canal system. The Elbe flows through the rich industrial section around Dresden and the lower agricultural plainlands about Magdeburg. Commerce on the Upper Elbe is unimportant although there is some traffic as far as Prague.[1] Hamburg's great ambition is to share in the commerce of the Saar, the Ruhr, and other Rhine lands. In eight years over $60,000,000 have been spent in building canals and clearing streams, in the effort to bring Westphalian coal and other bulky commodities to Hamburg for shipment. Her share, however, in this traffic remains small.

Railway traffic, operating under a system of long hauls, is gradually undermining transport by canal and river. Already most of the lighter goods travel by rail. Hamburg has admirable railway facilities that connect her not only with all parts of Germany but with practically every country in Europe. Thus by rail she competes with Genoa for the business of Switzerland. Five great trunk lines reach Hamburg from all parts of Germany. She has entered the industrialized Rhine lands and 12 per cent of her business by rail comes from that section. Antwerp and Rotterdam, however, have not been idle. They, too, have adopted the long haul and the former offers a system of

[1] Praha.

premiums (rebates) that shrewd industrialists cannot afford to over-look.

Since the war Hamburg has administered half the foreign trade of Germany. Most of the trade of Czechoslovakia flows through her quays and warehouses because she has granted more advantageous leases than Stettin, Trieste, and other competitors. By developing Cuxhaven, nearer the sea, she meets the requirements of the large passenger ships and has thus undermined the traffic of Bremen. Her commerce, like that of Antwerp and Rotterdam, is diversified, and touches all parts of the globe. The imports exceed the exports in bulk by almost two to one, but the latter exceed the former in value. A lasting factor in her prosperity has been her transhipment trade with the Baltic states. Since Hamburg is a Free Port, she has laid apart a zone that is not subject to the customs duties of the German Reich. Yearly, thousands of tons of goods are reshipped on demand to various Baltic ports via the Kiel Canal. The establishment of a Free Port is an advantage to the shipping of any state whose ports are situated along one of the chief arteries of trade. For years American shippers have petitioned for the establishment of a Free Port service near New York. Staten Island has met with favor in their eyes. Here, it is thought, American shippers could perform a valuable and profitable service as intermediaries between Canada and Europe on the one hand, and the Latin American states on the other. In spite of the complexity and the diversity of Hamburg's commercial relationships, the work of the port, controlled in the interests of efficiency by the state, has been compared to a frictionless machine. Not only do goods move rapidly, but the Bank of Hamburg, enjoying a great liberty of action within the German fiscal system, works in close conjunction with all the demands of trading. Since the World War the shipping and merchant lines of Hamburg have practically pooled their resources in order to achieve greater efficiency.

Rotterdam and Antwerp alone vie with Hamburg among the ports of Continental Europe. Bremen and Havre are great ports, but in comparison with the others they are distinctly smaller in importance. Hamburg has a total traffic of 21.2 million tons; Rotterdam 20.7 million tons; Antwerp, twenty million tons; Bremen, 8.6 million tons; and Havre, 7.7 million tons. The traffic of the Rhine Valley, estimated at nearly sixty million tons, is the prize for which both Rotterdam and Antwerp contend. Rotterdam commands the mouths of the Rhine and therein lies its chief advantage. Much of the commerce is of a bulky character, for Rotterdam's connection by water is unrivaled. The harbor itself, constantly improved, is excellent. It has a depth of thirty-five feet at high water and thirty-one feet at low water. It is protected from wind and wave, and unlike Hamburg, suffers neither fog nor choking ice. The port equipment is marvelous and the harbor is so well managed that three rows of ships can be unloaded simultaneously in the river. Floating cranes discharge the cargo on barges whence it proceeds up the river. Over 70 per cent of Rotterdam's commerce is of this type; bulky goods such as coal, iron ore, oil, wheat, and cotton which are transferred from ship to barge. The leading imports are iron ore and cereals; the leading export, coal. Rotterdam, however, has serious handicaps in competing with Antwerp. Its connections by rail are poor; its immediate hinterland is agricultural; and its industrial function has failed to develop because of the small consuming capacity of the agricultural population. A large proportion of the goods entering and leaving Rotterdam are carried in foreign bottoms. Because of the simplicity of its shipping relationship the commercial function is not so highly developed as at Hamburg. But by virtue of geographical advantages, its easy access to a large part of industrial Europe, its unexcelled water communications along the Rhine-Meuse, and the interior canal network Rotterdam is enabled to hold an important portion of the Rhineland and Westphalian transports and compete successfully for the movement of bulky commodities from Alsace-Lorraine and Switzerland.

Antwerp enjoys most of the geographical advantages common to Rotterdam. This port, too, derives a large portion of its business by moving goods to and from the Meuse and the Rhine. Rotterdam is eighteen miles from the sea; Antwerp is fifty; hence goods, especially those that are to proceed inland by rail, have the advantage of a shorter haul by way of Antwerp. Needless to say Antwerp serves, in the same manner, a dense population and a vast and diverse economic sphere. Not only does she compete with Rotterdam for the trade of Rhineland and Westphalia, but she serves a small but compact industry in Belgium and extends her operations into adjoining regions of France. Like Rotterdam, Antwerp must overcome certain nationalistic prejudices in order to maintain her status, but this she is able to do owing to a port efficiency that functions swiftly and cheaply and to the coöperation of a government that maintains friendly relations with all her neighbors.

Antwerp, like Rotterdam, is a very old port and like her rival came into prominence with the discovery of America and the development of the Atlantic trade. Since the sixteenth century Antwerp has kept abreast of the improvement of shipping, and has adjusted her harbor facilities to meet its exacting requirements. Her harbor is in constant state of improvement and extension. At high tide the harbor is thirty-five feet deep. Antwerp, as has been mentioned, is especially suited to traffic by rail and the state has insured her advantage by building a network of fine railways throughout Belgium and linking it up with the chief rail arteries of Europe. Unlike Rotterdam more goods enter and leave by rail than by river and canal. In fact 50 per cent of the imports and 60 per cent of the exports are carried to and from the interior by rail. An analysis of this traffic indicates the international position of Antwerp. Roughly 65 per cent of the rail traffic is national, 7 per cent is with France, 7 per cent with Alsace-Lorraine, 4 per cent with Germany, 12 per cent with Luxembourg, 2.8 per cent with the Saar, 2 per cent with Holland, and fractional amounts with Italy and Switzerland. In general her imports are raw materials and her exports finished wares. In keeping with her situation in a manufacturing region Antwerp lost no time in developing the industrial function. To-day there are several thousand industrial establishments located near the port where raw materials can be readily obtained and finished goods conveniently disposed of.

We have remarked the importance of the geographical factors in the prosperity of a really great port. Each of the ports discussed has derived inestimable advantages from its location near the great Euramerican trade artery; each has easy communication with a rich hinterland; each acts as a distributor of raw materials and finished goods entering the world trade; and each participates in the tremendous intra-European commerce. Man's relationship, however, cannot be denied. The physical harbor never corresponds exactly with his changing needs; hence the modern harbor is in a constant state of repair. To compete with other ports every facility must be developed efficiently and each service must be as cheap as possible. Means of credit and exchange must be provided at every turn. Yet as certain states are learning, trade does not flow uphill and policies for the national good, however well-intentioned, must conform to the limitations of geography. Human geography is the relationship between the physical and the social environment, and human economy is best served where it interferes least with their interrelation.

INDEX

Acorns, 215
Adriatic Sea, 211
Africa, 71-91
Agriculture: in Congo basin, 73; in the Sudan, 80; in the Sahara oases, 87-91; in Java, 97-108; in India, 118-130; in China, 140-147; in Japan, 167-172, 179; in Russia, 184-185, 201-208; in Mediterranean lands, 217-220; in South America, 234, 238, 239, 251, 256-257, 258-261, 263-273; in the West Indies, 280, 283-292; in the United States, 309-352; in Western Europe, 380-391
Aleutian Islands, 69
Alfalfa, 260, 315, 322, 330
Algeria, 210
Alps Mountains, 386
Altiplano, 232, 252, 253
Altitude, effect of, upon climate, 51, 58, 59, 234, 239, 276, 296-298, 386
Amazon River, 233, 235, 236
Amazonia, 235-236, 267-269
Amur River, 136, 187, 188
Anatolia, 209, 222-228
Andes Mountains, 231-232, 236, 239, 241
Antarctica, climate of, 69
Anticyclones, 45, 48
Antwerp, 415-418
Aperiodic winds, 44-48 *passim*
Aphelion, 18
Arabs, 78, 79, 82, 214, 217
Arctic Drift, 50, 51
Arctic regions, 70
Argentina, 241-248 *passim*, 257-261, 262
Atacama Desert, 238
Atlantic trucking region (U. S.), 349-352
Atmosphere, 35-36
Azov Sea, 187

Bahamas, 285

Baku, 198
Balkans, 216, 219, 220, 371
Baltimore, 359, 362, 365
Bamboo, 165, 170, 177, 179
Bananas, 73, 220, 264, 271, 293
Bantu, 73
Barley, 142, 166, 169, 217, 256, 298, 316, 342, 383-388 *passim*
Batum, 198
Belgium, 394, 395, 403-404, 415-418
Birmingham (Eng.), 393
Birmingham (U. S.), 354-355
Black Sea, 186, 187, 191, 207
Black soil belt (U.S.S.R.), 189, 201, 208
Bogotá, 239, 270
Bolivia, 243, 246, 253-254
Boll weevil, 334
Bolshevism, 184-185, 201
Bombay, 57, 132, 133
Bora wind, 211
Borax, 321
Bores, 33
Borneo, 97, 98, 159
Boston, 358, 362, 365
Brahmaputra River, 113, 127
Brazil, 243, 245, 247, 263-269
Brazilian Highlands, 233, 237-238, 264-265
Bremen, 415
British Isles, 373, 377, 378, 384; agriculture in, 386-388; resources of, 392-393; manufactures of, 393-395, 395-399; trade of, 406-407, 407-414
British West Indies, 277-279
Brussels, 379
Buckwheat, 142, 169, 386
Buenos Aires, 230, 243, 259
Buran wind, 186
Burma, 112, 131
Bushongo tribe, 73

Cacao, 101, 102, 252, 254, 264, 267, 270-271

419